COATINGS OF HIGH - TEMPERATURE MATERIALS

PART 1:

By G. V. Samsonov and A. P. Epik

Ukrainian Academy of Sciences

PART 2:

By W. A. Gibeaut and E. S. Bartlett

Battelle Memorial Institute

PART 3:

By D. H. Leeds

Aerospace Corporation

Edited and with a Foreword by
HENRY H. HAUSNER

PLENUM PRESS
NEW YORK
1966

The text for Part 1, which has been expanded and updated for this edition
by the authors, was translated from a Russian language work published in
Moscow in 1964 by the Metallurgy press under the title:

ПОКРЫТИЯ ИЗ ТУГОПЛАВКИХ СОЕДИНЕНИЙ

(POKRYTIYA IZ TUGOPLAVKIKH SOEDINENII)

Library of Congress Catalog Card Number 65-12156

© 1966 Plenum Press
A Division of Consultants Bureau Enterprises, Inc.
227 W. 17th St., New York, N. Y. 10011
All rights reserved

FOREWORD

The properties of materials depend on the characteristics of the bulk and on those of the surface. Any change in surface characteristics affects a wide variety of material properties.

During the last few years the role of surface phenomena in metallurgy has been the subject of many studies. Surface energy, surface tension, the activity of surfaces, and related problems are under discussion in the western world* as well as in the eastern world.† The relation between volume and surface properties in metals and alloys has been investigated and is still under investigation.

Materials are frequently exposed to environments which change their physical and chemical characteristics on account of a reaction going on between the material surface and the environment. The science and technology of surface preparation to improve material properties have gained importance during the last decade in many parts of the world. Main efforts have been concentrated especially on the coating of material surfaces in connection with the exposure of these materials to space environment.

The problems of coating metals are complex. The coating should act as an air barrier; it should be ductile; and the process of coating should guarantee a perfect continuity of the coated layer. Physical and chemical stability of the coated layer is a prime factor in coating technique. The problems of bond formation between the material to be coated and the coated layer offer an entire new series of problems. These are only a few of the aspects which have been under investigation during the last few years. Work in this field is going on especially in the United States and USSR in their competitive exploration of space and the development of space technology. The results of the coating investigation for space technology purposes, however, have found many other applications in other fields of technology where materials are exposed to high temperature.

---

* "Metal Surfaces, Structure, Energetics and Kinetics," American Society for Metals, Metals Park, Ohio (1960).
† "The Role of Surface Phenomena in Metallurgy," ed. by V. N. Eremenko (English translation), Consultants Bureau, New York, N.Y. (1963).

This book deals with the problems of coating high-temperature materials and the progress made in the solution of these problems in the United States and USSR. The book is divided into three parts, in which coating problems are discussed from different angles.

In the first, and largest, part of the book, which represents a rather comprehensive text on the subject, G. V. Samsonov and A. P. Épik of the Ukrainian Academy of Science in Kiev, have discussed and analyzed the coating problems for high-temperature materials and have organized their material according to the various types of coatings, such as borides, carbides, nitrides, silicides, etc. The information given by the two Soviet authors is taken from 149 references of which more than 75% are from the Russian literature, and many of them refer to Professor Samsonov's own work in the field.

The second part of the book, by W. A. Gibeaut and E. S. Bartlett of Battelle Memorial Institute, Columbus, Ohio, is based on 49 American references. The authors have arranged their information according to the materials to be protected by coating, and have discussed the coating of columbium, molybdenum, tantalum, tungsten, and the alloys based on these materials. In this way a duplication of presentation is practically avoided between Parts I and II of the book.

The third part is directed mainly to the application of coated materials in space technology, and is by D. H. Leeds of the Materials Sciences Laboratory, Aerospace Corporation, El Segundo, Calif. He discusses first material problems in space technology, the fabrication and structure of coated refractory metals, possible failures, and the testing of these coated materials. The information given in this part of the book is also based exclusively on American references. It was not possible to avoid some duplication of information in Parts II and III; however, it is believed that it would not benefit the reader if this duplication had been eliminated.

The information in this book is substantiated in a total of 106 figures and 83 tables. The reader will find much useful information in the following pages. The main purpose of the book, however, is to stimulate new ideas for more extensive studies for those readers who are involved in material problems in connection with high-temperature applications.

The problems of coating, the properties of coated materials, and the characteristics of the coating are of importance, not only to metallurgists and ceramists, but also to mechanical engineers and space technologists. The chemical engineer will also find stimulating thoughts in this book.

For the reader who wants more information on high-temperature materials, attention is called to the "Plenum Press Handbooks of High-Temperature Materials,"* especially to No. 1., "Materials Index," by P. T. B. Shaffer, and No. 2., "Properties Index," by Professor Samsonov. These two books were published approximately a year ago, and have become known as standard works since then.

----

*Plenum Press, New York, N. Y.

The field of coating, and especially of coating high-temperature materials, is in a state of steady development. It is hoped that the large amount of practical work in this field will result in a better understanding of the fundamentals of the complex problems of coating.

Henry H. Hausner
Adjunct Professor
Polytechnic Institute of Brooklyn

CONTENTS

PART 1. Coatings of High-Temperature Materials
By G. V. SAMSONOV AND A. P. EPIK

PART 2. Properties of Coated Refractory Metals
By W. A. GIBEAUT AND E. S. BARTLETT

PART 3. Coatings on Refractory Metals
By D. H. LEEDS

PUBLISHER'S NOTE

The following Soviet journals cited in this book are available in cover-to-eover translation:

Russian Title	English Title	Publisher
Fizika metallov i metallovedenie	Physics of Metals and Metallography	Acta Metallurgica
Fizika tverdogo tela	Soviet Physics - Solid State	American Institute of Physics
Metallovedenie i termicheskaya obrabotka metallov	Metals Science and Heat Treatment of Metals	Consultants Bureau
Metallurg	Metallurgist	Consultants Bureau
Ogneupory	Refractories	Consultants Bureau
Poroshkovaya metallurgiya	Soviet Powder Metallurgy and Metal Ceramics	Consultants Bureau
Vestnik mashinostroeniya	Russian Engineering Journal	Production Engineering Research Assoc.
Zhurnal fizicheskoi khimii	Russian Journal of Physical Chemistry	Chemical Society (London)
Zhurnal neorganicheskoi khimii	Journal of Inorganic Chemistry	Chemical Society (London)
Zhurnal prikladnoi khimii	Journal of Applied Chemistry USSR	Consultants Bureau

PART 1

Coatings of High-Temperature Materials

G. V. Samsonov and A. P. Epik

PREFACE TO THE ENGLISH EDITION

The constant development of research into methods of applying coatings of oxygen-free high-temperature compounds to various materials and into the properties of these coatings has called for the introduction of some additions and amendments despite the fact that the Russian edition of the book appeared in 1964.

As in the Russian edition, the authors have not considered publications on the plasma, flame-spraying, and detonation methods of applying coatings. The additions relate only to coatings produced by thermodiffusion saturation or by deposition from the gas or vapor phase. The chapters dealing with carbide coatings and coatings on graphite have been amplified. The chapter on silicide coatings in particular has been considerably enlarged. The list of literature references has been amplified to include publications appearing in 1963-1964, and also some publications previously omitted.

The authors hope that the book will prove useful to American readers interested in coatings of metal-like, high-temperature materials, and that it will encourage the further development of work in this promising field of the science of materials.

G.V.S. and A.P.E.

PREFACE

Technical progress is closely bound up with the development and application of new materials which improve the working conditions of technical process (temperature, velocity, stress, service life) and promote their fuller mechanization and automation. Among promising materials of this kind may be included high-temperature, metal-like compounds, principally carbides, nitrides, borides, and silicides of the transition metals and alloys based on them.

A new branch of the application of high-temperature materials has recently been developed in the form of coatings on metallic and nonmetallic materials. In a number of cases, the production of such coatings is most effective, and sometimes it is the only method of imparting special physicochemical properties to the surfaces of components. Components coated with high-temperature materials possess great hardness, resistance to wear, and resistance to corrosion and high-temperature oxidation, and also possess special electrophysical and semiconductor properties.

A sufficiently thorough development of the technology of the various coatings, as well as a comprehensive study of their properties, will result in a considerable expansion of their fields of application. Information on the technology of the production of the various coatings, their properties, and use is currently very scattered, which makes it almost impossible for large numbers of scientists and engineers to become acquainted with these developments, and impedes the conduct of corresponding work of research, engineering, and design.

This small monograph represents an attempt to review information available in Soviet and other literature on methods of producing coatings based on high-temperature materials, together with some of their properties and fields of application. Attention is focused mainly on coatings consisting primarily of carbides, nitrides, borides, and silicides of refractory transition metals, and produced by the thermal diffusion method.

This first attempt to collect information on coatings of high-temperature materials is naturally not without its shortcomings, and the authors will be grateful for critical comments which could be taken into consideration in their future work.

Chapter 1

BORIDE COATINGS

Boriding of metals and alloys increases their hardness, wear resistance, and corrosion resistance, as well as their erosion resistance and resistance to seizing at high temperatures. In the boriding process, simple or complex boride phases are formed, the composition and structure of which are determined by the choice of the conditions of the process and by the nature of the materials to be coated.

The following fundamental methods of applying boron-containing coatings to metals and alloys are known and are in practical use: diffusion boriding from the solid, liquid, or gaseous phase, electrolytic application of coatings, and the building-up of borides on the surface of parts.

Boriding of Iron and Steel

The technology and mechanism of the boriding of iron and steel have been investigated in very great detail. The first work in this field was done by N.P. Chizhevskii [6] and I.E. Kontorovich and M.Ya. L'vovskii [7]. A review of work on the boriding of iron and steel is given in the well-known book by N.S. Gorbunov [8].

The boron-containing reagents usually employed for boriding in the solid state are either boron itself in the form of powder or ferroboron (for boriding ferrous metals and alloys), or boron carbide mixed with borax. For activating the diffusion of boron in the surface of the metal or alloy, the process is carried out with additions of ammonium chloride to the boriding agent or (in isolated cases) in an atmosphere of hydrogen chloride and similar activators, which form volatile compounds with boron (chlorides, boranes), which dissociate on the surface of the material to be coated, with the formation of active boron atoms. At the same time, the diffusion activators effect cleaning (when hydrogen is used) or pickling of the surface (hydrochloric acid or chlorides), which accelerates the production of quality coatings. With the use of such diffusion activators or stimulators, the coating process amounts principally to the diffusion of active boron atoms in the activated surface of the article, i.e., the process really takes place from the gaseous phase, while the rate of diffusion is relatively low, owing to the direct contact between the metal and boron-containing solid reagent.

Gorbunov [8] carried out boriding of iron and steel from backs containing amorphous boron or amorphous boron mixed with Al_2O_3 (1:3 parts by weight); when the

TABLE 1. Variation of Thickness of Boride Diffusion Layers on Iron with Boriding Conditions, μ

Time, hr	Amorphous boron In H$_2$ atmosphere at temperature °C			Amorphous boron In H$_2$ + HCl atmosphere at temperature °C		Amorphous boron + Al$_2$O$_3$ (1:3) In H$_2$ atmosphere at temperature °C		
	850	900	950	850	900	950	1000	1050
1	–	–	–	–	–	45	60	120
2	30	35	70	42	95	50	110	180
3	43	60	110	48	180	70	150	220
4	56	77	120	70	200	90	190	300
5	75	100	130	100	300	120	250	330

TABLE 2. Variation of Thickness of Boride Layers on Iron and Steel St. 3 with Temperature and Duration of the Boriding Process, μ

Temperature, °C	Time, hr	Armco iron	St. 3	Temperature, °C	Time, hr	Armco iron	St. 3
700	4	75	26	900	8	186	78
800	4	90	56	900	17	237	–
900	1	16	6	1000	4	186	173
900	2	29	31	1100	4	245	225
900	4	116	70	1200	4	326	–

latter mixture is used, the thickness of the diffusion layers is less, but denser and more uniform coatings are obtained. As shown by these investigations, when boriding is carried out in a hydrogen atmosphere with additions of hydrogen chloride, the growth of the diffusion layers is substantially accelerated (owing to the reduction of boron chloride by hydrogen with the formation of active atomic boron) but the resultant coatings are of lower quality than when a hydrogen atmosphere is used without the addition of chlorine-containing compounds. The data on the thickness of the coatings on iron obtained in [8] are given in Table 1.

This investigation also showed that the thickness of the diffusion layer decreased with increase in the carbon content of the steel, owing to the formation of boron carbide during diffusion, thereby preventing further penetration of the boron into the steel (on changing over from steel 45 to steel U12, the thickness of the layer produced after 5 hr at 1000°C decreased from 160 to 50 μ).

Similar data were obtained in [9] for the boriding of steel St. 3 and Armco iron from backs of amorphous boron, using ammonium chloride as diffusion stimulator (Table 2).

For the production of high-boron surface coatings, considerable practical interest is afforded by the use of boron carbide with various additions. In a series of experiments carried out by G. V. Samsonov and I. L. Zagyanskii, potassium chloride, sodium chloride, ammonium chloride, calcium chloride, boric acid, and borax were used as such additions.

TABLE 3. Thickness of Layer in the Boriding of Steels in a Bath of B_4C with Different Quantities of $Na_2B_4O_7$ at a Temperature of 950°C

Steel	Borax, %	Time, hr	Thickness of layer, μ	Steel	Borax, %	Time, hr	Thickness of layer, μ
Steel 45	12	6	55	Steel 45	60	24	0
Steel 45	16	6	60	Steel 45	12	36	250
Steel 45	12	12	112	Steel 45	16	36	250
Steel 45	16	12	175	Steel 40 Kh	12	6	60
Steel 45	12	24	250	"	12	12	100
Steel 45	16	24	250	"	16	12	125
Steel 45	40	24	150				

Steels 45, 40Kh, 50, U10, and Armco iron were borided for 3 and 6 hr at temperatures of 700-1000°C.

The results of these experiments show that no layer is formed at all when additions of $CaCl_2$, $BaCl_2$, and H_3BO_3 are used; good results are obtained when NaCl, HCl, NH_4Cl, and particularly borax are used as additions. The mechanism of the action of these additions varies; chlorides evidently react with the boron carbide forming boron trichloride, which in its turn decomposes with the liberation of active boron atoms:

$$B_4C + Me\,Cl \rightarrow BCl_3 + Me + C \rightarrow B + Cl_2 + Me\,C.$$

On the addition of borax, the latter reacts with boron carbide, liberating elementary boron according to the schematic reaction

$$Na_2B_4O_7 + B_4C \rightarrow B + CO + Na_2O.$$

Experiments were made to ascertain the optimum relationship between the borax and boron carbide contents of the bath in the boriding of steels 45 and 40 Kh, as well as the influence of the duration of boriding on the thickness of the layer. The results of these experiments are shown in Table 3.

Table 3 shows that 16% of borax is to be preferred to 12% of borax; on increasing the borax content to 40%, the layer rapidly diminishes, and at 60% is not formed at all. Increasing the time to 24 hr results in an increase in thickness of the layer, but beyond that the influence of time is negligible.

The mechanism of the diffusion of boron in iron and steel was investigated in [8, 9]. In [9], the following values were obtained for the activation energy in the diffusion of boron in Armco iron and steel:

	Temperature, °C	Activation energy, kcal/g-atom
Armco iron	700-900	15.9
	1000-1200	21.2
Steel 3	700-900	7.1
	1000-1100	18.4

9

These data show that the activation energy for the diffusion of boron in α and γ iron is much higher than for the diffusion of boron in steel, which may be explained by the formation of strong B−C bonds in the second case, i.e., by the formation of boron carbide and possibly also iron carboboride.

X-ray analysis of the borided layer on iron shows predominantly the boride FeB with a rhombic crystal lattice, and on steel St. 3, a tetragonal lattice of a compound similar in structure type to the boride Fe_2B, but with parameters of the elementary cell of half the value. Presumably, this compound is iron carboboride.

The formation of iron borides and carboborides during the diffusion of boron in iron and steel is also indicated by the high hardness of the borided layers amounting to 730-790 kg/mm^2 on Armco iron and 1400-2100 kg/mm^2 on steel St. 3.

N.S. Gorbunov also discovered the high hardness of borided layers, but he pointed out that it decreased with increase in the carbon content of the steel (from 1340 for steel 10 to 1070 kg/mm^2 for steel U12). N.S. Gorbunov explains the increase in microhardness on passing from steel U12 to steel 10 by the supposedly high hardness of ferroboron formed in the case of the lower carbon content. A more likely assumption, however, is that with increase in the carbon content of the steel the Fe−B−C equilibrium is shifted in the direction for the formation of boron carbide with corresponding depletion of the matrix of the alloy in carbon, and decomposition of the iron carboborides.

Similar results have been obtained by Yu. M. Lakhtin and M.A.Pchelkina [10]. Steel was borided in an atmosphere of $BCl_3 + H_2$ at temperatures of 750-950°C and for times of 3 - 6 hr. The mixture of $BCl_3 + H_2$ was formed by admitting hydrogen to a vessel containing solid boron trichloride. At the above-mentioned temperatures, as the result of the reaction between BCl_3 and H_2, active atomic boron and hydrogen chloride are formed. The boron is adsorbed on the treated surface and diffuses in the treated part. At the initial moment of boriding, the HCl activates the treated surface by removing the oxide film. The best results are obtained with a ratio of $BCl_3 : H_2$ = 0.05. To produce this ratio, the temperature of the BCl_3 must be -50°C (BCl_3 freezes at a temperature of -12.7°C and a pressure of 1 atm). The apparatus for gaseous boriding in an atmosphere of $BCl_3 + H_2$ is shown in Fig. 1.

The diffusion layer, after saturation with boron under the conditions: temperature 850°C, boriding time 3-6 hr, ratio of $BCl_3 : H_2$ = 0.05, consists of characteristic columnar crystals, perpendicular to the surface of the saturated metal and representing iron borides. The rhombic boride FeB (η-phase) is formed on the surface, and at a greater depth the tetragonal boride Fe_2B (ε-phase). It should be noted that with increase in the carbon content, the total depth of the diffusion layer diminishes; there is less of the boride FeB (for steel U12, the η-phase is practically absent and the borided layer consists of Fe_2B), and the hardness of both borides is somewhat lower. The hardness, measured with the PMT-3 tester under a load of 100 g, was 2340-1890 kg/mm^2 for FeB, and 1680-1290 kg/mm^2 for Fe_2B. Boriding in a $BCl_3 + H_2$ atmosphere is much more intensive than boriding from the solid phase; in 3 hr at a temperature of 750°C, the thickness of the diffusion layer was 60 μ, while at 950°C for the same time it was 250 μ (cf. the results in Tables 1 and 3).

10

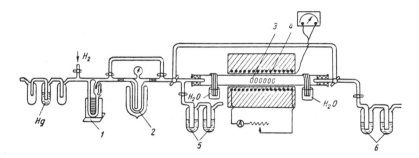

Fig. 1. Diagram of apparatus for boriding with a mixture of $BCl_3 + H_2$.
1) Flowmeter; 2) vessel containing BCl_3; 3) specimens; 4) furnace;
5, 6) water traps.

Investigation of the structure of borided layers [9] has shown that diffusion in Armco iron proceeds mainly along a front, and in steel between the crystallites with the formation of "feelers" or "wedges" (Fig. 2), ensuring high bonding strength of the borided layers to steels. The cause of such a difference in character of the diffusion layers is evidently the action of carbon and other constituents of the steel, which are concentrated on the grain boundaries of the structure and exert an influence on the diffusing boron, similar to the action of boundary-attracted precipitates in the theory of V.I. Arkharov [11]. Unlike the reaction of diffusing reagents with boundary-attracted additions, in boriding there is a reaction diffusion, accompanied by the formation of thermodynamically highly stable compounds, which makes this effect particularly pronounced.

Fig. 2. Photomicrograph of boron-saturated layer on steel St. 3; boriding
at 1100°C for 4 hr, × 60.

11

In its turn, the rate of the reaction diffusion depends on the degree of influence of the incompleteness of the d-electron levels of the transition metals and the ionization potential of the diffusing metalloid [3, 4]. In the case of diffusion in steel, where the influence of the d-level is already neutralized to a considerable extent by electrons of the carbon atoms, boron penetrates much more slowly (and to a lesser extent, the higher is the carbon content) than in iron, where this influence is the principal motive force of the diffusion.

The explanation of the influence of ordinary alloying elements (Cr, Ni, Co, Mn, W, Mo, Si, Al) and carbon on the kinetics and properties of borided layers on commercial iron was discussed by M.E. Blanter and N.P.Besedin [12], who proposed an original method of saturating a metal surface by any element, based on the use of a liquid bath consisting of a mixture of a carbide MeC and oxide MeO of the saturating element. When such a bath is heated, the following reaction takes place

$$Me\,O + Me\,C \rightarrow Me + CO,$$

culminating in the formation of active atoms of the element and the liberation of CO. This reaction is principally important for producing coatings of high-melting metals on various materials.

In the above-mentioned investigation, boron carbide B_4C mixed with borax was used, it being found experimentally that the optimum composition of the mixture from the point of view of maximum thickness of the borided coatings was 55% B_4C and 45% borax. Experiments on the influence of additions of neutral salts (NaCl and $BaCl_2$ in the proportion of 1: 1), for improving the fluidity of the melt, showed a sharp drop in the saturating capacity of the bath on the introduction of these additions.

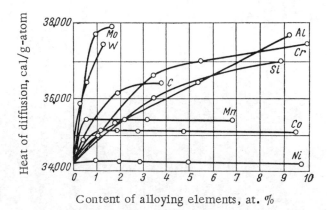

Content of alloying elements, at. %

Fig. 3. Influence of alloying elements on the heat of
diffusion of boron (cf. Fig. 4).

The following are recommended as optimum boriding conditions: Bath composition 40% boron carbide and 60% borax, temperature 1100°C, holding time at this temperature 5 hr.

In the course of the investigation, a determination was made of the relationships between the content of alloying additions, on the one hand, and the depth of the diffusion layer, and also the heat of activation of the diffusion of boron in the alloyed austenite, on the other. The corresponding data are shown in Figs. 3 and 4.

It may be concluded from an analysis of these results that the retardation of the rate of diffusion of boron in steel is directly associated with the presence of alloying elements (including carbon) in the steel, increasing the activation energy of diffusion. Such elements, in addition to those mentioned in [12], also include niobium, tantalum, titanium, hafnium, and vanadium. With regard to titanium and niobium, this conclusion has been confirmed experimentally by Yu. A. Lakhtin and M.A. Pchelkina in a study of the boriding of high-alloy steels [13].

Boriding was carried out in a mixture of diborane and hydrogen ($B_2H_6 : H_2 = 1:25$) at 950°C for 6 hr. After boriding, the specimens were kept for 4 hr at the saturation temperature. The specimens for boriding were heat-resistant stainless steels on a chromium—nickel basis. The results obtained in this investigation confirm the data and conclusions of [12]. It was found that chromium and nickel, especially when their content in the steel was not high, considerably reduced the depth of the diffusion layer; tungsten in an amount of 2.2% decreased the borided layer on chromium steel, and the introduction of up to 8% manganese into the latter did not appreciably affect its depth or structure. The influence of niobium and titanium on the depth and hardness of the borided layer of type 18-8 steels is shown in Figs. 5 and 6. Figure 7 shows the distribution of hardness over the depth of the diffusion layer in steel ÉI612 (Kh15N37V3T).

The distribution of hardness over the depth of the borided layer is similar in other austenitic steels.

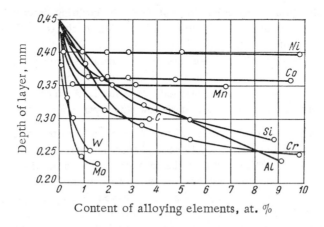

Fig. 4. Influence of alloying elements on depth of diffusion layer (standard experimental conditions).

13

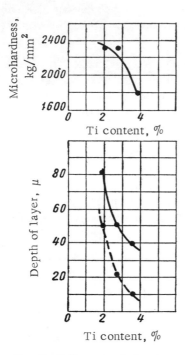

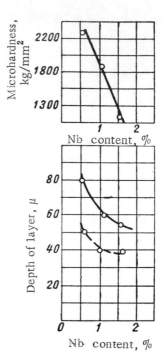

Fig. 5. Influence of titanium on depth of borided layer and microhardness of steel containing 0.15% C, 18.39% Cr, 8.4% Ni, 2.05% W. ——— total depth of layer; ----- depth of continuous layer of borides.

Fig. 6. Influence of niobium on depth of borided layer and microhardness of steel containing 0.27% C, 17.5% Cr, 8.1% Ni, 2.3% W. ——— total depth of layer; ----- depth of continuous layer of borides.

According to an assumption made in [13], the boriding process in high-alloy steels takes place as follows. After the solid solution on the treated surface has reached the limit of saturation with boron, borides are formed in addition to the saturated solid solution. The borides are present inside the solid solution in isolated regions, the number of these regions increasing with increase in the amount of boride-forming elements (Ni, Cr, etc.) contained in the steel. A continuous layer of borides is gradually formed on the surface, and below this layer is an austenitic boride zone.

A microstructure investigation of the influence of temperature on the structure of the borided layer in steel Kh23N18 showed that short-time saturation at high temperature (1100°C, 2 hr) results in the formation of an austenitic boride zone. There is no continuous, clearly defined layer of borides in this case, owing to the intensive withdrawal of boron atoms from the surface to deeper layers, and, as shown by a study of the microstructure, the formation of boride phases, i.e., the diffusion of boron, takes place mainly along the grain boundaries. At lower temperatures and longer times (950°C, 6 hr) a continuous layer of borides is formed on the surface, the austenitic boride zone being situated below this layer.

14

X-ray structural phase analysis of the borided layer showed it to consist of complex borides of iron and alloying elements (Cr, Ni, etc.). The formation of pure borides of alloying elements of various compositions is not precluded.

Table 4 shows the depth of the borided layer in steels and the composition and microhardness of the layer in relation to the boriding conditions.

The investigation [13] confirms the possibility of the extensive application of boriding for producing hard and wear-resistant coatings, consisting principally of complex borides, on high-alloy steels.

A mixture of diborane and hydrogen was also found effective for boriding ordinary steel 45 [14]. Investigation of the boriding process showed that the optimum conditions for the production of high-hardness and wear-resistant surface layers are: Ratio $B_2H_6 : H_2$ equal to 1:75, and rate of flow of gas mixture 75-100 liters/hr; in this case (other conditions being equal) very deeply borided layers are produced.

For a time of 4 - 5 hr, the appearance of borided layers commences at 500°C, at 650°C the thickness of the layers is 30 μ, at 750°C, 75 μ, at 850°C, 110 μ, and at 1050°C, 150 μ. The surface microhardness of the borided layer attains 3000 kg/mm^2, falling to 1500-2000 kg/mm^2 as the depth increases.

The production of coatings of complex borides on different metallic materials is of considerable interest. A description is given in [15] of one such process in which the diffusion method is used first of all for applying to a metallic surface a coating of another metal or nonmetal, which is then borided. Articles of cast iron, steel, titanium, zirconium, molybdenum, tungsten, cobalt, nickel, or their alloys may be subjected to such treatment. Titanium, zirconium, vanadium, niobium, chromium, molybdenum, tungsten, aluminum, and silicon may be used as saturating

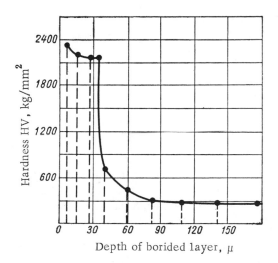

Fig. 7. Distribution of hardness over depth of borided layer of steel ÉI612.

TABLE 4. Influence of Conditions of Boriding Chromium—Nickel Steels on the Depth, Composition, and Microhardness of the Borided Layers

Steel	Boriding conditions		Depth of layer, μ		Surface microhardness, kg/mm^2
	T, °C	time, hr	borides	total depth	
Kh18N9T	950	6	25	100	2200
	1100	2	20	120	2200
Kh18N12M3T	900	4	20	100	2290
Kh18N25S2	900	4	25	115	2290
	1100	2	70	150	2200
Kh23N18	950	6	15	130	2190
	1100	2	20	130	2190
Kh25N25T	950	6	12	130	2090
	850	2	15	60	2190
	850	4	25	75	2190
Kh15N37V3T	850	6	30	125	2190
	850	10	45	160	2190
	950	2	30	80	2190
	1050	2	30	120	2190

elements for the production of the primary coating. Thus, for the production of coatings of chromium borides on specimens of low-carbon steel, the specimens were saturated with chromium in a closed container in a mixture consisting of 40% Cr, 60% Al$_2$O$_3$, and 0.19% NH$_4$Cl at a temperature of 1050°C and for a time of 4 hr. After this treatment, a diffusion coating 75 μ thick, with a mean chromium content of 22%, had been formed. The specimens were then borided at 1000°C for 4 hr in a back containing 5% B, 7.5% Cr, 87.5% alumina, and 0.1% NH$_4$F. After this treatment, the diffusion zone had a depth of about 90 μ and a hardness of 450 kg/mm^2 close to the boundary with the metal, and 1400-1500 kg/mm^2 on the surface.

Combined boro-aluminizing processes for steel, and the properties of the layers produced in these processes have been investigated [16]. Boro-aluminizing was carried out by one of three processes:

1. Aluminizing followed by boriding;
2. Boriding followed by aluminizing;
3. Simultaneous boriding and aluminizing.

A bath consisting of 97% ferroaluminum and 3% NH$_4$Cl was used for aluminizing, a bath of 84% B$_4$C and 16% borax was used for boriding, and a bath of mixed composition, consisting of ferroaluminum, boron carbide, borax, and ammonium chloride was used for simultaneous boriding and aluminizing.

The parts were treated in a shaft furnace having Silit heating elements. The parts were charged into the furnace in steel containers with lids, luted at their joint with the containers with refractory clay or asbestos paste thinned with water glass. The processes were carried out on steels St. 3 and ShKh15 at temperatures of 700-1000°C and for durations of 2-4 hr.

TABLE 5. High-Temperature Oxidation Resistance of Boro-Aluminized Layers, Increase in Weight, % (Oxidation Time 2 hr)

Oxidation temperature in air, °C	Steel St. 3				Steel ShKh15			
	Without treatment	Aluminizing followed by boriding	Boriding followed by aluminizing	Simultaneous boriding and aluminizing	Without treatment	Aluminizing followed by boriding	Boriding followed by aluminizing	Simultaneous boriding and aluminizing
500	0.036	0.078	0.001	0.049	0.005	0.041	0.002	0.016
600	0.128	0.154	0.073	–	0.006	0.135	0.683	0.023
700	0.714	0.316	0.092	0.098	0.24	0.762	0.140	0.264
800	3.520	2.042	0.25	0.43	7.67	0.930	0.293	0.335
900	–	–	–	0.46	–	–	–	0.382

In simultaneous boriding and aluminizing, the thickness of the layers was usually greater than in the case of the individual processes. At 1000°C, the thickness of the layer on steel St. 3 was 300 μ (hardness of layer 793 kg/mm^2) and on steel ShKh15 it was 134 μ (hardness of layer 928 kg/mm^2). The oxidation resistance of the layers produced by the three methods is shown in Table 5.

As will be seen from the data given in this table, boriding followed by aluminizing and simultaneous boro-aluminizing substantially increase the oxidation resistance of steels, especially at 700-900°C.

These data are in agreement with the results obtained in [8] in oxidation-resistance tests in an air atmosphere at 700°C of specimens of commercial iron subjected to boriding directly and also after previous aluminizing, siliconizing, and chromizing (Table 6).

As will be seen from the data in Table 6, boriding appreciably increases the oxidation resistance of iron in an atmosphere of air at 700°C (3 to $3\frac{1}{2}$ times).

Aluminizing and siliconizing before boriding do not appreciably increase the oxidation resistance, since the borided layer obtained in this case is less dense, which is the cause of the considerable oxidation of the surface.

Chromizing before boriding considerably increases the oxidation resistance of iron at elevated temperatures.

Various modifications of "pure" aluminizing have already long been used in practice for imparting high-temperature oxidation resistance to various materials, and have been sufficiently discussed in the literature [8, 17]. One reference [18] must be mentioned here, since the aluminizing technique proposed in it enables the oxidation resistance of low- and medium-carbon steels to be increased (Fig. 8) 6 to 8 times (at 950°C) and that of oxidation-resistant steels to be increased 8 to 10 times (at 1150°C).

TABLE 6. Increase in Weight of Specimens in Relation to Duration of Heating in Air at 700°C, mg/cm²

Material	Duration of test, hr				
	5	10	15	20	25
Iron	12.1	20.1	26.5	32.2	35.7
Borided iron	6.4	8.5	8.9	9.8	10.1
Iron borided after aluminizing	23.3	24.9	26.9	29.3	32.1
Iron borided after siliconizing	4.9	7.8	12.9	13.2	13.6
Iron borided after chromizing	0.5	0.5	0.5	0.6	0.8

The aluminizing process is in principle as follows. The surface of the article, before being coated with aluminum by metal spraying, is subjected to sandblasting or shot-beening. Spraying of a layer 0.5 to 2 mm thick is carried out by means of a gas or electrical apparatus (in the second case, the quality of the coating is better). The applied aluminum layer is then provided with an oxidation-resistant paste for protecting the aluminum from the oxygen of the air and promoting diffusion and uniform distribution in the surface layer of the article. Experiments have shown that the optimum composition of the coating is 20% refractory clay, 30% quartz sand, 50% graphite, with an addition of 8 to 10% (of the total weight) of water glass.

The articles thus treated are subjected to diffusion annealing at a temperature of 920-1000°C for 1.5-2 hr. The depth of the diffusion layer increases with increase in annealing temperature and duration, and correspondingly the concentration of aluminum on the surface decreases and becomes more uniform over the depth of the layer.

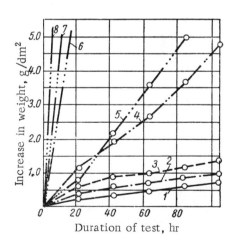

Fig. 8. Oxidation resistance of aluminized (1-4) and nonaluminized (5-8) specimens. 1, 5) Chromium steel; 2, 6) steel 20; 3, 7) steel 55L; 4, 8) gray iron.

18

The following materials were aluminized: Chromium steel Kh23N13, steel 20, steel 55L, and gray iron.

Metallographic examination of the investigated specimens of steel 20 and chromium steel showed that the diffusion layer consisted of an external and an internal zone, the composition of which was not studied. After annealing, no intermetallic compounds, usually situated along the grain boundaries, were found in any of the specimens.

Comparative tests of the high-temperature oxidation resistance of aluminized and nonaluminized specimens of steel Kh23N13 showed that after 16 hr at 1150°C, the increase in weight of the former was 5 mg/cm^2 and of the latter 80 mg/cm^2. With increase in the heating time, the difference between the increase in weight of the nonaluminized and aluminized specimens increased; consequently the advantage of aluminizing appears to an even greater extent for parts used under conditions of long-continued heating.

The results of tests on aluminized and nonaluminized parts of the gas-producer apparatus of a tractor and muffles for bright annealing of strip are shown in Fig. 9.

Aluminized molds for precision casting of low-carbon steel had a service life of 700 hr at a temperature of 920°C, while that of nonaluminized molds was only 72 hr.

Aluminized case-hardening boxes had a service life of 1400 hr at 950°C, while nonaluminized boxes were completely oxidized in 270 hr.

It may be concluded from the test results that carbon-steel parts aluminized in this way may be successfully used in a number of cases instead of stainless steel parts.

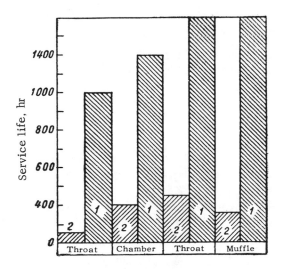

Fig. 9. Comparative data of tests on aluminized (1) and nonaluminized (2) parts of gas-producer apparatus and muffles.

Electrolytic boriding is also used in industry. The boriding medium is molten borax $Na_2B_4O_7 \cdot 10H_2O$; its decomposition is accompanied by the separation of boron ions on the cathode, formed by the parts to be borided, the boron ions subsequently diffusing into the depth of the material. The anode is usually a graphite electrode. The temperature of the process is 920-980°C.

Electrolytic boriding has been used [19] for increasing the wear resistance of linear plates of the molds in the semidry production of refractory bricks and the dies for continuous wire-drawing machines. The plates are used under conditions of intense abrasive wear and the dies at high pressures and temperatures.

Investigations have shown that the thickness of the borided layer increases with increases in the duration of boriding, and with increase in current density and temperature, but the structural character of the layer is not affected. For steel 40, from which the parts were made, the optimum boriding conditions were found to be as follows: Temperature 950-960°C, duration 5-6 hr, current density 0.20 A/cm². Under these conditions, the borided layer had a depth of 0.15-0.25 mm, good adherence to the base, and a surface hardness of 1700-1800 kg/mm².

Electron microscope, metallographic, and x-ray structural examination showed that the order of arrangement of the phases in the depth of the layer was as follows: On the surface of the layer was a zone consisting of α-phase and boron carbide distributed in it in the form of very finely dispersed inclusions. The microhardness of this zone was the highest, being 1800-1880 kg/mm². The second zone consisted mainly of the boride FeB with inclusions of the phase Fe_2B; its microhardness was 1670-1770 kg/mm². Following this zone was a zone of the boride Fe_2B with a microhardness of 1480-1670 kg/mm².

As shown by the results of tests, the borided plates with a mean surface hardness of 1750 kg/mm² were 2-3 times more resistant than the case-hardened plates previously used. The borided dies of the wire-drawing machines had a life $13\frac{1}{2}$ times longer than dies having a chromized working surface.

It has been shown [20] that the addition of 60% by weight of boric anhydride to the borax considerably increased the rate of growth and depth of the borided layer on steels (steels 10, 50, and U8 were investigated). At the same time, the hardness and brittleness of the layer were increased. The borided layer had maximum hardness on steel U8 of approximately 1520 HV, somewhat lower on steel 50, i.e., 1500 HV, and 1400-1450 HV on steel 10.

A study has been made [21] of the electrolytic boriding of steel electroplated with nickel and copper. Nickel plating of specimens of steels 35 and 50 was carried out in a complex $NiSO_4 \cdot 7H_2O$ electrolyte, and copper plating in a $CuSO_4 \cdot 7H_2O$ electrolyte. Boriding was then carried out at a temperature of 950-960°C for 1, 1.5, 2, and 4 hr.

The results showed that nickel does not prevent the diffusion of boron into the steel; for a nickel-coating thickness of 0.008 to 0.036 mm, the thickness of the borided layer remained equal to 0.15 mm (boriding at 950-960°C for 2 hr). The microstructure and hardness (1500 kg/mm²) of the diffusion layer showed it to consist of complex borides of nickel and iron.

Boron does not react with a copper layer. If the copper layer is sufficiently dense, and has no cracks or pores, the boron does not diffuse through it into the steel. A layer of copper 0.15 mm thick protects steel from penetration by boron (Fig. 10).

Thus, copper plating of the necessary quality may be used as local protection of inoperative surfaces from boriding. In the investigation referred to above, it was found that neither brass nor bronze could be borided.

Heating of the parts undergoing boriding by high-frequency currents greatly reduces the boriding time, and results in the production of deep diffusion layers. In [22] parts of steel U8 were borided by coating them with 50% of boron carbide (200-400 mesh) and 50% cryolite and then heating them with high-frequency current to 1200°C (after first drying the coating at 200°C for 1 hr). After 1 min heating, the thickness of the layer attained 35 μ, after 2 min, 80 μ, after 3 min, 125 μ, i.e., the heating time was reduced 100-200 times or more, compared with the usual heating. Similar results were obtained when steel 45 was borided. In the surface layer, the hardness of which attained 1000 HV, x-ray analysis showed the presence of borides of iron and boron carbide.

The use of a mixture of boron carbide and cryolite for boriding is similar to the method of M.E. Blanter described above, since it is based on the reaction of B_4C with the oxygen of the cryolite and the formation of active boron.

Boriding of steel by the surfacing method is usually carried out with steel electrodes coated with a composition containing ferroboron or boron carbide, while recently chromium boride or a mixture of ferrochrome with chromium and borides has been used [23]. Thus, BKh-2 electrodes are used, with a coating based on chromium boride containing 80% CrB, 10% graphite, 8% mica flour, and 2% potash. The hardness of the surface layer, built up by means of BKh-2 electrodes, is 79.8 RA, and its wear resistance is 2.1 times greater than the wear resistance of a layer built

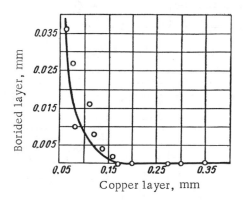

Fig. 10. Variation of depth of penetration of boron in steel 50 with thickness of copper layer on its surface in boriding for 2 hr at 950-960°C.

21

up with chromium–manganese mixtures. The outer part of the layer consists of lamellar eutectic with inclusions of a ternary compound of chromium, boron, and iron. A mixture containing 60% ferrochromium, 30% iron powder, 5% chromium boride, and 5% chromium carbide gives built-up layers having a hardness of 78.9 RA and a wear resistance 1.4-1.7 times greater than the wear resistance of layers built up with chromium–manganese mixtures. For hard facing of articles subjected to abrasive wear, a mixture containing 50% chromium boride and 50% iron powder is used. The wear resistance of a layer, produced by hard facing with such a mixture, increases the wear resistance of steel St. 3 by 10-12 times, three times greater than the wear resistance of a layer built up with a chrome–manganese mixture. In addition, electrodes are used having a coating of 80% chromium carbide Cr_3C_2, giving a layer having a hardness of 79.8 RA.

Boriding of Refractory Metals and Alloys

The result of boriding refractory metals is to produce on their surface a boride layer of varying composition with valuable inherent technical properties: high hardness, and resistance to the action of most inorganic acids and to oxidation in air at relatively high temperatures.

When titanium, niobium, tantalum, molybdenum, and tungsten were borided in a pack consisting of amorphous boron and 3% NH_4Cl, as described in [24], it was found that as a rule single-phase layers were formed, consisting of TiB_2, NbB_2, TaB_2, Mo_2B, and W_2B, respectively.

According to the results of this investigation, when titanium is saturated with boron, porous layers are formed, which exfoliate from the main body of the specimen,

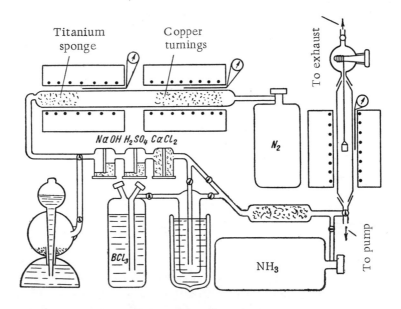

Fig. 11. Diagram of apparatus for boriding metals in $BCl_3 + H_2$, $BCl_3 + NH_3$, and $BCl_3 + N_2$.

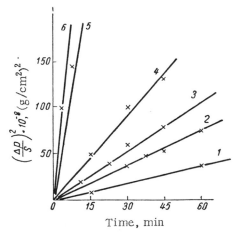

Fig. 12. Square of the increase in weight
of niobium specimens versus time in an atmosphere of $BCl_3 + H_2$ for various temperatures. 1) 700; 2) 800; 3) 900; 4) 1000;
5) 1100; 6) 1200°C.

possibly on account of the considerable difference in volume between Ti and TiB_2.
The boride layer on niobium is dense, uniform, and joins closely onto the base.
Borided layers on tantalum, molybdenum, and tungsten are found to exfoliate in a
very definite manner; in addition, boride layers on molybdenum often have appreciable porosity.

In the electrolytic boriding of molybdenum in a molten bath [25] consisting
of 33% HBO_3 and 67% NaF (under the conditions of cathode current density 9.6
A/cm², voltage 11 V, temperature 980-1200°C, time 1-2 hr), two layers are formed,
an outer layer, having a hardness of 2650 kg/mm², and an inner layer with a hardness of 1680 kg/mm², adjacent the pure molybdenum. The thickness of the inner
layer depends little on temperature and time, varying from 8 μ at 980°C to 16 μ at
1100°C (with saturation time of 1 hr), and from 7 μ to 12 μ when the saturation time
is increased from 20 to 170 min (at 1050°C). The outer layer, on the contrary, grows
more rapidly; its thickness is about 40 μ for saturation in 1 hr at 980°C. The total
thickness of the electrolytically produced diffusion layer differs little from the
thickness of coatings produced by solid-phase boriding.

Boriding of refractory metals from the gas phase is often carried out, as in the
case of steels, by using the reaction between BCl_3 and hydrogen at temperatures of
700-1200°C [26, 27]. An account is given in [27] of an investigation of the boriding
of niobium, in which the effect of the absence of nitrogen in the reaction mixture
on the diffusion process was studied. Figure 11 shows the boriding apparatus diagrammatically. The specimens were attached to a molybdenum wire suspension (suspen-
sions of Nichrome, platinum, and quartz failed due to their reaction with BCl_3),
and were placed in a porcelain tube situated in an electric furnace. The apparatus
was designed for the use of hydrogen, molecular nitrogen, and ammonia as carrier
gas, the ammonia being admitted to the reaction space directly from a cylinder.

After boriding in $BCl_3 + H_2$, the surface of the niobium had a metal-like layer, varying from light to dark brown in color as it became thicker. The coating was mechanically strong, compact, and adhered well to the metal. The results of x-ray structural analysis showed that the formation of niobium borides commenced at only 700°C.

When different amounts of ammonia were added to the $BCl_3 + H_2$ mixture (atmosphere of $BCl_3 + H_2 + NH_3$), the process of the reaction diffusion was similar to that described above with regard to the phase composition of the diffusion zone and its rate of formation. Solubility of nitrogen in niobium diboride was not detected. The observed facts indicate that under experimental conditions the chemical affinity of boron for niobium is greater than that of nitrogen, such that nitrogen does not participate in the process of reaction diffusion.

In the absence of hydrogen in the boron-containing gaseous medium, the boron is not reduced and does not react with the niobium. Under these conditions, only diffusion of nitrogen in niobium with the formation of niobium nitrides is observed. The observed reduction in weight of the specimens in the initial period of the process may possibly be explained by the formation of volatile niobium chlorides as the result of the thermal dissociation of the BCl_3. The results of x-ray, metallographic, and kinetic investigations are shown in Table 7 and Fig. 12.

The parabolic time curve of the increase in growth of the diffusion boride layer, and the absence of texture and porosity in the metal-oxide scale zone indicate that the surface is saturated with boron mainly by diffusion of the latter, through the crystal lattice of the reaction products, in the form of positive ions and free atoms.

The absence of pores and cracks in the boride diffusion layer was also confirmed by corrosion tests: After being kept for 500 hr in 50% solutions of sulfuric, hydrochloric, and nitric acids, the borided specimens showed no loss in weight or coating defects (at 20°C). Tests on resistance to oxidation at 1000°C in air showed that boride coatings on niobium are unable to protect the latter from high-temperature oxidation. This conclusion is in agreement with the results of other investigators [28, 29].

Reaction diffusion in the system molybdenum—[boron + silicon] has been investigated [140]. Saturation of molybdenum was carried out in an atmosphere of $BCl_3 + SiCl_4 + H_2$ in the temperature range 800-1200°C for a duration of from 0.5 to 4 hr. For comparing the kinetic data of boriding, siliconizing, and combined saturation with boron and silicon under comparable conditions, all three processes were studied separately. It was found that siliconizing in a $SiCl_4 + H_2$ atmosphere took place more intensely than boriding in a $BCl_3 + H_2$ atmosphere, while the process of the combined saturation with boron and silicon in a $BCl_3 + SiCl_4 + H_2$ atmosphere occurred more slowly than boriding and siliconizing separately. Furthermore, in the case of combined saturation, the diffusion zone according to x-ray diffraction and metallographic examinations, for temperatures below 1000°C, consisted of a layer of Mo_2B_5, closely adjacent the metal and firmly bonded to it. At temperatures above 1000°C, a second very thin layer of α-MoB appeared between the outer layer and the metal. No silicide phases were found.

24

TABLE 7. Results of an Investigation of the Niobium Boriding Process (Boriding Time 1 hr, No Texture Discovered in the Layers)

Boriding medium	Temperature, °C	Results of x-ray phase analysis	Diffusion law
$BCl_3 + H_2$	700	NbB_2	—
	800	$NbB(Nb_3B_4)$	—
	800	NbB_2	Parabolic
	900	NbB	—
	900	NbB_2	—
	1000–1200	NbB_2	Complex, loss
$BCl_3 + H_2 + NH_3$	800–1000	NbB_2	in weight ob-
$BCl_3 + N_2$	800	NbN (cub.)	served
	1000	Nb_2N (tetr.)	
	1200	X-phase*	

* The structure and composition of this phase were not investigated.

In the opinion of the authors of [140], the lower rate of combined borosili-conizing may be explained on the assumption that silicon dissolves in small amounts in molybdenum borides, particularly in the phase Mo_2B_5, and produces an increase in the activation energy of the elementary act of the diffusion of boron through this phase. For explaining the somewhat unexpected fact, however, of the formation of borides alone in the combined saturation of molybdenum by boron and silicon, a quantitative thermodynamic analysis of the investigated system will be necessary, for which insufficient data have, as yet, been collected.

Full investigations of the process of boriding cobalt, nickel, iron, tungsten, molybdenum, niobium, zirconium, tantalum, and rhenium have been made by A.N. Minkevich [30]. Boriding was carried out in the following media: 1) in a bath containing molten borax and boron carbide (about 40%); 2) in boron powder in a vacuum at a pressure of $5 \cdot 10^{-4}$ mm Hg (furnace TVV-2); 3) in boron carbide powder in the same vacuum furnace; 4) in a bath of molten borax (electrolytic boriding).

Boriding of iron, cobalt, and nickel was carried out at a temperature of 950°C, taking into account the position of the solidus line of the corresponding Me–B binary diagrams, and bearing in mind the brittleness of the boride phases, increasing with increase in temperature. The boriding rate of cobalt and iron was found to be the same and (in medium 1), after 3 hr, ensured the production of a diffusion layer hav-ing a thickness of 0.13 mm. The boride layers on these metals consisted of boride needles penetrating into the core and perpendicular to the surface. As shown by the experiments, the kinetics of the formation of boride layers is similar for cobalt and iron. Initially, needles are formed of the lowest borides Fe_2B and Co_2B (tetragonal lattice having a boron content of 8.8 and 8.4%, respectively), and then with increase in the boron content, a second series of needle-shaped borides FeB and CoB is formed. The microhardness values for FeB and CoB were, respectively, 2000 and 1850 kg/mm^2, and for Fe_2B and Co_2B, they were 1850 and 1550-1600 kg/mm². Medium 4 was found to be more active than medium 1 (Fig. 13); after 3 hr in medium 1, Co_2B was mainly formed, while in medium 4, Co_2B and CoB were formed.

The diffusion of boron in nickel took place rather more slowly, and the layer consisted of two distinct boride zones, one of which, according to the author's proposal, represented the phase Ni_2B and the other, Ni_3B. The microhardness of the diffusion layer was rather lower (1500-1650 kg/mm²) than in the case of cobalt and iron. In an investigation of the boriding process of nickel in a $BCl_3 + H_2$ medium at a temperature of 900°C, however, three layers were found, an outer layer having a microhardness of 1700 kg/mm², an intermediate layer with 1500 kg/mm², and an inner layer with 1150 kg/mm². The phase composition of the layers was not determined particularly, but according to the Ni-B diagram, in the authors' opinion, these layers consist of NiB, Ni_3B_2, and Ni_2B.

The needle-like structure of borided layers on iron and cobalt and sometimes on nickel may be explained, as suggested in [30], by the preferred migration of the diffusing element (boron) in a definite structurally determined direction of the intermetallic phases undergoing formation. This phenomenon was also discovered and investigated previously [32] in the example of the Fe_2Al_5 phase in the aluminizing of iron. The feature of the structure of this intermetallic phase was that individual atomic rows of its lattice were only 70% full. Such abnormally high concentration of vacancies on parallel planes of the lattice resulted in the preferential movement of the aluminum atoms along these planes.

Boriding of molybdenum, tungsten, niobium, zirconium, tantalum, and rhenium was carried out at temperatures of 1100-1500°C, since at higher temperatures the porosity and brittleness of the layer are appreciably increased. The results of the investigation of the diffusion layers are shown in Figs. 14 and 15. Analysis of the curves allows one to conclude that: 1) under any conditions, the depth of the borided

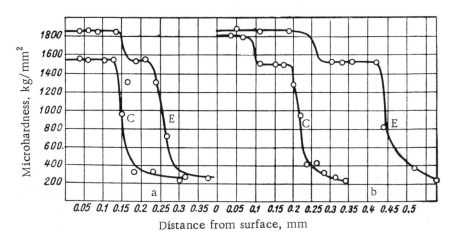

Fig. 13. Distribution of microhardness over the depth of a borided layer (cobalt). a) 950°C, 3 hr; b) 950°C, 6 hr; C) boriding in bath of molten borax and boron carbide; E) electrolytic boriding.

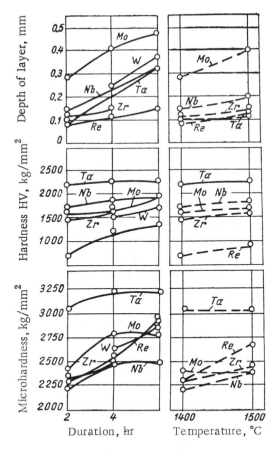

Fig. 14. Depth of boride layer, Vickers hardness
on surface (load 5 kg), and microhardness of
borided layers on Mo, W, Nb, Ta, Zr, and Re
versus duration of the process at 1400°C and temperature of the process for a duration of 2 hr.

layer is a maximum on molybdenum and much less on tungsten, niobium, zirconium,
tantalum, and rhenium; 2) maximum hardness of the borided layer on tantalum is 2000-
2200 kg/mm² HV, microhardness 3000-3200 kg/mm² (this value of the microhardness is considerably higher than all the other published values); 3) with increase in temperature and duration, the surface hardness as a rule increases.

X-ray structural analysis of the surface layers formed on the above-mentioned
metals as the result of treatment in medium 3 at a temperature of 1400°C and duration 1 hr showed lines of different intensities, belonging to different phases. The
diffusion layer on molybdenum consisted of Mo_2B (faint lines) and Mo_2B_5, that on
tungsten of W_2B, WB (very faint, broad lines), and W_2B_5 (faint), that on niobium of
NbB_2 and other phases, that on zirconium of lower borides and ZrB_2, that on tantalum of Ta_2B, and that on rhenium of ReB.

The phase composition of the surface zones obtained in medium 2 (1400°C,
1 hr) and in medium 1 (1200°C, 1 hr) on molybdenum, tungsten, and niobium was

27

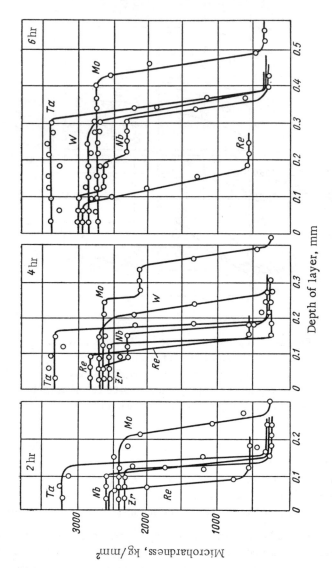

Fig. 15. Variation in microhardness with depth of borided layer on Mo, W, Nb, Ta, Zr, and Re. Treatment in boron carbide powder in vacuum at 1400°C for 2.4 and 6 hr.

28

close to that mentioned above with the sole difference that the lines relating to the higher borides were stronger. Under these conditions, on zirconium, instead of two borides, only one boride ZrB was found, and on tantalum, instead of one boride, two were found: Ta_2B and TaB_2. It may be concluded on the basis of these results that media 1 and 2 are more active than medium 3. Measurements of the depth of the boride layers confirmed this conclusion.

The wear resistance of borided molybdenum, tungsten, and niobium was found to be several times higher than the wear resistance of quenched steel U10 and case-hardened steel 30KhGT. In tests on the Amsler machine for 2 hr with a load of 50 kg, the borided layers on tungsten showed weight loss of $0.0175 \, g/m^2$ and those on molybdenum and niobium weight losses of $0.0148 \, g/m^2$ and $0.0120 \, g/m^2$, respectively, while a case-hardened steel layer tested with them lost $0.046 \, g/m^2$.

The scaling resistance of the borided metals, determined at 950°C for a duration of 24 hr, for zirconium was found to be 20 times, for tantalum 30 times, and for titanium 14 times that of the untreated metals. The scaling resistance is increased, particularly in the case of rhenium. After 10 hr at 1000°C, untreated rhenium showed a loss in weight of $10,940 \, g/m^2$, while the treated rhenium showed a loss of only $288 \, g/m^2$.

The hot hardness (at 900°C) of borided molybdenum was substantially higher than that of niobium. A comparison of the hot hardness of the boride layers of some metals, cermet hard alloys, and steel R18 is given in Fig. 16. The value of this property is approximately the same for the borides and standard cermets, but the first have a higher scaling resistance than the latter.

We have studied the process of boriding titanium, zirconium, niobium, tantalum, molybdenum, and tungsten as carried out in a mixture of 84% (wt) of boron carbide and 16% (wt) of borax at temperature of 1100-1400°C for 1-8 hr [33]. Saturation was effected in graphite cartridges in an electric resistance furnace, through which dry hydrogen was passed at a rate of 0.8-1.2 liters/min.

X-ray diffraction, chemical, and metallographic analysis of the surface diffusion zones showed the formation on tungsten and molybdenum of at least two layers, separated by a fairly sharp boundary and differing in microhardness, structure, and etchability, the inner layers being close in composition to W_2B and Mo_2B, and the outer layers to $WB + W_2B_5$ and $Mo_2B_5 + MoB_2$. On tantalum, niobium, titanium, and zirconium, single-phase layers were found, consisting, respectively, of TaB_2, NbB_2, TiB_2, and ZrB_2. The results we have obtained on the composition of the boride layers on tungsten and molybdenum are in good agreement with the data in [25, 30], and on tantalum, niobium, titanium, and zirconium, with the data in [24]. Figure 17 shows typical microstructures of boride layers on the investigated metals.

The microhardness of the inner layers produced at maximum saturation temperatures on tungsten was equal to 2326-2460 kg/mm^2 and that of inner layers on molybdenum 2450-2580 kg/mm^2, while for the outer layers, the values were, respectively, 1960-2150 and 1120-1250 kg/mm^2. The microhardness of the boride layers on tantalum, niobium, titanium, and zirconium were, respectively, 2350-2500, 2500-2650, 2950-3100, and 2000-2200 kg/mm^2, i.e., they were close to the microhardness of the diborides of the corresponding metals.

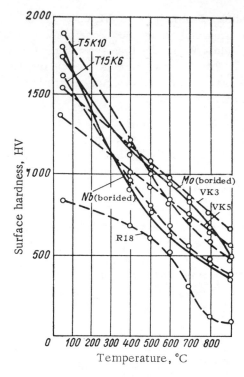

Fig. 16. Variation of hardness of boride layers on niobium and molybdenum, cermet hard alloys and high-speed steel when heated in a vacuum.

In all cases, the microhardness of the layers decreased insignificantly with decrease in boriding temperature. There was practically no appreciable variation in microhardness over the depth of the layer.

The following structural features of the boride layers were revealed by metallographic examination. On molybdenum, and particularly on tungsten, layers of a thickness of up to 100 μ were retained relatively strongly, were difficult to flake off even when struck, and practically did not crumble during the preparation of polished sections. Adhesion between the inner and outer layers was much weaker than that between the inner layer and the metal. This may evidently be explained by the fact that under all boriding conditions, the inner layer consists of columnar crystallites, extending in a direction perpendicular to the surface of the metal and penetrating the latter wedge fashion.

Boride layers on tantalum and niobium are dense, nonporous, and closely contiguous to the metal base. Even at saturation temperatures of 1400 and 1500°C, no gaps appear between the layers and the metal, but in the layers themselves cracks extending to the surface of the metal begin to form. At saturation temperatures of 1100-1200°C no cracks were found in the layers, and they adhered so strongly to the metal that they were not detached even when the metal was appreciably deformed.

30

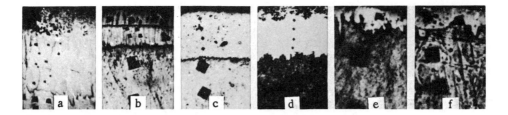

Fig. 17. Microstructure of boride layers: a) Tungsten, 1400°C, 1 hr, × 340; b) molybdenum, 1300°C, 1 hr, × 340; c) niobium, 1400°C, 1 hr, × 200; d) tantalum, 1400°C, 4 hr, × 200; e) titanium, 1400°C, 2 hr, × 450; f) zirconium, 1300°C, 4 hr, × 450.

The boundary between boride layer and metal base has a zigzag shape, with sharp but small projections and depressions (see Fig. 17), obviously promoting firm adhesion to the metal.

The boride layers on titanium and zirconium are much thicker than on tungsten, molybdenum, niobium, and tantalum for the same saturation conditions. These layers, being more porous, are more or less well bonded to the base. The structure of the boride layers on titanium and zirconium is much the same as on commercially pure iron, nickel, and cobalt [30], and consists of elongated wedges of boride phase, extending into the body of the metal along the intercrystalline boundaries, and growing densely together at the surface.

TABLE 8. Variation in Thickness of Diffusion Layers with Boriding Temperatures and Time

Metal	Temperature, °C	Time, hr	Total thickness of layer, μ	Metal	Temperature, °C	Time, hr	Total thickness of layer, μ
Tungsten	1100	6	45	Molybdenum	1100	6	50
		8	64			8	65
	1200	1	60		1200	1	40
		2	90			2	48
		4	120			4	63
Niobium	1100	1	4	Tantalum	1100	1	7
		2	6			2	10
		4	12			4	16
	1200	1	20		1200	1	12
		2	30			2	20
		4	45			4	42
Titanium	1100	6	7	Zirconium	1100	6	6
		8	8			8	9
	1200	1	6		1200	1	5
		2	7			2	6
		4	9			4	8

31

TABLE 9. Activation Energy and Equations of the Diffusion of Boron in Tungsten, Molybdenum, Tantalum, Niobium, Titanium, and Zirconium

Metal	Activation energy, cal/mole	Diffusion equation
Titanium	30,600 ± 7,800	$D = 8.9 \cdot 10^{-5} \cdot \exp\left(-\dfrac{15,300}{T}\right)$
Zirconium	34,500 ± 8,100	$D = 1.26 \cdot 10^{-4} \cdot \exp\left(-\dfrac{17,250}{T}\right)$
Niobium	59,000 ± 8,500	$D = 2.94 \cdot \exp\left(-\dfrac{29,500}{T}\right)$
Tantalum	47,000 ± 6,000	$D = 9.44 \cdot 10^{-4} \cdot \exp\left(-\dfrac{23,500}{T}\right)$
Molybdenum	45,000 ± 5,800	$D = 6.96 \cdot 10^{-2} \cdot \exp\left(-\dfrac{22,500}{T}\right)$
Tungsten	64,000 ± 6,300	$D = 1.48 \cdot \exp\left(-\dfrac{32,000}{T}\right)$

With increase in thickness of the boride layers, their brittleness, porosity, and number and size of the cracks increase, and their bond to the metal deteriorates in every case. As a rule, layers of a thickness not greater than 100 μ are sufficiently dense and firmly bonded to the base.

Investigation of the kinetics of the boriding process showed that the increase in thickness of the diffusion layer and the increase in weight of the specimens were represented by almost parabolic curves, which are characteristic of processes of re-action diffusion, and indicate the high density of the diffusion layers and the prefer-ential diffusion of the boron atoms through the lattice of the new phase formed in the metal [27, 30]. Table 8 shows the variation of layer thickness with time and temperature for some boriding conditions.

Using the method described in [24, 34], we determined the diffusion para-meters and found the temperature relations of the coefficients of diffusion of boron in the investigated metals (Table 9).

It has been shown [24] that when a nonmetal diffuses in transition metals of groups IV-VI of the periodic system, the unfilled d-levels of the metal atoms are "filled" because of the valence electrons of the nonmetals. At the same time, this process takes place more easily (with a lower activation energy) the higher the elec-tron deficiency of the d-level, i.e., the smaller the number (n) of electrons on it, and the lower the energy state of this level, the less is the degree of screening from the nucleus, i.e., the smaller is its principal quantum number (N). It is proposed to express the combined action of these factors qualitatively by the ratio 1/Nn, called the criterion of acceptor capacity of the d-electron shells. The greater this ratio, i.e., the smaller the numbers n and N, the more readily is a chemical compound hav-ing a total electron complement formed on diffusion of a nonmetal in the transition metals, and the lower is the activation energy of this process.

The values we have obtained for the activation energy confirm this supposition. In fact, with increase in the ratio 1/Nn, the activation energy is less (for titanium, the ratio 1/Nn is 0.176, for zirconium it is 0.125, tantalum 0.67, niobium 0.63, molybdenum and tungsten 0.05). It is interesting that the diffusion of boron (and carbon) in molybdenum takes place with a lower activation energy than in tungsten, although the ratio 1/Nn for these metals is the same, being 0.05; tungsten contains 4 electrons on the 5d-level, and molybdenum 5 electrons on the 4d-level. It may evidently be assumed that the energy state of the d-shell, characterized by its principal quantum number N, plays a greater part in the processes considered than the degree of its incompleteness, as defined by the number n of electrons in it.

Chapter 2

CARBIDE COATINGS

Without considering the carburization of iron and steel, which is a conventional, widely adopted, thoroughly developed, and fully described method of chemical heat-treatment [35-37], we shall dwell briefly on the production of layers of high-temperature carbides, principally on refractory metals. It is possible to produce them on steel and cast iron, as well as any other metals and alloys, for which the surface of the corresponding articles must be subjected to surface saturation by refractory metals and then by carbon.

A study has been made [38] of the influence on the wear resistance of steels, containing from 0.03 to 1.18% C, of the diffusion saturation of their surface by carbide-forming elements—chromium, vanadium, niobium, tungsten, molybdenum, and manganese. Saturation was effected from the gaseous phase under conditions ensuring the formation, on the surface, of layers consisting predominantly of carbide phases of the corresponding element. Chromizing, vanadizing, and niobizing were carried out at 1100°C for 6 hr, tungstenizing and molybdenizing at 1200°C, saturation with manganese at 800°C, also for 6 hr. Owing, evidently, to intense decarburizing in tungstenizing and molybdenizing, it was not possible to produce a single-phase carbide zone on the surface of steel. Saturation with manganese also failed to result in the formation of a carbide phase, with the exception of steel containing 1.03% C. The wear resistance of the surface layers, subjected to diffusion treatment with tungsten, molybdenum, and manganese, was approximately the same and somewhat lower than the wear resistance of the unsaturated steels. This may evidently be explained by the presence of texture and anisotropy of the surface layer of steels saturated with the above-mentioned elements, and also by the fact that the tests were carried out in a medium of a 0.5% aqueous solutions of potassium dichromate.

Chromium, which also does not form a single-phase carbide layer, increases the wear resistance of steels only 1.5 times. On the other hand, niobium and vanadium, for a carbon content of the steel of 0.15% or more, form carbides in the surface layers, and increase the wear resistance of the latter by 20-30 times.

The high properties of titanium carbide coatings, applied to the surface of cast iron and steel by deposition of titanium by means of plasma flame-spraying or by its deposition from a gaseous mixture containing $TiCl_4$, volatile hydrocarbons, and hydrogen, are discussed in [39]. The results of the investigations showed that after annealing at 930°C for 4 hr, a dense, light gray coating, consisting of TiC, was formed on cast iron and a number of steels. Traces of oxygen in the gases resulted

35

in the formation of a dull gray layer, and nitrogen colored TiC coatings dark gray, black, or yellow. Chromium steels and carbon steels are particularly favorable for the formation of TiC coatings. As has been remarked [45], the kinetics of the formation of titanium carbide is not yet sufficiently clear, but it was pointed out that the activation of the process is not due to the $TiCl_4$ and hydrogen contents, but to the carbon of the material and to the hydrocarbons. The rate of increase in thickness of the titanium carbide layer is a minimum in the first stage of the process of its formation and depends largely on the nature of the metal of the base. The cooling conditions of the coated parts in general do not affect the strength of adhesion of the TiC layer to the substrate metal, but a sharp variation in temperature from 0 to 1000°C may cause exfoliation of the coating, since the coefficient of linear expansion of titanium carbide is approximately half that of steel.

Despite the fact that the method of deposition of carbides (like other refractory compounds) has long been known [134], and a complete monograph has been written on the subject [131], the mechanism of carbide formation has not been adequately elucidated.

It is only recently that this question has begun to attract more attention.

In a discussion of the deposition of silicon carbide from the gas phase [135], the suggestion was made that its formation passes through a stage in which free silicon is liberated. This hypothesis is based on the fact that it was found impossible to deposit SiC from a mixture of silicon tetrachloride and toluene, if argon was used instead of hydrogen.

A detailed investigation [136] of the conditions for the formation of titanium carbide from the vapor-gas mixture $TiCl_4 + CH_4 + H_2$ led to a similar conclusion: The process of formation of TiC passes through a stage in which metallic titanium is liberated by the reduction of the titanium tetrachloride by hydrogen. It will be of interest to consider this investigation in more detail.

Deposition of titanium carbide was carried out in a special apparatus, ensuring a high degree of purity of the starting products and a wide variation of the deposition conditions. The substrates, on which the titanium carbide was deposited, were filaments of titanium, tungsten, and carbon. A study was first made of the possibility of depositing on incandescent filaments (1090-1630°C) metallic titanium from the mixture $TiCl_4 + H_2$ under conditions of a hundredfold excess of hydrogen. The results of these experiments amounted to the following.

The titanium filament was dissolved in every case, the rate of solution at first increasing, with increase in temperature, to a maximum (at 1350°C), after which it decreased. The explanation given for this fact was that at low temperatures (<1350°C) there was reduction of titanium according to the overall reaction

$$Ti + 3TiCl_4 = 4TiCl_3.$$

At higher temperatures (>1350°C), the function of hydrogen as reducing agent increased. The temperature of the commencement of the separation of metallic titanium, found by extrapolation of the experimental data, was 1750°C, in agreement with published data, according to which the formation of titanium occurred at a temperature lying above its melting point [137].

36

In experiments with tungsten and carbon filaments carried out under similar conditions, an increase in weight was found. X-ray diffraction analysis of the surface layers showed that in the case of tungsten, the surface layer consisted of tungsten—titanium alloy, while in the case of the carbon filament, the surface layer consisted of titanium carbide. The formation of the TiC or the W—Ti alloy is not due to the reduction of the titanium tetrachloride by the material of the filament, but to the fact that the carbon or tungsten, dissolving in the titanium, reduces its concentration, with the result that the equilibrium of the reaction

$$TiCl_4 + 2H_2 = Ti + 4HCl$$

is shifted in the reduction direction. In the case of the formation of titanium carbide, the process is greatly facilitated.

To assess the possibility of the reduction of $TiCl_4$ vapor by carbon, an incandescent graphite filament was held in a current of helium, saturated with titanium tetrachloride. X-ray diffraction analysis of the surface layer of the filament treated in this way failed to disclose any characteristic lines of titanium carbide or metallic titanium. Carbon was found to be incapable of reducing titanium tetrachloride not only to titanium or its carbide, but even to titanium trichloride.

According to [136], reduction of titanium tetrachloride vapor by hydrogen to the metal is impossible while the temperature of the reaction surface is below 1750°C. In the presence of carbon, this process is accompanied by the formation of TiC, the carbon acting solely to combine with the metal, liberated by the reduction of $TiCl_4$ by hydrogen, to form carbide. Thus, the rate of formation of TiC is determined by the rate of liberation of titanium and the rate of its carburization.

In the case of the deposition of TiC from the mixture $TiCl_4 + CH_4 + H_2$, liberation of the carbon combining with the titanium to form carbide is due, according to the authors' suggestion, to the reaction of the elementary decomposition of methane taking place on the incandescent surface. Methane is thermally unstable and readily decomposes at a temperature above 1000°C. Special experiments showed that with increase in the partial pressure of methane in the mixture, the rate of formation of TiC increased according to a linear law. With increase in the partial pressure of methane above $1.4 \cdot 10^{-2}$ atm, the rate of deposition of TiC as a function of the temperature (deposition was carried out on a tungsten filament at temperatures of 1320, 1680, and 1900°C) either increased insignificantly or remained constant. The linearity of the rate of deposition of TiC with increase in the partial pressure of the methane, and the absence of free carbon, are evidence of the fact that in the region of low partial pressures, the limiting link in the process of TiC formation is the rate of decomposition of the methane.

The authors of [136] thus arrive at the conclusion that the processes of the formation of titanium carbide on a carbon surface over which is passed a mixture of $TiCl_4 + H_2$ and the deposition of carbide from the mixture of $TiCl_4 + CH_4 + H_2$ differ merely in the fact that in the first case, the carbon is provided by diffusion from the carbon base, while in the second case, it is provided by the decomposition of methane from the gas mixture. In both cases, the first preliminary stage of the process is the separation of metallic titanium, due to the reduction of the titanium tetrachloride by hydrogen.

In cases where steels are coated with carbide-forming elements, but carbides are still not formed, they may be produced by subsequent carburization in the usual way.

Thus, for example, in [40], electrolytically deposited chromium coatings on steel were carburized to increase their wear resistance. The carburizing pack was a mixture of 50% wood charcoal, 20% calcined sodium carbonate, and 30% iron powder. The temperature of the process was 850-950°C, and the time was determined by the required depth of the diffusion layer. A time of 2-3 hr was sufficient for producing a layer 40-60 μ thick. Examination of the diffusion layer showed that it consisted of chromium carbides and double carbides of chromium and iron. With a hardness of 1500-1800 kg/mm^2, such a layer has a wear resistance several times greater than that of electroplated chromium.

According to the results of much earlier work [41], the wear resistance, resistance to high-temperature oxidation, and resistance to corrosion of electrolytic chromium coatings on steels 18KhNMA, GKh, and Armco iron were increased many times by carburizing, carried out in a mixture of gasoline vapor and hydrogen at temperatures of 950 and 1050°C for periods of 3 and 8 hr.

Metallographic and x-ray structure examinations of the structure of the coating (thickness 45 to 50 μ) revealed the presence of three successively deposited carbide layers: 1) a thin outer layer consisted of a higher chromium carbide (Cr_3C_2); 2) an intermediate thicker layer, assumed to consist of Cr_7C_3; 3) a thin inner layer, etching slightly, evidently consisting of $Cr_{23}C_6$. There was also a residual layer of uncarburized chromium, and below that the base metal, in which chromium had partly diffused. This diffusion layer ensured good mechanical bonding of the coating to the base. In the intermediate thicker layer, a network of veins was observed, formed on the site of cracks, which as a rule are produced in the process of the electrolytic deposition of chromium and penetrate the deposit throughout its entire depth. Diffusion of carbon takes place with particular intensity along these cracks, the space of the cracks being filled up with a higher chromium carbide. The formation of the veins is of importance in connection with the properties of the coating for two reasons. First, the system of cracks, along which corrosive reagents could penetrate to the base metal, is suppressed, and secondly, the veins as it were "reinforce" the coating, thereby increasing its mechanical strength.

Comparative tests on the wear resistance of specimens chromium-plated only, and chromium-plating followed by carburizing, showed that the latter had considerably better properties. Thus, a chromium-plated Armco iron specimen paired with steel with 0.1% C, after 100,000 revolutions had a loss in weight of about 50 mg, and fine, annular scratches were left on its surface. A carburized specimen (1050°C, 3 hr), under the same conditions, showed a loss in weight of only 0.4 mg and traces of abrasion were absent. A specimen, carburized at a temperature of 1050°C for 8 hr, after 10 cycles (1,000,000 revolutions) suffered no loss in weight and showed no traces of abrasion. Steel 18KhNMA, chromium-plated only, and carburized at 1050°C for 3 hr, after chromium plating, paired with antifriction cast iron, showed the following results. The chromium-plated specimen, after 400,000 revolutions, showed a loss in weight of 4 mg, and after 800,000 revolutions, one of 15 mg, and deep scores and holes were visible on its surface. The specimen which was chromium-plated, and then carburized, showed no signs of wear, even after 1,000,000 revolutions. The authors assume that carburized chromium coatings should have high wear-resistance properties also at elevated temperatures (including 1000°C).

The high-temperature oxidation resistance of the specimens was determined by heating them in an open furnace in an air atmosphere at a temperature of 1000°C. After heating for 6 hr, the specimen which had been only chromium-plated could no longer be tested, since its entire chromium layer was oxidized.

Corrosion tests in 30% sulfuric, hydrochloric, and nitric acids at room temperature showed sufficiently high acid resistance of the carburized chromium coatings.

It is also possible to treat the surface of articles simultaneously with, for instance, mixtures of powders of a refractory metal and carbon, or to precipitate high-temperature compounds on the surface from the gas phase. These methods, of which there are numerous modifications, have scarcely been investigated and await development. For example, a description is given in [42] of the production of chemically stable and wear-resistant coatings of titanium carbide on cast iron, formed by the deposition of TiC from the gas phase according to the reactions:

$$TiCl_4 + 2H_2 + C = TiC + 4HCl,$$
$$TiCl_4 + 2Fe + C = TiC + 2FeCl_2$$

followed by heat-treatment.

Carbide diffusion coatings on refractory metals may be produced by ordinary carburization with solid carbon, as a rule in a protective atmosphere, or in an atmosphere of a stimulator, for example, hydrogen, which forms hydrocarbons, the carbon being thus transferred through the gas phase.

The diffusion of carbon in titanium, zirconium, niobium, tantalum, molybdenum, and tungsten has been studied [24]. The specimens were saturated with carbon in cartridges containing lampblack, which had been heated for the removal of moisture and volatile matter, and contained 99.8% C. The protective gas used was well-purified hydrogen. The carburization time at the selected temperatures was 2 hr. According to the results of x-ray and metallographic examinations, when carbon diffuses in titanium and zirconium, the monocarbides TiC and ZrC are formed, while in niobium, tantalum, molybdenum, and tungsten, carbides of the composition Me_2C are formed. On titanium a porous, exfoliating carbide layer is formed; on zirconium, the layer has a needle-like structure and is well applied to the coated metal. It is assumed that the growth of the zirconium carbide grains and their occurrence in the form of needles is due to the reduction in specific volume in the formation of the carbide from the metal. In the diffusion of carbon in niobium, the layer is applied closely to the base, but is not held very strongly, owing to the frontal character of the diffusion. The layers on tantalum are porous, but are applied closely to the base, and have a frontal character. On tungsten, apart from the principal layer of W_2C adjoining the metal, there is also a very thin outer layer of the carbide WC. The same phases of tungsten carburizing were found in a previous investigation [34].

TABLE 10. Influence of the Conditions of the Diffusion Treatment of Titanium by Wood Charcoal on the Properties of Carburized Specimens

Temperature, °C	Time, hr	Depth of layer, μ	Surface hardness, HV, kg/mm^2	Hardness at a depth of 100μ, HV, kg/mm^2	Hardness at a depth of 200μ, HV, kg/mm^2	Ultimate tensile strength, kg/mm^2	Elongation, %
850	8	106	1500	640	250	46,4	30,8
	16	86	3200	550	355	40,3	20,0
	24	85	3200	575	430	41,3	12,5
	48	140	3200	705	540	46,4	10,8
900	8	183	1500	880	540	44,4	19,5
	16	143	1500	720	490	41,3	6,0
	48	157	1500	760	555	49,6	8,0
950	8	87	3200	585	405	45,8	6,0
	16	88	3200	530	460	40,7	—
	24	172	3200	740	545	41,8	6,0
	48	205	3200	760	605	25,5	4,0

In the diffusion layers of carbides on titanium, zirconium, niobium, and tantalum, the carbon content varies according to the homogeneity regions of the corresponding carbide phases, this appearing in a variation in hardness, which falls from the peripheral part of the layer to the layer adjoining the coated metal. Data are given in [43] on the carburization of titanium articles in wood charcoal in tightly closed iron containers. The results obtained are shown in Table 10.

In an examination of the microstructure, it was found that the outer layer of the carburized part consisted principally of titanium carbide, the transition layer consisted of globular precipitations of a solid solution of carbon in titanium on a background of a lamellar solid solution, and the central portion of the article had a relatively fine-grained structure of lamellar character.

The data of Table 10 show that the reduction in strength of carburized titanium is considerable, but much less than, for example, in nitriding. With suitable choice of the carburizing conditions, it is possible to produce surface strengthening, thereby retaining the possibility of using carburized titanium as constructional material.

A study has been made [44] of the carburization of commercial titanium mark VT1 in a vacuum furnace in metal capsules with ground carbon and graphite. At a temperature of 950°C and in a time of 4 hr, a TiC layer having a thickness of up to 0.02 mm with a microhardness of 1290 kg/mm^2 was obtained. The layer was well bonded to the base metal.

An investigation was made of gas carburization of titanium in an argon atmosphere containing additions of 0.5-5% CO, propane, or methane. It was found that at 5% CO, a solid solution of oxygen in α-Ti was formed, but there was a TiC skin 10 μ thick. The layer had high wear resistance. Thinner layers (2.5-5 μ) were attached better to the metal and had better wear resistance. Carburizing with methane and propane considerably increased the hydrogen content of the metal (by about ten times).

A method for the surface saturation of titanium by diffusion in a current of a mixture of 0.5-1% (vol) of gaseous hydrocarbons of the series C_nH_{2n+2} (for example, methane, propane) or the series C_nH_{2n} (for example, propylene) with an inert gas (argon) forms the subject of a patent [45]. Optimum conditions of the process are: Temperature 930-980°C, propane content of gas mixture 0.8% (vol), time 8 hr, rate of flow of mixture about 11 cm^3/min for each 100 cm^2 of area of the article. The articles should be cooled in an inert medium. These conditions ensure the formation of hard carbide layers, firmly bonded to the base metal and having good wear and erosion resistance. Examination of the structure of the layer showed it to consist of a titanium carbide lattice with a deficit in carbon (8-12% C), hardness 1200-1500 Knoop. Optimum properties were also found in a layer 5 μ thick, applied to a polished surface.

The carburizing process is greatly accelerated when the metal being saturated is heated by high-frequency currents. Thus, in the carburization of titanium alloys of the type VT4 and VT6, with the application of a paste and high-frequency induction heating in a helium atmosphere [138], a diffusion layer having a thickness of ~ 0.25 mm and a hardness of 1780 HV and high wear resistance was produced in 15 min at a heating temperature of 1000-1100°C. The carburizing paste consisted of silver graphite and binder, and after being applied to the surface of the part by means of a compressed air spray-gun, was air dried before heating. After the articles have been heated, the paste cakes and comes off the surface in the form of a crust. It is stated that wear resistance is determined by the thickness of the layer, and its optimum value must be selected for specific wear conditions.

Carburizing of high-purity tantalum in a mixture of argon, hydrogen, and hydrocarbons has been investigated [139]. A tantalum wire 0.25 mm thick was carburized for 20 sec, 1.4 min, and 30 min at a temperature of 2400°C, the wire being carburized throughout after 30 min. Comparative investigation of the carburizing of polycrystalline wires and single-crystal wires showed no appreciable difference in the rate of the process. It is interesting to note that in the opinion of the authors [139], satisfactory carburizing of tantalum cannot be effected by means of gases other than hydrocarbons, with a low partial pressure of the latter in the gaseous mixture. For successful carburizing, all the gaseous components used must be subjected to careful purification (from O_2, CO_2, N_2, etc.).

On the basis of available data, for producing a high-grade carburized layer on titanium, it is recommended [44] that carburization should be carried out from the solid phase in a vacuum, and from the gas phase in an atmosphere of neutral gas containing an exactly proportioned amount of carburizing gas. We have investigated the carburizing process of titanium, zirconium, molybdenum, and tungsten under conditions similar to those described in [24]. Saturation of titanium and zirconium was carried out in the temperature range 900-1300°C, molybdenum 1400-1700°C, and tungsten 1600-1900°C. The duration of treatment at each temperature was 1-8 hr.

X-ray diffraction, chemical, and metallographic analysis, as well as microhardness measurements of the diffusion zones, showed that under all the conditions investigated, two layers were formed on tungsten, an outer thin layer consisting of

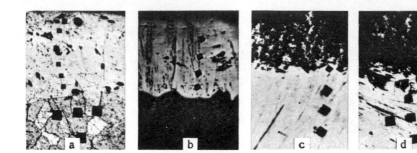

Fig. 18. Microstructure of carbide layers: a) Tungsten, 1900°C, 1 hr, × 200; b) molybdenum, 1500°C, 4 hr, × 170; c) titanium, 1200°C, 1 hr, × 200; d) zirconium, 1100°C, 4 hr, × 200.

the carbide WC and an inner thick layer consisting of the carbide W_2C, while on molybdenum, titanium, and zirconium, only single-phase layers were formed, consisting, respectively, of the carbides Mo_2C, TiC, and ZrC. These results are in agreement with the results in [24, 34, 43-45].

Figure 18 shows typical microstructures of the carbide layers on tungsten, molybdenum, titanium, and zirconium. Metallographic analysis of these layers, produced under different carburizing conditions, enables the following conclusions to be made.

The thickness of the W_2C layer increases with increase in the carburizing time and particularly the temperature, while the WC layers grow very slowly. The boundary between the W_2C layer and the metal is relatively flat and smooth, which confirms the conclusions made in [34] regarding the absence of any appreciable difference in the rate of diffusion of carbon along the grain boundaries of polycrystalline tungsten compared with the rate of diffusion through the body of the grain. The boundary between the MoC_2 layer and molybdenum has a similar character. A boundary of this form between the carbide phase and metal is evidently one of the causes of the relatively poor adhesion of the carbide layers to the metal base. In addition, weak adhesion is due to the considerable difference in the specific volume of coefficients of thermal expansion of tungsten and molybdenum, on the one hand, and the carbides W_2C and Mo_2C, on the other. In practice, layers not exceeding 50-70 μ in thickness adhere satisfactorily to the metal base.

Layers of W_2C, regardless of their thickness, had thin, radial cracks passing through the entire thickness of the layer as far as the metal, while in layers of Mo_2C (only for a thickness greater than 80 μ) longitudinal cracks were found in places, but no radial cracks.

The microhardness of W_2C and Mo_2C layers, obtained at the maximum saturation temperatures, was, respectively, 1650-1780 and 1420-1500 kg/mm^2. At lower carburizing temperatures, only a slight decrease in microhardness was observed, which may evidently be explained by the relatively narrow homogeneity ranges of the W_2C and Mo_2C phases. No variation was found in the microhardness over the depth of the layers.

The carbide layers on titanium and zirconium, produced at temperatures of 900-1000°C for a treatment time of 1-8 hr, were compact, practically without cracks, and well applied to the metal base. The boundary between the carbide layers and metal under all treatment conditions was relatively even and smooth, which, as in the case of tungsten and molybdenum, is evidence of the approximately identical rate of diffusion of the carbon along the boundary and through the body of the titanium and zirconium grains.

The microhardness of the carbide layers formed at these temperatures was 1140-1300 kg/mm^2 for titanium and 1020-1100 kg/mm^2 for zirconium. The results obtained are in good agreement with those given in [44, 45], in which carburizing of titanium was studied under conditions similar to ours.

With increase in the carburizing temperature (1100-1300°C), the hardness of the layers increased, but their density decreased, porosity increased, adhesion to the metal deteriorated, brittleness increased, and longitudinal and transverse cracks were formed in the layers. The microhardness of a TiC layer formed at a temperature of 1200°C was 1820-2000 kg/mm^2 and that of a ZrC layer was 1600-1800 kg/mm^2, while at a temperature of 1300°C, the corresponding values were 2600-2700 and 2500-2650 kg/mm^2. Such a pronounced increase in the microhardness of the carbide diffusion layers on titanium and zirconium, occurring with increase in saturation temperature, has also been noted previously [24], and may be explained by the wide homogeneity ranges of TiC and ZrC phases, and their higher carbon content with increase in carburizing temperature.

Determination of the increase in weight of the specimens and the thickness of the layers as a function of the duration of treatment at each temperature showed that the kinetics of the carburizing processes for tungsten, molybdenum, titanium, and zirconium follow a parabolic time law, characteristic of reaction diffusion.

TABLE 11. Thickness of Carburized Layers on Titanium, Zirconium, Molydenum, and Tungsten in Relation to Saturation Temperature and Time

Metal	Temperature, °C	Time, hr	Total layer thickness, μ	Metal	Temperature, °C	Time, hr	Total layer thickness, μ
Tungsten	1600	1	15	Molybdenum	1400	1	10
		2	32			2	35
		4	45			4	45
	1700	1	30		1500	1	40
		2	47			2	48
		4	60			4	110
Titanium	1900	1	18	Zirconium	900	1	23
		2	35			2	30
		4	60			4	36
	1000	1	50		1000	1	35
		2	60			2	60
		4	85			4	80

TABLE 12. Activation Energy and Equations of the Diffusion of Carbon in Tungsten, Molybdenum, Titanium, and Zirconium

Metal	Activation energy, cal/mole	Diffusion equation
Ti	33,000 ± 5,950	$D = 2.04 \cdot 10^{-3} \cdot \exp\left(-\dfrac{16,500}{T}\right)$
Zr	41,000 ± 9,600	$D = 3.44 \cdot 10^{-2} \cdot \exp\left(-\dfrac{20,500}{T}\right)$
Mo	83,000 ± 8,600	$D = 7.80 \cdot 10^{2} \cdot \exp\left(-\dfrac{41,500}{T}\right)$
W	104,000 ± 9,200	$D = 1.56 \cdot 10^{3} \cdot \exp\left(-\dfrac{52,000}{T}\right)$

Table 11 shows how the thickness of the diffusion layers depends on the carburizing conditions.

Using the method described in [24, 34], the diffusion constants were calculated, and the temperature relationships of the coefficients of diffusion of carbon in the investigated metals were determined (Table 12).

Comparison of the data of Tables 9 and 12 shows that the values of the activation energy for the diffusion of carbon in the transition metals are higher than the corresponding values for the diffusion of boron in the same metals. This has already been noted and explained [24], the authors basing their considerations on the assumption that in the case of reaction diffusion of nonmetals in transition metals, inhibition of the process is determined not by the size of the atom of the diffusing nonmetal, but by its ionization potential, characterizing the ability of the nonmetal atom to give up its valence electrons for the formation of a common electron group with the atoms of the metal. The lower is the ionization potential of the nonmetal atom, the easier (with less activation energy) will the process of the reaction diffusion in the transition metal take place (the ionization potential of carbon is 11.24 eV and that of boron is 8.28 eV).

Chapter 3

NITRIDE COATINGS

The nitriding of steel and cast iron has been thoroughly studied and discussed in the relevant literature [35-37]. We shall deal merely with investigations which concern the nitriding of refractory metals, carried out as a rule in an atmosphere of nitrogen or ammonia. According to the conditions of the process and the purity of the nitriding gases, simple or complex solid solutions may be formed, or chemical compounds, consisting of atoms of the metal subjected to saturation, and atoms of the metalloids: nitrogen, oxygen, hydrogen. The process of nitriding powdered refractory metals (titanium, zirconium, vanadium, niobium, tantalum, and chromium) has been studied in detail [46]. Investigations on the nitriding of compact refractory metals and alloys, however, are still definitely insufficient. The nitriding of titanium and its alloys has been studied the most.

The nitriding of titanium by nitrogen and ammonia in the case of the latter results in large depths of the diffusion layer and high hardness of the latter, but at the same time, the diffusion of hydrogen causes increased brittleness [43]. Although the hydrogen may be removed to a considerable extent by vacuum treatment, the method of nitriding by means of ammonia, however, is uneconomical. The thickness of the layers and the properties of titanium after nitriding in a nitrogen atmosphere [43] are given in Table 13. In nitriding by means of ammonia in the same temperature range, elongation falls to 2%, and impact toughness to 0.3-0.5 kg-m/cm². The data given show that the depth of the growth layer does not obey a parabolic time law.

Similar results were obtained by A.N. Minkevich et al. [47]. Pure titanium and titanium alloyed with chromium and tungsten were nitrided in ammonia at temperatures of 850, 950, and 1050°C for different lengths of time. It was found that with low rates of flow of ammonia, the layer was deeper in a number of cases than with high rates of flow, and in addition, with increase in temperature, the optimum rate of flow of ammonia also increased for the production of a layer of maximum depth. It was noted that the depth of the nitrided layer did not vary according to a curve similar to a parabola, but according to a curve with a maximum. X-ray diffraction study of the surface layer showed that at a temperature of 1050°C, it consisted of a solid solution of titanium nitride and hydride (in the case where the ammonia had not been purified sufficiently from oxygen and TiO). The formation of solid solutions of TiN, TiH, and TiO is facilitated by the uniformity of the crystal lattice of these compounds and the similarity of their lattice constants. At a temperature of 950°C, only a solid solution of nitrogen and hydrogen in titanium was found.

45

TABLE 13. Influence of the Conditions of the Diffusion Treatment of Titanium by Nitrogen on the Properties of Nitrided Specimens

Temperature, °C	Time, hr	Depth of layer, μ	Surface hardness, HV, kg/mm²	Hardness at a depth of 100 μ, HV, kg/mm²	Elastic limit, kg/mm²	Ultimate tensile strength, kg/mm²	Elongation, %	Impact toughness, kg-m/cm²
	8	25	1132	250	29.0	37.8	36.5	22.8
	16	42	1206	360	26.0	36.4	45	27.6
700	24	33	1332	285	23.5	37.3	45	26.0
	48	35	1246	445	27.0	36.6	48.5	25.4
	8	13	1003	205	26.0	36.7	43.0	25.1
	16	40	1333	325	26.4	36.4	45.0	21.1
800	24	25	1520	280	24.5	39.5	45.0	26.8
	48	44	1426	360	26.0	37.4	39.5	23.5
	8	53	1500	375	36.0	41.7	36.5	17.1
	16	61	1500	470	22.5	46.7	25.0	11.0
900	24	76	1500	500	39.0	47.7	30.0	10.6
	48	31	1500	390	43.5	48.1	43.5	9.0

According to the results of this investigation, the nitriding of titanium in ammonia increases its wear resistance by tens of times, but reduces its strength and ductility, especially if the process is carried out at high temperatures and for considerable lengths of time. This is because of the grain growth of the titanium and saturation of the latter with hydrogen with increase in temperature and nitriding time. The conditions for the nitriding of titanium in ammonia must therefore be selected with the technologically minimum parameters.

Alloying of titanium with tungsten results in a sharp decrease in the depth of the nitrided layer. An alloy of titanium with 5% chromium, when nitrided, showed an increase in wear resistance of 42-167 times (depending on the saturation conditions) compared with nonnitrided commercial titanium. Since nitriding in ammonia inevitably leads to embrittlement of the articles, investigations were conducted [44, 48, 49] on the nitriding of titanium in a mixture of argon and nitrogen. It was found [48] that a vacuum accelerated the diffusion of nitrogen in the metal. Evidently, in rarefied nitrogen, there is no formation of a TiN skin, retarding the solution of nitrogen in titanium. Nitriding in a medium containing an adjusted proportion of nitrogen is accompanied by the difficulty of introducing the small quantity of nitrogen which has to be added to the argon. According to [48], the optimum amount of nitrogen at 800°C is 0.1% (Fig. 19).

The nitriding of titanium in a mixture of carefully purified argon and nitrogen has been described [49]. The nitriding apparatus is shown diagrammatically in Fig. 20. The quantity of argon was adjusted to 50 cm³/min by means of a bubbler con-

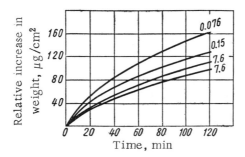

Fig. 19. Influence of nitrogen pressure on the
increase in weight of specimens as a function
of heating time at 800°C.

taining concentrated H_2SO_4. The quantity of nitrogen was equal to 6, 4, 2, 1, and
0.5% in relation to the argon and was adjusted in the same way.

The specimens were prepared from iodide titanium and alloys of titanium with
small additions of aluminum, manganese, silicon, and tin. Before nitriding, all the
specimens were subjected to vacuum annealing ($2 \cdot 10^{-3}$ mm Hg) at 800°C for 2 hr.
Nitriding took place at 850°C for periods of from 2 to 30 hr, and various partial
pressures of nitrogen in the argon. It was found that the depth of the nitrided layer
decreased with increase in the nitrogen content of the working mixture (Fig. 21).

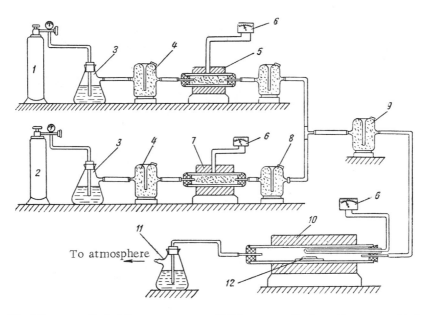

Fig. 20. Diagram of nitriding apparatus. 1) Nitrogen cylinder; 2) argon cylinder;
3) bubbler; 4) Tishchenko bottle containing asbestos fibers saturated with sodium
hydroxide; 5) furnace with copper turnings; 6) potentiometer; 7) furnace with titanium turnings; 8) vessel with aluminum; 9) vessel with $CaCl_2$; 10) working
furnace; 11) bubbler; 12) specimens.

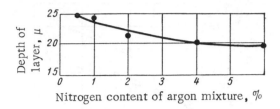

Fig. 21. Depth of nitrided layer of an iodide titanium specimen as a function of the nitrogen content in the argon mixture (850°C, 4 hr).

X-ray structure analysis showed that the surface layer of nitrided specimens consisted of TiN + TiN$_2$ when the nitrogen content of the mixture exceeded 0.5%. This nitride skin prevents the diffusion of nitrogen into the body of the metal, and at the same time diminishes the thickness of the total saturated surface layer. A reduction in the amount of nitrogen to 0.5% or less results in the formation on the surface of a solid solution of α-Ti with inclusions of TiN with a gradual transition to a pure solution of nitrogen in α-titanium. Increase in the nitriding time produces an increase in weight and in the depth (Fig. 22) of the diffusion layer of the specimens, while when the treatment time exceeds 24 hr, even with a 0.5% nitrogen content of the mixture (partial pressure 0.005 atm), a nitride skin is formed on the surface of the specimens. The partial pressure of nitrogen accepted as the optimum, 0.005-0.04 atm, depends on the total surface area of the treated parts, temperature, and duration of the process, as well as on the chemical composition of the material of which the parts are made. By means of a nitriding mixture of such a composition, it is possible to produce at 850°C in 20 hr on commercial titanium a strengthened layer without a titanium nitride skin on the surface. The depth of the layer is 0.10-0.12 mm and the surface microhardness is 1200 kg/mm^2, corresponding approximately to 62-63 HRC.

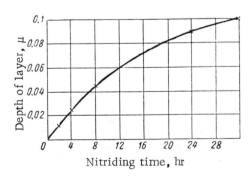

Fig. 22. Dependence of diffusion layer on nitriding time of iodide titanium specimens at constant partial pressure of nitrogen (0.005 atm) and 850°C.

TABLE 14. Influence of Alloying Titanium on the Depth of Diffusion of Nitrogen, Increase in Weight of Specimens, and Microhardness Distribution at 850°C

Alloying element	Amount of alloying element, %	Presence or absence of nitride layer (according to micro- hardness and color)	Microhardness, kg/mm², at a depth of 0.1 mm and load 100 g	Depth of layer, μ	Increase in weight of specimens, mg/cm² of surface	Duration of treatment, hr
Aluminum	1.74	Absent	824	50	0.92	4
	3.00	''	1000	56	0.95	4
	3.75	''	1000	50	0.85	4
	5.00	''	1100	48	0.73	4
	5.00	Present	1200	120	–	24
Manga-	1.35	Absent	824	27	0.72	4
nese	2.45	''	1000	–	0.71	4
	3.76	''	1100	28	0.70	4
	6.54	Present	1200	25	0.70	4
	6.54	–	1500	68	–	24
Silicon	0.66	Absent	1100	20	0.52	4
	1.62	''	1100	18	0.46	4
	1.62	Present	1200	65	–	24
Tin	0.86	Absent	824	28	0.53	4
	1.58	''	824	24	0.74	4
	1.58	Present	1100	83	–	24
Iodide ti-	–	Absent	824	25	0.82	4
tanium	–	Present	1200	90	1.05	24

Table 14 shows the effect of alloying with aluminum, silicon, tin, and manganese on the titanium nitriding process.

Analysis of the data presented shows that aluminum accelerates the diffusion of nitrogen in titanium, increasing the depth of the diffusion layer and the increase in weight of the specimens, while manganese, tin, and particularly silicon act in the opposite direction.

The process of nitriding titanium in a stream of pure nitrogen at a temperature of 700-1050°C for periods of up to 10 hr has been studied [50]. The increase in weight and hardness of the specimens was determined, and the surface layer was studied by the methods of microstructure examination and electron diffraction analysis. It was found that an appreciable increase in weight commenced at 800°C and followed a parabolic law up to 1000°C. Electron diffraction analysis showed that after nitriding at temperatures of 800°C and above, titanium nitride TiN was formed in the surface layer. There was no very noticeable increase in hardness at 800°C, but at a temperature above 900°C, the thickness and hardness of the layer gradually increased with time. For example, after nitriding for 1, 5, and 10 hr at a temperature of 900°C, the HV surface hardness was, respectively, 325, 425, and 475 kg/mm^2. It is pointed out [50] that according to the combination of properties and structure of the nitrided layer and core, the optimum results were obtained at 850-900°C. According to [49], nitriding in molecular nitrogen gives optimum results in the temperature range 850-950°C for a duration of up to 24 hr. According to these results, however, nitriding with 100% nitrogen has a number of drawbacks compared with nitriding at low partial pressures of nitrogen. These drawbacks are mainly due to the formation of a nitride skin which reduces the rate of diffusion of the nitrogen into the body of the metal, whereby the depth of the strengthened layer is decreased, and which is detrimental from the point of view of the subsequent treatment of the article. According to other authors, nitriding of titanium and its alloys in pure, molecular nitrogen ensures the production of the necessary properties of the surface layer [51-53].

Titanium was nitrided in a current of nitrogen at a temperature of 850°C and duration of treatment of 16-80 hr for the purpose of increasing its wear resistance, resistance to corrosion, and its mechanical properties [51]. As shown by tests, the nitrided titanium satisfactorily operated without lubricant when paired with cast iron, hard chromized coatings and nonnitrided titanium. In operation with a lubricant, good results were found when the nitrided titanium was paired with bronze, carbon steel, low-alloy steel, bakelite, and chromium-plated surfaces. Nitrided titanium showed high corrosion resistance in heated hydrochloric, sulfuric, phosphoric, hydrofluoric, nitric, and other acids. As pointed out by the authors [51], nitriding does not appreciably affect the mechanical properties of titanium. In [52], specimens of commercial titanium and heat-resistant titanium alloy with 6% Al and 4% V were nitrided in purified nitrogen at 980°C for 4-168 hr. The nitrided layer on commercial titanium was considerably thicker than on the alloy containing 6% Al and 4% V, and its hardness attained 1650 HV. It was found that the values of impact toughness of nitrided and nonnitrided titanium were almost the same, while they were considerably lower in the case of the alloy. This was explained by the presence in the alloy of nitrided grains situated at an angle of 45° to the surface and extending to a considerable depth. They evidently acted as stress concentrators, resulting in a considerable drop in impact toughness. According to the results of this investigation, the thickness of the nitrided layer on titanium varied with increase in the duration of treatment according to a parabolic law, and was 0.2 mm after nitriding for 168 hr.

Nitriding of titanium and its alloys in pure nitrogen has also been studied in [53]. The optimum nitriding conditions adopted were as follows: Saturation temperature 950°C, time 24-30 hr, rate of supply of nitrogen 0.12-0.15 liter/min. At lower temperatures nitrogen diffusion was slow, while at higher temperatures, brittleness of the layer and of the metal itself increased considerably. Treatment for longer than 30 hr failed to give any appreciable increase in thickness of the nitrided layer. Under optimum nitriding conditions, a layer 80 μ thick with a surface hardness HV = 780-850 kg/mm^2 was produced on forged commercially pure titanium mark VT1.

TABLE 15. Influence of Nitriding and Additional Treatment after Nitriding on the Mechanical Properties of Specimens of Alloy VT1

Treatment	σ_b, kg/mm²	δ,%	ψ,%	a_k, kg-m/cm²
Initial alloy, annealed in vacuum at 800°C for 2 hr	45.1	33.0	65.2	14.8
Nitrided at 950°C, 30 hr (nitrided layer not removed)	55.5	15.1	39.2	5.3
The same, layer removed for a depth of 0.5 mm	51.0	20.1	53.9	7.6
The same, layer removed for a depth of 1 mm	48.2	23.2	54.2	9.7
The same, layer removed for a depth 1.5 mm	–	–	–	12.0
Nitrided at 950°C, 3 hr + annealing in vacuum 800°C, 2 hr, pressure $3 \cdot 10^{-4}$ mm Hg (nitrided layer not removed)	54.2	19.4	35.0	10.6

The nitrided layer consisted of several zones. On the surface was a golden film of TiN having a thickness amounting to tenths of a micron, below it was a zone 8-10 μ thick having a microhardness of 1500 kg/mm² and a nitrogen content of 10-12%, and consisting of titanium nitrides, according to x-ray structural analysis. The nitride zone was followed by the thickest zone (60-80 μ) with gradually diminishing microhardness (from 1300 to 700 kg/mm²) and containing 4 to 1.5% N. X-ray structural analysis showed that this zone consisted of α-Ti with increased lattice parameters. Investigation of the mechanical properties of the nitrided specimens subjected to various additional treatments showed (Table 15) that annealing in a vacuum at a temperature of 800°C for 2 hr at a pressure of $3 \cdot 10^{-4}$ mm Hg reduces the brittleness of the layer and increases the ductility characteristic by 10-15%.

As has been pointed out [53], the principal cause of the reduction (by 25-30%) of the ductility of titanium after nitriding is grain growth as the result of long high-temperature heating. Another cause of the reduction in ductility is the rather deep penetration of nitrogen into the tested specimen in the nitriding process, evidence of which is provided by Table 15. The ductility of the titanium increases with increase in depth of layer removed.

An investigation of the influence of alloying titanium with various elements showed that 2-2.5% Al, up to 2% Si and 1.5% Mn produced an increase in depth of the nitrided layer. At a higher content of these elements in the alloy, the depth of the layer decreased. Chromium and iron reduced the depth of the nitrided layer independently of their content in the alloy. A trial was made in this investigation of the nitriding of some ternary alloys of titanium, and it was also shown that the alloys VT2, VT3, VT5, and VT6 did not nitride as well as alloy VT1. The advantages of nitriding titanium in an atmosphere of pure nitrogen, using the high-frequency method of heating the specimens, are given in [54]. The investigations were made on cylindrical specimens of alloys VT4 and VT6, using the apparatus GZ-46 with a 40-kva 500-kc tube oscillator. After filling the chamber containing the specimens with purified and dried nitrogen, the specimens were heated to temperatures

51

of 850-1100°C (on the surface) and held at the selected temperature for 6, 10, 15, and 20 min. The pressure of the nitrogen in the chamber was kept within the limits of 40-50 mm water gauge.

At the maximum temperature, after 20 min, a layer 30 μ thick and a micro-hardness of 2000 kg/mm^2 had been formed. Wear tests on specimens paired with hardened steel U12A under conditions of dry friction showed practically no change in the nitrided specimens.

The high-temperature oxidation of the nitrided specimens 3 mm in diameter and 200 mm long in air at 1000°C, heated by direct passage of current, was found to be four times that of the nonnitrided specimens (testing was carried out to failure of the specimens). As stated in [54], induction heating by high-frequency currents during nitriding considerably increases the rate of formation of the dif-fusion layer, cuts down the length of the saturation process to tenths of its previous value, and is thus an effective method of strengthening the surface of titanium and its alloys. In addition, heating by high-frequency currents makes it possible to raise the temperature of the surface layer only, without affecting the body of the metal, the optimum structure and properties of which are provided by the prelimin-ary treatment.

V.I. Arkharov and his collaborators have investigated the reaction diffusion in complex metal-gas systems [55-57].

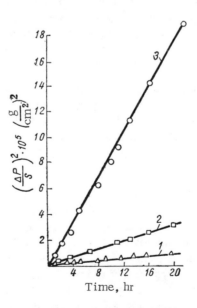

Figure 23. Increase in weight of specimens at 1100°C versus duration of carburizing (1), carbonitriding (2), and nitriding (3).

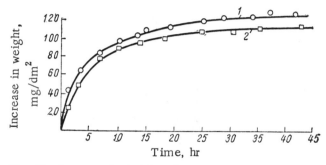

Fig. 24. Increase in weight of specimens versus time at 1000°C in an air atmosphere. 1) Carbide coatings; 2) carbonitride coatings.

The structure and properties of carbonitrided coatings on chromium have been studied [55]. Specimens of steel St. 3, after chromium plating, were treated in a mixture of gasoline vapor and nitrogen at temperatures of 700, 900, 1000, and 1100°C. The composition of the medium was determined by means of the temperature of a thermostat, which contained the saturator with the gasoline and through which oxygen-free nitrogen was passed from a cylinder at a rate of 10 liters/hr. X-ray structural and metallographic analysis of the coating showed its outer layer to consist of Cr_3C_2, its middle layer of Cr_7C_3, and its inner layer adjacent the metallic base of Cr_2N. Furthermore, if the applied chromium layer had a textured structure, the Cr_2N layer also had a texture, following the principle of orientational and dimensional correspondence.

The kinetic characteristics of carburizing, carbonitriding, and nitriding are shown in Fig. 23.

The form of the curves shows that reaction diffusion in Cr−N, Cr−C, Cr−C−N systems obeys a parabolic law, the diffusion mobility of the nitrogen atoms being substantially higher than that of the carbon atoms.

Acid-resistance and wear-resistance tests, carried out by the method described in [41], showed that carbonitrided chromium coatings were not inferior in properties to carburized coatings. Comparative tests of the high-temperature oxidation of carbonitrided and nitrided chromium coatings also gave the same results (Fig. 24). Such agreement in the properties of the coatings was quite natural since in both cases the surface layers consisted of the same phases − rhombic (Cr_3C_2) and hexagonal (Cr_7C_3) chromium carbides. These layers also determined the above-mentioned properties of the coatings.

The carbonitrided layer was formed as the result of the diffusion of nitrogen and carbon atoms through corresponding layers of chromium carbides and nitride. "Interdiffusion" of chromium atoms was not observed. The front of the reaction between nitrogen and chromium was situated at the Cr−Cr_2N interface, while that between carbon and chromium was situated at the boundary between Cr_2N and Cr_7C_3. The well-defined boundary between Cr_2N and Cr_7C_3 indicates the limited solubility of these phases.

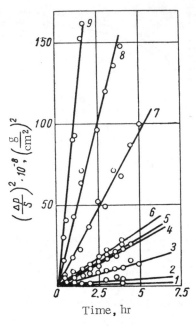

Fig. 25. Increase in weight of molybdenum specimens
in an ammonia medium versus time at various temperatures. 1) 700; 2) 750; 3) 820; 4) 880; 5) 900; 6) 940;
7) 1000; 8) 1050; 9) 1120°C.

Nitrided, carburized, and carbonitrided molybdenum were studied in [56].
Saturation with nitrogen was effected in atmospheres of ammonia and molecular
nitrogen at temperatures of 700-1150°C and 800-1200°C, respectively, no reaction
being detected between molybdenum and nitrogen in the second case, at atmospheric pressure. In an ammonia atmosphere saturation of molybdenum with nitrogen
followed a parabolic time law in the entire temperature range (Fig. 25). Up to a

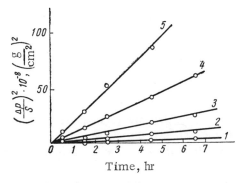

Fig. 26. Increase in weight of molybdenum specimens
in a medium of gasoline vapor and hydrogen versus time at
various temperatures. 1) 1000; 2) 1050; 3) 1100;
4) 1150; 5) 1200°C.

54

TABLE 16. Results of Nitriding, Carburizing, and Carbonitriding of Molybdenum

System	Temperature range, °C	Number of metallographi- cally revealed layers	Results of x-ray phase analysis of the layers	Presence of texture
Mo−N	700-900	2	Outer layer MoN, inner layer Mo$_2$N	None
	940-1150	1		
	1150-1250	−	Mo$_2$N	ʻʻ
			Mo	−
Mo−C	800-1200	1	Phase with Mo$_2$C lattice	None (texture at 1200°C)
Mo−C−N	900-1200	1	Phase with Mo$_2$C lattice	None

temperature of 940°C, two layers were formed on the surface of the molybdenum: an outer layer of MoN and an inner layer of Mo$_2$N. At a temperature above 940°C, only the Mo$_2$N phase was stable, and this phase also disappeared at a temperature above 1150°C.

Carburization of molybdenum in a mixture of gasoline vapor and hydrogen was noticeable only at 1000°C, and also took place according to a parabolic time law up to 1200°C (Fig. 26). According to the results of x-ray structural analysis and metallographic examination, under these conditions, the diffusion layer consisted only of the lower carbide Mo$_2$C (the carbide MoC was not found).

The combined saturation of the surface of molybdenum with nitrogen and carbon was carried out like that of chromium [55], with the sole difference that molecular nitrogen was replaced by ammonia. The formation of a diffusion layer, consisting of molybdenum carbonitride with Mo$_2$C lattice, was found at a tempera- ture of 1000-1200°C and obeyed a parabolic law (Fig. 27). An investigation of the

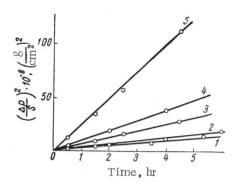

Fig. 27. Increase in weight of molybdenum speci- mens in an atmosphere of a mixture of gasoline va- por and ammonia versus time at various temperatures. 1) 1000; 2) 1050; 3) 1100; 4) 1150; 5) 1200°C.

55

System	Temperature range, °C	Number of metallographically revealed layers	Results of x-ray phase analysis	Presence of texture
W−N	1000-1100	2	Outer layer WN, inner layer W_2N	None
W−C	1000-1200	2	Inner layer W_2C, outer layer WC	"
W−C−N	1000-1200	2	Outer layer with WC lattice, inner layer with W_2C lattice	"

formation of diffusion layers in molybdenum−nitrogen, molybdenum−carbon, and molybdenum−carbon−nitrogen systems showed that their growth increased, owing to the preferred diffusion of nitrogen and carbon through the reaction products to the metal, the nitriding rate of molybdenum being much higher than its carburizing rate, while the rate of the combined saturation with nitrogen and carbon had an intermediate value. The results of x-ray structural analysis and metallographic examination of the surface diffusion layers in the above-mentioned systems are shown in Table 16.

The diffusion of carbon and nitrogen in tungsten has been similarly studied [57]. The results of x-ray analysis and metallographic examination of the surface layers formed are given in Table 17.

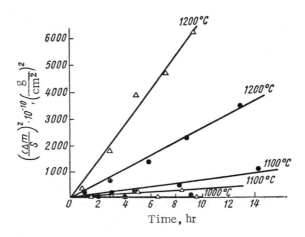

Fig. 28. Square of increase in weight of tungsten specimens versus duration of process in W−C and W−C−N systems. Δ) W−C system; ●) W−C−N system.

The kinetics of the diffusion layer formation in W−C and W−C−N systems is shown in Fig. 28.

From a comparison of the form of the kinetic curves, it may be concluded that the presence of nitrogen in the carburizing atmosphere retards the diffusion of carbon in tungsten (the opposite is found to be the case with molybdenum and chromium). Since both in carburizing and carbonitriding, the partial pressure of carbon in the reaction space was the same (the temperature of the gasoline satura-tor was kept constant), the authors of [57] assumed that the tungsten carbide formed in the diffusion zone contained dissolved nitrogen, which inhibited the diffusion of the carbon atoms through the carbide phases further into the body of the metal. The surface layer growth observed in all the systems obeyed a parabolic time law, which points to the preferred diffusion of nitrogen and carbon through the crystal lattices of the phases formed.

An interesting method of coating materials with nitrides of metals of groups IV and V of the periodic system, titanium, zirconium, and niobium, is described in [58]. It is based on the fact that in the reaction of the halides of these metals with ammonia, complex compounds of varying composition are formed, which decompose at high temperatures. Apparently, in this decomposition, active atoms of the metals and nitrogen are liberated and diffuse into the saturated surface. For the application of coatings of titanium nitride, it is advisable to carry out the reaction between $TiCl_4$ and NH_3 at temperatures of 900-1200°C. To avoid the precipitation of nitride particles in the free state, the $TiCl_4$ and NH_3 must be introduced into the reaction zone separately, the former in a stream of H_2.

Chapter 4

SILICIDE COATINGS

The siliconizing of metals and alloys as a method of increasing their resistance to corrosive liquids and gaseous media at different temperatures is widely employed in modern technology. The siliconizing of graphite and other nonmetallic materials is also practiced on an extensive scale. The surface of articles may be saturated with silicon from solid, gaseous, and liquid media. The most effective are the first two methods, regarding which much has been published [4, 8, 35, and others].

In siliconizing in powder mixtures, the source of silicon employed is elementary silicon, ferrosilicon, or silicon carbide. It is customary to add to the mixture aluminum oxide, ground fireclay, and other inert materials to prevent caking of the reaction mass and its sticking to the surface of the metal to be coated. The diffusion stimulator used is mainly NH_4Cl in an amount of 2-5% of the weight of the mixture.

The first Russian work [59-61] on the siliconizing of Armco iron and low-carbon steels in powder mixes of different compositions showed that to produce a layer 0.3-0.9 mm thick, saturated with silicon, a length treatment period (more than 10 hr), high temperatures (1100-1200°C), and a considerable consumption of silicon-containing materials were necessary. Table 18 shows the way in which the thickness of the siliconized layer depends on the working conditions, according to these results.

The mechanism of the siliconizing of nonsilicon and low-silicon iron was investigated by Fitzer [62]. The siliconizing medium was ferrosilicon containing 6-20% Si. The medium was heated to 1500°C and kept at this temperature for from 5 to 30 hr. Examination of the siliconized layers showed: 1) The siliconizing process was suitable for producing on the surface of iron articles coatings containing 6-11% Si, protecting the metal from corrosion in weakly corrosive media; 2) it was impossible to produce layers having a higher silicon content (14-15%), and consequently more resistant to corrosive media, since in this case, a porous layer, readily detached from the surface of the articles, was produced; 3) in siliconizing in media having a higher silicon content, the volume of the boundary layer between the coating and base metal appreciably increased, owing to the formation of the compound Fe_3Si in this zone. These drawbacks, to which must also be added the undesirable increase in grain size of core and siliconized layer of the articles, caused by long treament periods and high temperatures, resulted in the fact that the process of siliconizing from the solid phase was not adopted on any considerable scale in industry.

59

TABLE 18. Effect of Siliconizing Conditions on the Thickness of Siliconized Layer on Armco Iron and Steel 10

Material	Siliconizing mixture	Siliconizing mixture Temperature, °C	Duration, hr	Depth of layer, μ	Literature reference
Armco iron	Ferrosilicon containing 79% Si	1100	2	0.1	[59]
		1100	12	0.22	
		1200	3	0.3	
Steel 10	80% ferrosilicon + 20% fireclay	1100	2	0.02-0.05	[60]
		1100	12	0.20-0.23	
		1200	2	0.33-0.50	
		1200	12	0.60-0.80	
Steel 10	75% ferrosilicon + 20% fireclay + 5% NH$_4$Cl	1200	10	0.88-0.90	[60]
Steel 10	Ferrosilicon containing about 60% Si	1100	9	0.08	[61]
		1100	18	0.16	
		1100	60	0.47	

The process of gas siliconizing, carried out at lower temperatures and with shorter treatment periods, gives compact and sufficiently thick siliconized layers containing 13 to 16% Si. Gas siliconizing is carried out in hermetically closed muffles or in furnaces having revolving retorts, similar to the furnaces for gas carburization. The principal source of the silicon diffusing into the metal is silicon tetrachloride (SiCl$_4$) in vapor form, produced by passing gaseous chlorine or hydrogen chloride through the muffle with the silicon-containing pack (silicon carbide, ferrosilicon, and so forth). The silicon tetrachloride is decomposed on the surface of the metal with the precipitation of atomic silicon, which diffuses actively in the body of the metal. In the case of iron, the reaction may be written in the form

$$4Fe + 3SiCl_4 = 4FeCl_3 + 3Si.$$

In addition, the surface layer is saturated with silicon also as the result of the direct contact of the parts with the silicon-containing pack.

In gas siliconizing, packing of the parts in a silicon-containing composition is not essential. The parts may be placed in the middle of the muffle or retort and toward the gas outlet, while a suitable silicon-containing mixture is fed to the gas inlet. In such a method of siliconizing, the thickness of the layer formed is less and its inhomogeneity is rather higher, but the surface of the article is much cleaner and more even, which is sometimes more advantageous.

Table 19 gives data [35] on the depth of the siliconized layer as affected by the working conditions. As will be gathered from the table, the depth of the diffusion layer, even in the absence of direct contact between charge and articles, is much greater than for siliconizing in the solid phase, other conditions being the same.

In the case of continued passage of chlorine or hydrogen chloride, if they are in excess, the surface of the coated metal and the siliconized layer itself are strongly eroded, which results in the parts becoming completely useless [8]. In this connection, N.S. Gorbunov and collaborators proposed a modified gas siliconizing process, in which instead of passing chlorine during the whole of the siliconizing process, the reaction space was filled with the gas only once (before the commencement of siliconizing) and at room temperature [63, 64]. Even under these conditions, however, a large excess of chlorine must be avoided when filling the reaction space with it. Investigations showed that the optimum concentration was 1-2 ml Cl_2 per square centimeter of surface to be coated.

Siliconizing was carried out on iron packed in silicon powder. The optimum temperature, at which a diffusion silicon layer of adequate thickness and density was, lay in the range 950-1100°C. Table 20 shows the effect of siliconizing temperature and time on the thickness of coatings on iron.

With increase in carbon content of the iron, the thickness of the silicon-containing layer decreased, and amounted, for example, for steel 25 to 125 μ, for steel 45 to 106 μ, for steel U8 to 65 μ, and for steel U10 to 42 μ in the case of siliconizing for 2 hr at 1000°C. The authors ascribe the decrease in thickness of the siliconized layer on steels having a high carbon content to the formation of silicon carbides, impeding the diffusion of silicon on the iron. The microhardness of the siliconized layers was fairly high, and decreasing with decrease in the carbon content of the steel:

Steel	Microhardness, kg/mm^2
U12	765
U8	210
45	148
10	137
Iron	128

TABLE 19. Effect of Gas Siliconizing Conditions on the Depth of Siliconized Layer (Treatment Conditions: 980°C, 2 hr)

Siliconizing material	Gas supplied to muffle	Specimens exposed directly to gas stream	Specimens covered from above with powder
Ferrosilicon (60% Si)	Chlorine	0.53	1.38
Silicon carbide	''	0.51	1.07
Ferrosilicon (60% Si)	Hydrogen chloride	0.59	1.12
Silicon carbide	'' ''	0.62	0.95

TABLE 20. Effect of Siliconizing Conditions on Thickness
(μ) of Silicide Diffusion Layers

Time, hr	Siliconizing temperature, °C			
	950	1000	1050	1100
1	72	104	138	178
2	116	151	188	234
3	136	190	235	307
4	149	216	168	362

Other conditions being the same, the wear resistance of siliconized iron was three times that of nonsiliconized iron.

For studying the anticorrosion properties of silicon diffusion layers, compara- tive tests were made on siliconized and untreated iron in 10% aqueous solutions of sulfuric, hydrochloric, phosphoric, acetic, and oxalic acids, 3% NaCl solution, 5% $CaCl_2$ solution, and 50% Na_2SO_4 solution. The results of the tests are given in Tables 21 and 22.

As will be seen from these tables, the corrosion resistance of siliconized iron in salt solutions was 10 to 15 times greater than that of nonsiliconized iron, while it was 10 to 100 times greater in acid solutions.

High-temperature oxidation tests on siliconized and nonsiliconized specimens, carried out at temperatures of 500-900°C for a duration of 10-50 hr in an air at- mosphere, showed the former to be substantially superior, especially up to a tem- perature of 800°C (Table 23). At higher temperatures, there was appreciable diffusion of silicon into the body of the specimen, resulting in a decrease in silicon concen- tration in the surface layer and a reduction in the resistance of the coating to high- temperature oxidation.

TABLE 21. Corrosion of Untreated and Siliconized Iron in Acids

Time, days	Loss in weight, mg/cm^2, in 10% solutions of									
	hydrochloric acid		sulfuric acid		phosphoric acid		acetic acid		oxalic acid	
	untr.*	sil.	untr.	sil.	untr.	sil.	untr.	sil.	untr.	sil.
1	4.7	No loss	12.2	0.06	0.73	0.07	3.0	0.05	0.72	0.06
2	9.2	The same	26.4	0.11	1.51	1.51	4.3	0.07	1.00	0.11
3	13.6	» »	34.8	0.16	2.22	0.21	5.2	0.11	1.40	0.12
6	26.8	» »	67.3	0.32	2.08	0.35	8.5	0.22	3.25	0.27
8	34.4	0.03	85.2	0.35	5.57	0.40	10.3	0.22	3.80	0.27
10	61.37	0.08	103.1	0.36	7.02	0.41	12.1	0.22	5.27	0.27

*In Tables 21-23, "untr." = untreated iron, "sil." = iron, siliconized for 2 hr at 1000°C (thickness of siliconized layer about 200 μ).

TABLE 22. Corrosion of Untreated and Siliconized Iron in Salt Solutions

| Time, days | Loss in weight, mg/cm^2, in the solutions: | | | | | |
| | 3% sodium chloride | | 5% potassium chloride | | 50% sodium sulfate | |
	untr.	sil.	untr.	sil.	untr.	sil.
1	0.3	0.08	0.20	0.01	0.18	—
2	0.3	0.18	0.29	0.02	0.44	0.02
3	0.5	0.25	0.47	0.03·	0.71	0.04
6	0.8	0.43	0.93	0.05	1.27	0.12
8	1.1	0.48	1.31	0.06	1.82	0.12
10	1.4	0.48	1.72	0.06	2.15	0.12

The siliconizing of chromium steels has been discussed in [65]. The following steels were investigated: 20, 20Kh (1% Cr), Kh6 (6.3% Cr), and Kh13 (12.4% Cr). The method used for comparison was solid-phase siliconizing in powder mixtures (ferrosilicon, fireclay, and ammonium chloride) at a temperature of 1050-1200°C and for a period of 3-12 hr, and the gas siliconizing method, chlorine being passed through ferrosilicon and fireclay at 950°C for 1-6 hr. Figure 29 shows how the depth of the siliconized layer varied with the siliconizing conditions and the chromium content of the steels. As will be seen from the data presented, increase in the chromium content reduced somewhat the depth of the siliconized layer. The result obtained on iron and plain carbon steels, namely that gas siliconizing is more effective and economical than solid siliconizing, was confirmed. Thus in the case of gas siliconizing, after 2 hr at 950°C, a depth of diffusion layer 2-2.5 times greater was obtained than in the case of solid-phase siliconizing at 1150°C for 12 hr. The siliconized layer was uniform, dense, and well bonded to the base metal. The experiments showed that siliconized steel Kh13 had high resistance to gas corrosion up to 1000°C, while siliconized low-carbon steel showed this resistance only up to 800°C. This confirmed the supposition [66] that the combined influence of chromium and silicon on the corrosion resistance of steel is stronger than that of each element separately. These facts may apparently be explained by the formation of chromium silicides, which are quite resistant to oxidation in air at high temperatures [67].

TABLE 23. High-Temperature Oxidation Resistance of Silicon Coatings for Different Test Temperatures and Durations

| Time, hr | Increase in weight of specimens, mg/cm^2, at a temperature, °C, of | | | | | | | | | | | |
| | 500 | | 600 | | 700 | | 800 | | 850 | | 900 | |
	untr.	sil.	untr.	sil.	untr.	sil.	untr.	sil.	untr.	sil.	untr.	sil.
10	2.3	—	3.1	0.3	5.3	0.6	24.3	5.1	2.8	6.5	52.1	—
20	3.9	0.04	4.5	0.5	9.1	1.3	33.7	9.2	52.8	10.8	85.1	15.9
30	4.1	0.12	5.6	0.6	11.9	2.1	50.8	13.1	73.1	12.2	114	41
40	4.4	0.19	6.7	0.6	15.3	2.9	60.8	17.7	87.6	18.4	134	67.3
50	4.8	0.27	8.0	0.8	21.1	4.2	69.3	23.8	108.6	33.5	183	97.3

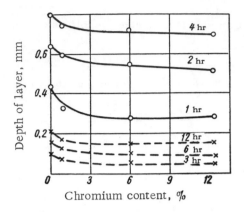

Fig. 29. Chromium content versus depth
of siliconized layer. ——— gas siliconizing at 950°C; ----- solid siliconizing at
at 1100°C.

In this connection, it must be pointed out that siliconizing complex alloy
steels, in particular chromium steels, may be promising for increasing their corrosion resistance in various media at high temperatures. It has, in fact, been found
[68] that siliconizing the chromium−nickel steel ÉI417 was more effective than
chromizing, aluminizing,and aluminosiliconizing for protecting this steel from the
action of media containing V_2O_5. All coatings, with the exception of the siliconized
coatings, were failed when tested upon heating for 500 hr in contact with ash containing 10 and 41.6% V_2O_5 at a temperature of 730°C.

According to the data of this investigation, simultaneous diffusion saturation
by silicon and aluminum gave poorer results compared with saturation by each element individually. With cyclic cooling of the specimens in the course of the tests
(40 cycles from 730 to 20°C during 15-20 min), no exfoliation or failure of the siliconized layer was found. Furthermore, when siliconized specimens were quenched
in water from 1150°C, no cracks were observed, nor was there any destruction of
the bond between the layer and metal base. On the basis of the results obtained
[68], it was recommended that diffusion siliconizing should be used for the protection
of gas-turbine guide blades from corrosion when burning oil fuel having a high vanadium content.

Steels 10, 20, U10, and gray iron mark SCh18-36 and SCh24-44 have been subjected to combined chromizing and siliconizing [69]. The specimens were heated
by high-frequency current and (for comparison) in an electric furnace. The temperature of the process was 1050-1100°C in both cases, the duration of the treatment
being 10 and 20 min from the moment at which the specified temperature was
reached. Saturation was carried out in a powder mixture consisting of ferrochrome
mark Chr0 and ferrosilicon mark Si75, and also in a powdered chromium alloy containing 5% Si. The inert mass was fireclay, and the initiator of the process was ammonium chloride, both added to the initial powders in a quantity of 30 and 4% (wt),
respectively. The thickness of the resulting chromosiliconized layers in the case
of heating by high-frequency current was 0.2-0.3 mm on the steel specimens, and

about 0.1 mm on the cast-iron specimens, while in the case of heating in the electric furnace, it was 0.01 mm for both types of specimens. The microhardness of the chromosiliconized layers on steel 10 did not exceed 180-200 HV, while on steel U10 and cast iron it was 800-950 HV.

A comparison which was made in this investigation between the processes of chromizing alone and chromosiliconizing showed that thicker diffusion layers were always produced in the second case, i.e., the silicon accelerated the diffusion of chromium in plain carbon steels. The authors assumed that this could be explained by the transformation of the iron from γ to α, in which the chromium diffuses more rapidly, and also by the fact that the silicon, by displacing the carbon in the body of the base metal, facilitated the diffusion of chromium. Without producing any quantitative evidence, the authors remark that the chromosiliconized layer was much tougher than the siliconized layer, and its resistance to high-temperature oxidation and to acids greater than the chromized layer.

The silicides of the refractory transition metals of groups IV, V, and VI of the periodic system of the elements have a number of valuable properties, among which it is necessary to distinguish above all their considerable resistance to high-temperature oxidation and their resistance to the action of various corrosive media. Refractory metal—silicon systems have been studied in a number of investigations, references to which are contained in the monograph [4]. The diffusion of silicon in refractory metals is carried out in the same way as for iron and its alloys, usually in solid-phase packs and gaseous media.

According to the results of an investigation [70], in which siliconizing of titanium, niobium, tantalum, chromium, molybdenum, and tungsten was carried out in a solid-phase medium, consisting of silicon powder with activating additions, the diffusion layers on all the above-mentioned metals were predominantly disilicides. In the same investigation, a determination was made of the value of the activation energy in the diffusion of silicon in the above-mentioned metals, these values being found to be less than the activation energy of boron and carbon. These results, as stated above, can be well explained on the assumption that the energy of activation in reaction diffusion processes is determined not by the radius, but by the ionization potential of the diffusing metalloid. The ionization potentials of Si, B, and C are, respectively, 8.28, 8.4, and 11.24 eV.

For siliconizing titanium, tantalum, molybdenum, and iron [71], a solid-phase pack of silicon powder with an addition of 3% ammonium chloride was used. The ammonium chloride was included in the pack so that in the reaction between Si and NH_4Cl, a certain quantity of $SiCl_4$ was formed, which by decomposing on the surface of the metal with the liberation of active silicon, accelerated the process of its diffusion in the metal, while the hydrochloric acid gas, formed at the same time, etched the surface of the metal, thereby also assisting the diffusion. The layer on titanium was found to consist of the silicides TiSi and $TiSi_2$, that on tantalum of the higher silicide $TaSi_2$, that on molybdenum of the silicides Mo_5Si_3 and $MoSi_2$, and that on iron of the silicide FeSi for temperatures of 900°C or higher, but of a solid solution in iron at lower temperatures. The data obtained for phase composition, thickness, and hardness of the layers as a function of temperature and saturation time are given in Table 24.

65

A study has been made of the protection of molybdenum against oxidation by the application of silicide coatings [146]. Siliconizing was carried out in a special container filled with a mixture of 90% Si and 10% Al_2O_3, the container being closed by porous refractory plugs through which was passed a gaseous mixture of H_2+HCl at a rate of 10 cm^3/min. To elucidate the influence of an addition of alloying elements to the silicide coatings, iron, chromium, and aluminum in powder form were added to the siliconizing mixture. The results of tests on the resistance to scaling under static conditions at temperatures of 1000 and 1450°C showed that the addition of Cr, Fe, and Al to the silicide coatings appreciably impaired the protective properties of the latter. In thermal shock tests in the range 0-1200°C, chromium and iron were found to have a favorable effect. It was shown that the optimum thickness of the diffusion coatings was not the same for tests under static conditions as under conditions of abrupt temperature fluctuations.

An investigation has been made on reaction diffusion in Mo−Si, W−Si, and Ta−Si systems [72]. The specimens were heated in silicon powder in a vacuum of 10^{-5} mm Hg at temperatures of 1150-1350°C for various intervals of time. X-ray diffraction analysis showed that lower silicides were formed on all three metals in the first stage of the process. After heating for 5 hr at 1150°C, the inner layers

TABLE 24. Effect of Siliconizing Conditions of Titanium, Tantalum, Molybdenum, and Iron on the Properties of the Silicide Layers

Metal	Temperature, °C	Time, hr	Layer thickness, μ	Phase composition	Microhardness at depth of 20μ from surface of specimen, kg/mm^2
Titanium	800	4	Individual grains	TiSi	1000
	900	4	46	TiSi, TiSi$_2$	1000
	900	8	50	TiSi, TiSi$_2$	1000
	1000	4	56	TiSi, TiSi$_2$	1000
	1100	4	70	TiSi, TiSi$_2$	1000
Tantalum	900	4	1	TiSi, TiSi$_2$	—
	1000	4	120	TaSi$_2$	1220
	1100	4	180	TaSi$_2$	1220
	1200	2	230	TaSi$_2$	1220
	1200	6	430	TaSi$_2$	1260
Molybdenum	800	4	40	Mo$_5$Si$_3$	1520
	900	4	50	Mo$_5$Si$_3$, MoSi$_2$	1520
	1000	1	50	Mo$_5$Si$_3$	800
	1000	2	75	Mo$_5$Si$_3$, MoSi$_2$	1310
	1000	4	110	Mo$_5$Si$_3$, MoSi$_2$	1950
	1000	8	174	Mo$_5$Si$_3$, MoSi$_2$	1950
	1100	4	127	Mo$_5$Si$_3$, MoSi$_2$	1150
	1200	4	165	Mo$_5$Si$_3$, MoSi$_2$	1070
Iron	800	4	10	Solid solution	—
	900	1	60	—	950
	900	2	165	—	610
	900	4	230	FeSi	—
	900	8	680	FeSi	650
	1000	4	180	FeSi	640
	1100	4	220	FeSi	900—1200

on molybdenum and tungsten consisted, respectively, of the phases Mo_3Si, W_5Si_3, and W_3Si, higher silicides being situated closer to the surface. At 1240°C, the disilicide was found on tungsten after $\frac{1}{2}$ hr, on tantalum after 1 hr, and on molybdenum after 3 hr. It is stated that with the appearance of the disilicide on the surface, subsequent growth of the layer occurred principally on account of this phase, and only after a certain thickness had been reached, did the growth of the disilicide layer become slower, and a layer of lower silicides began to grow appreciably. The occurrence of cracks normal to the surface of the silicide layers was not, in the authors' opinion, due to the difference in the thermal coefficients of expansion of silicide and metal, but could be explained by the increase in volume (in relation to the volume of the treated metal) during the formation of the silicides, leading to the development of tensile stresses on the external boundary of the layer. This deduction was confirmed by calculation based on the crystal-chemical characteristics of the initial metals and silicide phases. It was also found that the growth of the silicide layers occurred by preferential diffusion of silicon through the lattice of the phase formed in the metal, and that the most rapid phase transformation process (up to and including the appearance of the disilicide) took place on tungsten, and the slowest on molybdenum.

The kinetics of the vacuum siliconizing of metals, taking tantalum and molybdenum as examples, has been studied [73]. It was shown theoretically that in the vapor (gas)−solid system, at rates of admission of the volatile component to the reaction zone much below the rate of the mutual diffusion of the components through the compound formed, a linear law of growth of the layer with time ought to be observed. This conclusion was confirmed experimentally in the siliconizing of tantalum and molybdenum in silicon powder of a particle size of 0.5-1 mm, at temperatures of 1200 and 1250°C, and for periods of 0.5-1.5 hr. At temperatures of 1300°C and above, the linear law of the rate of growth of the layers was replaced by a parabolic law.

Consequently, the linear function of time of the thickness of silicide layers, observed at 1200 and 1250°C, is due to the slow rate of supply, compared with diffusion, of silicon from the vapor phase to the lattice of the compound being formed. According to the assumption made by the authors of [73] under certain conditions, the limiting link in the vacuum siliconizing process is not diffusion through the silicide layer, but chemisorption of the silicon vapor by the surface undergoing saturation. In fact, as has been shown [74], in addition to the process of chemisorption of the silicon vapor at temperatures of 1200-1250°C, the reverse process, namely the dissociation of disilicide and the desorption of silicon, takes place quite intensely. Consequently, the time required for the accumulation of silicon atoms, in sufficient number for the formation of a fresh elementary layer of disilicide, may be quite considerable in comparison with the time of diffusion of these atoms through the layer to the reaction boundary. At the same time, it is pointed out that according to experimental data, the finer the powder, the higher is the rate of siliconizing and the narrower is the linear range of the time function.

The characteristics of the vacuum siliconizing of the refractory metals molybdenum, tungsten, and tantalum have been the subject of further investigations [141, 142]. Saturation was carried out in saturated silicon vapor at a residual pressure in the reaction chamber of $1 \cdot 10^{-5}$ mm Hg and temperatures of 1200, 1250, and 1350°C. X-ray diffraction analysis and metallographic examination showed the outer thick layers of the diffusion zone to be composed of the disilicides of the corresponding metals, and the more deeply situated thin layers consisted of lower silicides. At temperatures of 1200 and 1250°C, a parabolic law of the rate of growth of the diffusion layers with time was found for all the metals, the rate of supply of silicon to the surface of the metal affecting only the absolute thickness of the layer, but not the law of their growth. The phase $TaSi_2$ was found to have inclusions of the silicide Ta_5Si_3, the crystals of which extended perpendicularly to the disilicide layer in the direction of diffusion of the silicon. This arrangement of Ta_5Si_3 enabled the authors to assume that this phase was not formed inside the $TaSi_2$ as the result of precipitation, but was formed during the diffusion of silicon at the $Ta_5Si_3-TaSi_2$ interface. Apparently, when tantalum is saturated with silicon, lower silicides are first formed, followed by a transition from lower to higher silicides. Similar conclusions have also been made with regard to the formation of molybdenum disilicide. Thus, in vacuum siliconizing the process of formation of disilicides from lower silicides may be represented by the following schematic reaction:

$$Me + Si \rightarrow Me_3Si + Si \rightarrow Me_5Si_3 + Si \rightarrow MeSi_2.$$

By means of inert markers and other methods, it has been shown convincingly that in the overall diffusion process in the Mo−Si system, the diffusion of silicon plays a predominant part. Apparently, this conclusion is also applicable to the siliconizing of other refractory metals.

In the vacuum siliconizing of refractory metals, the rate of growth of the silicide diffusion layers is less than in siliconizing from the gas phase, but in the opinion of the authors of [72, 73, 141, 142] the quality of these layers is higher.

The siliconizing processes of niobium, and the structure and phase composition of the silicide layer and its resistance to oxidation have been investigated [75]. It was found that as the result of saturation at temperatures of 1100-1300°C for 0.5 to 15 hr, a coating of complex structure and composition was formed on niobium. The outer layer consisted of niobium disilicide $NbSi_2$ (microhardness 1050 kg/mm^2), the intermediate layer was Nb_5Si_3 (microhardness 700 kg/mm^2), and the inner layer, adjacent the metal, was nearly Nb_4Si. The kinetics of the process followed a quadratic parabolic function.

Oxidation of the siliconized niobium in the temperature range 1100-1300°C resulted in the formation of a porous surface film, consisting of β-Nb_2O_5 and α-SiO_2 and affording the silicide layer little protection from oxidation. It was shown that simultaneous saturation of niobium with silicon and titanium enhanced the protective properties of the complex silicide coating (solid solution of titanium and niobium silicides). Thus, the surface of niobium, protected by silicon and titanium, oxidized at two-thirds the rate of that in the case of protection by silicon alone, and the oxide film formed, consisting mainly of rutile, TiO_2, and a small quantity of α-SiO_2, was relatively dense and well bonded to the surface of the metal.

The various methods of protecting niobium from high-temperature oxidation are discussed most fully in the book by Borisenko [76]. Analysis of the data presented shows that up to temperatures of 1000°C, metallic protective coatings (chromium, chrome—nickel, zinc, etc.) are quite effective. In the temperature range 1000-1150°C, mixed coatings are used, consisting of refractory oxides and metals. During heat-treatment the metals introduced into the coatings oxidize and form a layer consisting of complex oxides, which are resistant to the action of high temperatures. For temperatures exceeding 1150°C, it is possible to use coatings of various high-temperature materials, applied by means of a plasma gun.

It appears expedient to discuss more fully the coating LM-5 (40% Mo, 40% Si, 2% B, 8% Cr, 10% Al) which has been proposed and investigated in detail [77], since this coating has been found to be the best for protecting niobium from oxidation at temperatures above 1250°C. The coating was applied by flame spraying or by means of a plasma gun on pure niobium, or niobium previously provided with a high-temperature oxidation-resistant coating of Nb—Ti—Cr—Al alloy. Tests showed that such a duplex coating possessed approximately the same protective properties as a single coating of LM-5 of the same thickness. A coating of LM-5, 75-100 μ thick, protected niobium from oxidation in quiescent air at 1100°C for more than 1000 hr. In a thickness of 112 μ, it prevented gas corrosion of niobium at 1250°C for 840 hr, and at 1500°C, for more than 100 hr. The coating also showed satisfactory thermal shock resistance, withstanding 30 cycles of temperature fluctuations in air according to the cycle 1150-20-1150°C. On water quenching, it failed, even after only 3-5 cycles. The duplex coating withstood 20-30 water-quench cycles.

The high resistance to oxidation of the LM-5 coating is explained by the fact [77] that its principal component is molybdenum disilicide, the high-temperature oxidation resistance of which is further increased by the additional presence of chromium, boron, and aluminum. Since molybdenum disilicide has the best (of the silicides) high-temperature oxidation resistance, and molybdenum has high-strength characteristics which, however, cannot be utilized directly on account of the easy oxidizability of this metal, it is important to discuss the methods of protecting molybdenum from high-temperature oxidation by creating silicon-containing coatings on its surface.

In addition to the solid-phase method described above, molybdenum may also be siliconized by the gas-phase method, which provides the densest and strongest coatings. In the investigations described in [78, 79], molybdenum wire was siliconized by the reduction of silicon tetrachloride by hydrogen on the surface of the molybdenum at temperatures of 1100-1800°C. An apparatus for carrying out this process is shown diagrammatically in Fig. 30. Silicon coatings on molybdenum are usually duplex; a lower silicide, Mo_5Si_3, is formed at the interface with the metal, and a higher silicide, $MoSi_2$, grows on the lower silicide.

Experiments were made on the creation of silicide layers [78] on wire 2 mm in diameter; the silicon source was 99.8% $SiCl_4$, which was reduced by carefully purified and dried hydrogen (hydrogen of 99.8% purity was passed over copper turnings heated to 400-600°C, then dried with $MgClO_4$ and P_2O_5 and passed through magnesium turnings heated to 600°C). The hydrogen was then passed through $SiCl_4$ and supplied to the coating chamber. The wire was heated by the direct passage of current. At temperatures below 1420°C (melting point of silicon), a three-phase coat-

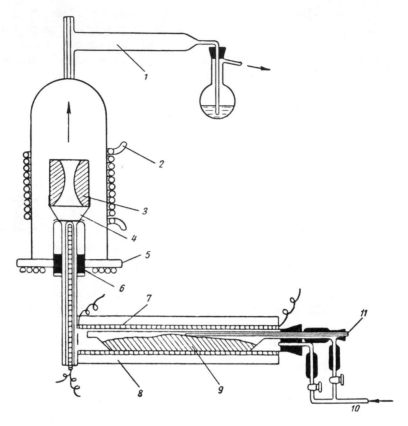

Fig. 30. Diagram of gas-phase siliconizing apparatus. 1) Condenser; 2) inductor; 3) part to be siliconized; 4) holder; 5) base of apparatus; 6) asbestos insulation; 7) heater; 8) thermal insulation; 9) metal halide; 10) hydrogen supply; 11) thermocouple.

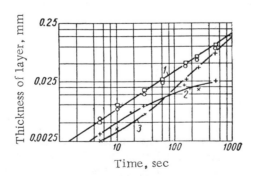

Fig. 31. Thickness of inner and outer layers versus coating time in the siliconizing of molybdenum wire. 1) Total layer; 2) inner layer; 3) outer layer.

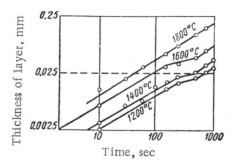

Fig. 32. Variation in thickness of coating on siliconized molybdenum wire, 2 mm in diameter,
with time and temperature.

ing was usually obtained, consisting of silicon, molybdenum disilicide, and a silicide
of lower silicon content. Above this temperature, the coatings contained only the
disilicide and silicon. The variation of thickness of the layers of $MoSi_2$ and the
lower silicide with time and temperature is shown in Fig. 31 (rate of flow of hydrogen 500 cm^3/min); Figure 32 shows the overall rates of growth of the coating at
temperatures of 1200-1800°C (rate of flow of hydrogen 800 cm^3/min). It follows
from Fig. 32 that the rate of formation of the inner layer (lower silicide) was less
than that of the $MoSi_2$ layer, i.e., there was the usual diffusion rate of growth. The
microhardness of the silicide layer on the surface of the molybdenum wire was 1410
kg/mm^2 compared with 370 kg/mm^2 for molybdenum. Molybdenum chlorides are
not formed in this process and under these siliconizing conditions. It should be
noted as one of the advantages that the depth and composition of the silicide layers
are not very sensitive to temperature fluctuations (in the limits of 1450-1700°C),
$SiCl_4$ concentration in the coating medium, and rate of flow of hydrogen.

According to [78], the oxidation resistance of molybdenum silicide coatings
on molybdenum wire may be expressed by the empirical formula:

$$\tau = K \cdot \delta^n,$$

where τ is the service life of the coating, hr; δ is the thickness of the coating, mm; K
is a coefficient, equal to 12,460 at a temperature of 1200°C and 2565 at a temperature of 1700°C; and n = 1.65 at 1200°C and 1.51 at 1700°C.

Coatings of a thickness greater than 0.075-0.1 mm are prone to split; stronger
coatings are found to be those of a thickness of 0.025-0.05 mm. Practically, the
thickness of the coatings should not exceed 0.025 mm. In an air atmosphere, saturated with water vapor, the oxidation resistance of the siliconized layer at a temperature of 1000°C is somewhat higher than in perfectly dry air. Impurities in the
molybdenum reduce the resistance of the layers to oxidation, and the impurities may
be arranged in the following order of diminishing degree of harmful effect: iron →
copper → nickel → chromium. Iron and titanium impurities reduce the service life of
the silicide coating at 1700°C by several tens of hours. The presence of chromium
and molybdenum in the layer reduces its service life insignificantly.

71

The mechanical properties of the siliconized layer are fairly high. Despite the high hardness of the layers under a load of 100 g (microhardness of the silicon phase is 940, that of $MoSi_2$, 1160, and that of the lower silicide, 890 kg/mm^2), the siliconized wire may be bent without cracking. Furthermore, the coatings are very resistant to thermal shock on rapid heating from 20 to 1700°C.

Molybdenum silicide resists well the action of CO_2, SO_2, or NO_2 at a temperature of 1000°C, and if protected by previous oxidation, also the action of hydrogen chloride. In the unprotected state, decomposition of molybdenum disilicide by hydrogen chloride and particularly chlorine proceeds very rapidly owing to the formation of volatile chlorides of molybdenum and silicon.

Siliconized molybdenum is extensively employed for the production of the heating elements of electric resistance furnaces, combustion chambers, nozzles, heat exchangers, and other components operating in an oxidizing atmosphere at high temperatures.

According to [80], molybdenum may also be siliconized by spraying silicon-containing alloys on the surface of molybdenum, followed by thermal diffusion heating. Table 25 shows the composition of the alloys used for spraying.

The technology of the application of coatings by the spraying method is as follows: The surface of the molybdenum is cleaned by blasting with metal (preferably iron) grit, the residues of which are removed from the surface by means of hydrochloric acid. The silicon-containing compositions are sprayed on by means of a mechanically operated spray gun until a layer thickness of 0.3-0.38 mm has been reached; the corners are coated last, and cylindrical or spherical specimens are rotated continuously during spraying. The articles with the coating layer applied are subjected to diffusion heating for 2 hr at 1100°C in a dry hydrogen atmosphere. To prevent the coating layer from adhering to the support on which the articles are placed, the support is previously painted with a slurry of aluminum oxide in methyl alcohol. After the heat-treatment, articles required to have accurate dimensions are machined with silicon carbide grinding wheels.

After the heat-treatment, the sprayed layers apparently consist of multicomponent silicide layers.

TABLE 25. Composition of Alloys for the Protective Coating of Molybdenum by the Spraying Method

Coating alloy	Si	Cr	Al	Mo	Fe	Ni	Others
Cr—Si	40.55	56	0.44	—	1.4	—	—
Cr—Mo—Si	33	31.3	—	31.3	0.7	—	—
Mo—Ni—Si	32.2	—	1.53	37	0.2	30.6	—
Fe—Si	51	—	—	—	Remainder	—	—
Ni—Si	30	—	—	—	7	60	3Ca

All the alloys shown in Table 25 are resistant to oxidation in air at 980°C for 500 hr. At a temperature of 1150°C, coatings of the Al—Cr—Si alloy are effective for more than 200 hr, but at 1300°C, the service life is reduced somewhat. Molybdenum articles coated with silicide have high thermal shock resistance. Under conditions of heating in a gas furnace to 980°C in 30 sec, this temperature then being held for 15 sec followed by cooling to 27°C in 45 sec in an air blast, molybdenum articles provided with such coatings withstood 420-560 cycles. In ballistic shock tests, in which a steel bullet 4.4 mm in diameter was fired at a velocity of 100 m/sec (from an air rifle) into a specimen heated to 980°C, followed by an examination for the presence of cracks, the results were not very good. On reducing the velocity of the bullet to 40 m/sec, however, the subsequent service life of the specimen at 980°C before failure was still 160-170 hr (compared with 500 hr for coatings with alloys containing boron and nickel). Erosion tests, in which a jet of aluminum oxide powder of 90 mesh particle size was directed on the specimen at an angle of 45° to the surface, and at a rate of 30 g/min, showed a relatively high resistance (20 to 30 min). In determining ductility by creep test at 980°C, the elongation of molybdenum specimens coated with the aluminum—chromium—silicon alloy was 2-5% without failure of the coatings (duration of test was 100-500 hr).

Similar processes for the protection of molybdenum from oxidation have also been investigated [81,82]. An account is given [81] of a study of various complex compositions of protective coatings for molybdenum, the coatings being applied by the method of thermal diffusion saturation from a solid-phase medium. The following method was used for applying the coatings. The specimens to be coated were packed in a mixture consisting of 1) a metal (Cr, Nb, Ta, W, etc.) or a nonmetal (B or Si), in the free or combined state, with which the surface of the specimen was saturated; 2) an activating substance (for example, NH_4Cl); 3) compounds for controlling the necessary atmosphere, in which the process took place; 4) an inert filler (Al_2O_3, fireclay, etc.). The retort was sealed with a ceramic mixture having a lower softening temperature than the boiling temperature of the compounds contained in the retort. The entire system was heated to a temperature of 950-1230°C, and kept at this temperature for 4-8 hr. When a temperature of 130-140°C was reached, the atmosphere control compounds [for example, urea, $Co(NH_2)_2$, which decomposed with the liberation of NH_3 gas and biuret, $(NH_2 \cdot CO)NH$] displaced the air from the retort and subsequently maintained a reducing atmosphere in the latter. On completion of the process, the retort was cooled, during which the sealing mixture solidified and prevented air from entering the retort and oxidizing the treated specimens.

In the investigation, the material to be coated consisted of sheets of a thickness of 0.8 and 0.254 mm of heat-resistant alloy Mo + 0.5% Ti. Two types of coatings were investigated. Coatings of the first type consisted of several elements, applied to the molybdenum simultaneously in one cycle. The principal component of the saturating mixture was silicon powder, and the alloying elements were B, C, Co, Cr, Nb, Ta, V, W, and Zr. Coatings of the second type also consisted of several elements, but they were applied in two cycles; in the first cycle, the surface of the molybdenum was saturated with chromium, and in the second cycle, with silicon and another element. The following compositions were tried for coatings of the second type: Cr—Si + B, Si + C, Si + Co, Si + Mo, Si + Ta, Si + V, Si + W, Si + Zr. For comparison, the following method of applying coatings of the second type was also used: In the first cycle, saturation with chromium and silicon was carried out, and in the second cycle, saturation with the alloying element.

In both cases, complex solid solutions and intermetallic compounds were formed, and the resultant coatings consisted of alloys of the applied elements and molybdenum, molybdenum silicides forming the principal component of the coating.

The applied coatings were tested for oxidation in an oxyacetylene flame having a temperature of 1650°C, the ratio O_2:C_2H_2 being 3:1. The resistance of the coatings in the oxyacetylene flame was estimated according to the time to failure of the coating. To test the coatings for ductility, the sheet specimens were bent around a die 19 mm in diameter, while being pressed by this die into a 21 mm female die. The load was increased to 17.5 kg/cm^2. If the coating failed before the load of 17.5 kg/cm^2 was reached, the relative ductility was expressed as the ratio (percent) of the load on failure to the load 17.5 kg/cm^2. It was considered that ductility was excellent if the coatings of two identical specimens did not fail under a load of 17.5 kg/cm^2; good if one specimen bent and one specimen failed at a bend greater than 50% of the maximum; fair if both specimens failed at a bend greater than 50%; and poor if both specimens failed at a bend less than 50%. The results of preliminary tests on specimens having the first type of coatings are given in Table 26.

As will be seen from the data presented in Table 26, the best coatings on molybdenum with regard to resistance to oxidation and ductility are coatings of Si + Ta and Si + Nb.

The results of tests made on the second type of coatings are given in Table 27. As will be seen from this table, coatings comprising chromium and silicon in the first layer had better properties than coatings in which the first layer consisted of chromium only. The following coatings present the maximum interest: Cr, Si + C; Cr, Si + Mo; Cr, Si + V.

TABLE 26. Technological Properties of the First Type of Coatings (for the Alloy Mo + 0.5% Ti) in Relation to Their Composition

Composition of coating	Time to failure on oxidation in an oxyacetylene flame at a temperature of 1650°C, hr	Ductility on bending for coatings applied to a sheet 0.8 mm thick	Thickness of coating	Porosity of coating
Si + B	0.2	Poor	0.038	Porous
Si + C	2.1	"	0.071	"
Si + Nb	3.8	Excellent	0.09	Not porous
Si + Co	2	Fair	0.063	Porous
Si + Cr	1.1	Good	0.063	Slightly porous
Si + Ta	6.7	"	—	The same
Si + V	1.5	Fair	0.101	Very slightly porous
Si + W	1.5	"	0.076	The same
Si + Zr	0.5	Excellent	0.101	Porous

74

TABLE 27. Technological Properties of the Second Type of Coatings (for the Alloy Mo + 0.5% Ti) in Relation to Their Composition

Composition of coating	Time to failure on oxidation in an oxyacetylene flame at a temperature of 1650°C, hr	Ductility on bending for coat-ings applied to a sheet 0.8 mm thick	Thick-ness of coating	Porosity of coating
Cr, Si + B	2	Fair	0.0635	Porous
Cr, Si + C	2.1	Good	0.0765	Slightly porous
Cr, Si + Mo	2	''	0.254	Not porous
Cr, Si + V	2.1	Fair	0.101	Slightly porous
Cr, Si + W	1.5	Good	0.0765	Very slightly porous
Cr + Si, B	0.8	Fair	0.051	Porous
Cr + Si, C	0.02	''	0.063	Very porous
Cr + Si, Mo	0.5	''	0.089	Very slightly porous
Cr + Si, V	0.03	''	0.0635	Very porous
Cr + Si, W	0.02	Poor	0.0765	The same

The low ductility of almost all the coatings is probably due to recrystallization of the base metal, which occurred when the process was carried out in two cycles.

Six of the best compositions were selected on the basis of the preliminary tests for further examination. For the selected coatings, the tests also included a number of heating cycles: Heating at 650°C for $\frac{1}{2}$ hr, followed by cooling in an air jet to room temperature. The oxidation resistance and ductility tests were the same as before. The results of the tests on the six selected coatings are shown in Table 28.

The table shows that the best coatings for the protection of molybdenum from high-temperature oxidation are Si + Ta, Si + Nb, Si + V, and Si + W, applied by the thermal diffusion method in one cycle.

In [82], two compositions of coatings, applied by means of a flame spray gun, were tested for protection of the alloy Mo + 0.45% Ti from high-temperature oxi-dation. A typical composition of the first coating was: 72% Ni, 15.5% Cr, 3% B, 4.5% Si, 4% Fe, 1% C, and of the second coating: 61.7% Cr, 34.9% Si, 1.95% Al, 0.6% Fe. Owing to considerable porosity, both coatings required additional sinter-ing, the sintering temperature substantially affecting the quality and service life of the coating. Experiments showed that the Ni−Cr−B coating had to be sintered in a hydrogen atmosphere for one hour at a temperature of 1100°C, while the Al−Cr−Si coating was protected by a slurry of aluminum oxide in alcohol.

The criterion on which the quality of the coatings was assessed was their ser-vice life, and not their rate of oxidation. The coatings were tested for oxidation resistance at 100-1200°C, and also for thermal shock resistance under the following conditions: Heating in 40 sec to 1000°C, cooling in 5 sec in an air jet to room temperature. At a temperature of 1000°C, the Ni−Cr−B coating did not fail after about 500 hr, while at 1150 and 1200°C, failure occurred even after 20 hr. After 4-20 thermal shock cycles, the coating disintegrated considerably.

TABLE 28. Technological Properties of Selected Protective Coatings for Molybdenum in Relation to Their Composition

Composition of coating	Time to failure when heated in an oxyacetylene flame at 1650°C, hr	Ductility on bending for coatings on sheets 0.8 mm thick	Number of thermal cycles of a duration of 0.5 hr	Time to failure at 1650°C for specimens subjected to bending tests, hr	Thickness of coating	Porosity of coating
Si + Nb	3.8	Excellent	7	1.9	0.09	NP*
	3.5	"	7			
Si + Ta	4.1	Fair	8	ND	0.114	SP
	4.1	"	8			
Si + V	3.4	Excellent	6	1.5	0.101	VSP
	4.5	"	9	1.8		
Si + W	4.8	Good	9	1	0.086	VSP
	4.9	"	9	ND	0.025	NP
Cr, Si + Mo	1.7	Poor	3			
Cr, Si	2.7	Fair	5	ND	0.101	—

* NP: not porous; ND: not determined; SP: slightly porous; VSP: very slightly porous.

Preliminary tests of single-layer Al−Cr−Si coatings showed that their resistance at 1000°C attained 300 hr, and at 1200°C, 50-75 hr. Metallographic examination of the coatings after 75 hr at 1200°C revealed good adhesion of the coatings to the base, but insignificant cracks were to be seen on its surface. To reduce the effect of cracks, after sintering, on the first Al−Cr−Si layer of a thickness of 0.25 mm, a second layer of analogous composition was applied. The service life of such a duplex coating at the temperature 1200°C increased to 150-200 hr. In addition, it was quite resistant to thermal shock: After 280-300 cycles, only slight disintegration was found. Further testing of the Al−Cr−Si showed that the service life was increased if the coatings were kept at 1000°C for 6 hr before thermal tests.

It is assumed [82] that the service life of a coating is determined by the diffusion of molybdenum through it. Chemical analysis showed the existence of an increase in the molybdenum content of the applied layer after 200 hr at 1200°C.

According to [83], a coating similar in composition to the compound Ni_4MoSi_2 is effective in protecting molybdenum and its alloys from oxidation and thermal and dynamic shock. The coating may be applied to the surface of parts in several ways: 1) Silicon is deposited on the heated part from $SiCl_4$ vapor, and forms a layer of silicides, on which nickel is deposited electrolytically or by decomposition of carbonyls; 2) fine Ni and Si powders in the proportion of 4.2:1 are mixed in a solvent, which evaporates on subsequent heating, and are applied to the base by painting, spraying, or dipping; 3) a powder of the alloy Ni_4MoSi_2, or a mixture of Ni, Mo, and Si powders in the same proportions by weight as in the compound Ni_4MoSi_2, i.e., approximately 61:25:14, is applied in the same way as in the second method. The coating is then subjected to a heat treatment, consisting of its fusion in an atmosphere of hydrogen or in a vacuum, resulting in a dense coating and good adhesion to the base. To increase fluidity and resistance to oxidation, inclusion of chromium, iron, or cobalt in the composition of the coating is recommended, and for increasing the density, vanadium or manganese. If cracks appear in the coating, the molybdenum is oxidized and forms nickel molybdenate, which is stable in the presence of silicon. There is no further oxidation of the base, i.e., the coating is "self-heating."

For protecting molybdenum from oxidation at a temperature of 1650°C or above, a coating of Al—Si alloy (12% Si) has been patented [84]. The process of creating the coating comprises spraying on a layer of the Al—Si alloy 0.12 mm thick, slight oxidation thereof either by heating in air to 650°C for $\frac{1}{2}$ hr, or by placing it in a solution of Na_2CrO_4 (30 g/liter) for 10 min at 100°C to form a film having a high surface tension, retaining the coating during its fusion in the subsequent treatment. After heat-treatment of the entire part of 1100°C for 1 hr in a vacuum or under a pressure of less than 1 mm Hg, a protective coating consisting of the following three layers is formed: $MoSi_2$, Al—Mo—Si alloy, SiO_2, and Al_2O_3. It is thus possible to apply protective coatings to molybdenum alloys, and also to parts coated with molybdenum for strength (for example, graphite articles).

The Al—Si alloy, proposed in the foregoing, and the method of applying it, may be employed for the protection of tantalum, tantalum—tungsten alloys, and graphite [85].

Before spraying the Al—Si alloy on metallic materials, the latter are sandblasted (tangentially to the surface) and washed with dilute HCl, while graphite is coated with a layer of molybdenum 50 μ thick by metallization, reduction of molybdenum halides by hydrogen, or by thermal decomposition of its hexacarbonyl. After the treatment described above, the coating shows good adhesion to the base, resistance to thermal shock, and does not exfoliate during heat-treatment under pressure. In quiescent air, the coating protects the parts at 1090°C for more than 100 hr, at 1370°C, for more than 24 hr, and in a slow air current for more than 1.5 hr at 1650°C and 0.5 hr at 1900°C; at a velocity of Mach 4, for 45 sec at 1900°C.

Good results have been obtained in siliconizing molybdenum in a liquid bath consisting of copper and 10-30%(wt) of silicon [86]. Satisfactory wetting of the molybdenum by a melt of such a composition and the formation of protective diffusion layers are obtained only at temperatures of not less than 1000°C. The wetting capacity of the bath is reduced with increase in its oxygen content or in the presence of an oxide film on the surface of the molybdenum. If the bath contains more than 10% Si, a compact, well-adherent layer of molybdenum disilicide is formed on the surface of the immersed molybdenum, the rate of growth of the layer depending on time and the temperature and composition of the bath. The thickness of the $MoSi_2$

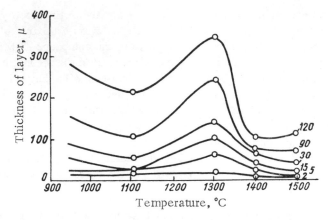

Fig. 33. Thickness of MoSi$_2$ layer versus bath temperature for different durations of treatment (the figures
against the curves indicate duration of treatment, min).

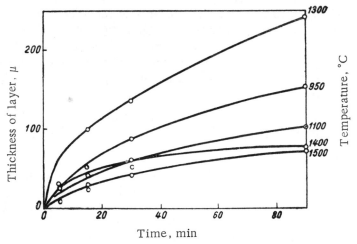

Fig. 34. Thickness of MoSi$_2$ layer versus time for dif-

ferent treatment temperatures.

layer and the kinetics of its growth are shown in Figs. 33* and 34.* As will be
seen from these curves, maximum rate of growth and layer thickness are obtained
at a temperature of the melt of 1300°C. The decrease in these values at higher
temperatures (1400-1500°C) is apparently due to the fact that the molybdenum disilicide layer dissolves appreciably in the Cu–Si melt, and at lower temperatures,
to the diminished activity of the silicon atoms.

Examination of the microstructure of the coating reveals two distinct coatings:
an outer coating consisting of MoSi$_2$ and an inner coating probably consisting of
Mo$_5$Si$_3$ (Fig. 35). After cooling, any melt which has solidified on the siliconized
surface may be readily removed by dipping the article in a zinc bath heated to
500°C.

* The bath contained 16.5% Si.

High-temperature oxidation tests on specimens heated by the direct passage of current in an air atmosphere showed that the most resistant and highest quality coatings were obtained at siliconizing temperatures of from 1200 to 1300°C. Such coatings satisfactorily withstand oxidation at 1600°C for 250 hr. The siliconized layer possesses a very valuable property, that of self-healing with low porosity. At an operating temperature above 1600°C, the service life of the protective layer is limited by increased diffusion mobility of all its components.

A bath of this composition may also be used for the production of protective coatings on tungsten, tantalum, niobium, and their alloys, while up to 50% of the copper may be replaced by silver, tin, lead, cadmium, or gold [87]. By adding to the Cu—Si melt up to 20% boron, small amounts of the latter may be introduced into the siliconized coating, thereby increasing the resistance of the latter to high-temperature oxidation and thermal shock.

In an investigation [144] on the siliconizing of molybdenum in a liquid bath, also consisting of copper and silicon, the optimum composition of the bath was found to be one containing 13-14% Si. According to the results obtained, the rate of liquid-phase siliconizing is higher than that of any other method, for otherwise the same conditions (temperature, time). Thus, in siliconizing at a temperature of 1200°C for 80 min, the thickness of the layer was twice that obtained in siliconizing in an atmosphere of silicon tetrachloride and hydrogen, other conditions being the same.

For producing high-grade protective coatings on molybdenum, the latter, according to the results of [88], should be immersed for 1 min in an Au—Si melt (2.5% Si) heated to 1400°C in a vacuum or an inert atmosphere. To prevent the liquid phase from running off the surface of the part, thin capillaries are formed artificially on the surface by depositing molybdenum on the part from an aqueous suspension of molybdenum powder of a fineness of 2-4 μ, followed by drying and heating. The intermediate molybdenum coating has a porosity of about 40%, the optimum size of the capillaries having been found to be a radius of 1 μ and a height of 0.38 mm. The protective coating will withstand heating to 1400°C for 1000 hr without loss of weight, and 88 cycles of heating of 1400°C and quenching in water; it withstands well the action of extraneous hard particles, and also has the property of self-healing of fissures and cracks, caused by plastic deformation of the part. Among the defects of the coating, reference is made to its ability to embrittle molybdenum at room temperature and its poor resistance to oxidation in the range 620-840°C. This poor resistance may be partly eliminated by reducing the rate of heating and cooling of the articles.

Molybdenum may be protected from high-temperature oxidation by coatings other than those containing silicon. The composition of such coatings and the methods of their application are discussed in the monograph [89]. For example, metallic protective coatings, consisting of one or more nonscaling metal alloys and, less frequently, intermetallic compounds, applied in layers, may be employed. Molybdenum may also be provided with duplex coatings of chromium and nickel [90, 91]. Nickel and aluminum alloys, applied to molybdenum after first coating it electrolytically with chromium, also protect it reliably from oxidation in air at 1100°C for hundreds of hours [92].

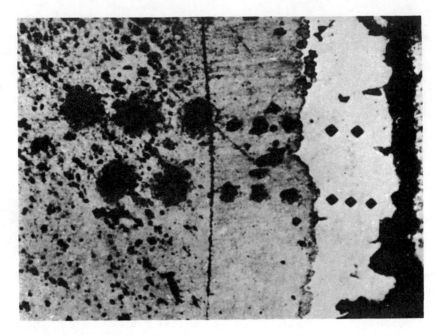

Fig. 35. Structure of siliconized layer on molybdenum in cross section
(bath temperature 1000°C), × 400.

Molybdenum may be protected by coating its surface with refractory oxides.
As pointed out in [83], however, oxide coatings applied to molybdenum are very
sensitive to mechanical and thermal shock, which considerably reduces their practical value. Nevertheless, the high resistance to oxidation and the possibility of
producing refractory compositions render such coatings very valuable for the protection of articles, operating at very high temperatures for short intervals of time.

Tungsten and its alloys may be effectively protected from oxidation by
producing on their surface a layer of WSi_2, which like $MoSi_2$ is highly resistant to
scaling. Siliconizing may be carried out by various methods. For example, saturation of the tungsten with silicon in pure silicon powder, to which has been added 5%
NH_4Cl or 10% NaF, is recommended [93]. The process is carried out at a temperature of 1010-1065°C in a hydrogen atmosphere for 4-8 hr. According to metallographic examination, the coating consists of two layers, an outer layer of WSi_2 and an
inner layer of W_3Si_2. At a temperature below 1815°C, the resistance of the coating
attains 10 hr. According to the same source [93], the application to tungsten of a
protective coating of ZrO_2, with an intermediate layer of WSi_2, did not offer any
advantages.

The investigation of protective coatings, including silicide coatings, on
tungsten, is dealt with in [147]. As pointed out by these investigators, the decisive
factor in the ability of a coating to perform its protective function is its behavior at
the "coating−environment" and "coating−substrate" interfaces. A detailed study
of the reactions taking place at these interfaces permits a rational choice of coating
in each specific case.

An original method of improving the properties of protective coatings on re-fractory metals and their alloys has been patented [94]. The principle of the method is that after applying to the article an electrolytic or thermal diffusion coating, it is coated in its turn by a foil of explosive substance, which is detonated by means of an electric fuse. The wave produced in the explosion strengthens the surface layer and increases its resistance to scaling and thermal shock. The explosion may be carried out under water, which acts as the medium for transmitting the detonation wave. Further improvement in the quality of the coating is obtained by annealing at tem-peratures below the recrystallization of the base metal. A suitable explosive which may be used is pentaerythritol tetranitrate.

The patent specification mentions that the method proposed was used for improving the properties of silicide coatings on molybdenum and electrolytically deposited nickel coatings on an alloy of 95% Mo + 5% Nb.

Interesting work has been done on the gas-phase application of protective silicide coatings to niobium, tantalum, and alloys based on them [95]. Two types of coatings were produced and investigated. Coatings of the first type were ap-plied by interaction of the metal or alloy with a gaseous mixture of $SiCl_4 + H_2$ at a temperature of 1450°C, as the result of which a silicide layer of the corresponding metal or alloy was formed on the surface. The composition of the coating and its resistance to high-temperature oxidation were determined by the base of the alloy. Coatings of the second type, called "duplex coatings," were produced by first ap-plying to the metal or alloy a high-molybdenum layer, followed by conversion of this layer into molybdenum disilicide by reaction with a mixture of $SiCl_4 + H_2$.

Coatings of the first and second types were applied to specimens prepared from sheets of niobium, tantalum, and alloys based on them, the composition of which is given in Table 29.

Figure 36 shows diagrammatically the apparatus for producing the coatings. The gaseous medium in the working space of the furnace contained 25-30% $SiCl_4$, the remainder being hydrogen. Heating was by high-frequency current (450 cps), the optimum temperature was 1450°C. Reaction with the gaseous atmosphere con-tinued for about 20 min.

After siliconizing, the sheet specimens were tested for oxidation at tempera-tures of 1260°C and above in an air atmosphere, for ductility by bending around a rod of 1.27 mm radius; they were also subjected to metallographic and x-ray examinations.

Coatings on niobium and its alloys had the best properties under the following production conditions: 1) Application of MoO_3 from the liquid phase; 2) reduction of the molybdenum trioxide by hydrogen at 800°C; and 3) formation of $MoSi_2$ as the result of interaction of the molybdenum with a mixture of $SiCl_4 + H_2$. The outer layer, consisting of molybdenum disilicide, had a thickness of from 0.05 to 0.076 mm, while the thickness of the inner layer, consisting of the disilicide of the base metal, was 0.05 mm. The molybdenum trioxide was applied to the surface of the specimen by immersion of the latter in liquid MoO_3 heated to 800°C. Attempts to deposit the molybdenum trioxide on the previously formed coating were unsuccess-ful since the disilicide was not wetted by it.

81

TABLE 29. Chemical Composition of Niobium and Tantalum and Alloys Based on Them, Subjected to Siliconizing, %(wt)

Material	Nb	Ta	W	Zr	Ti	Fe	Ni	Si	N	O
Niobium	Base	0.05	0.01	0.01	0.005	0.007	0.007	0.01	0.015	0.03
Tantalum	0.06	Base	0.01	—	0.01	0.005	0.005	0.01	0.002	0.003
Nb−Ta−Zr alloy	Base	32	0.02	0.7	0.02	0.007	0.007	0.001	0.018	0.07
Nb−Ta−W−Zr alloy	,,	28	4.5	0.6	—	—	—	—	0.012	0.051
Ta−W (tantalum) alloy	0.04	Base	10	—	0.02	0.008	—	0.02	0.004	0.004

For tantalum and its alloys, the best results were obtained by deposition of MoO_3 from the gas phase onto a coating of the first type, 0.025 mm thick. After reduction of the molybdenum trioxide by hydrogen at 800°C, followed by treatment in an atmosphere of $SiCl_4 + H_2$, a silicide layer 0.05 mm thick, containing a small quantity of molybdenum, was formed. For the application of MoO_3 from the gas phase, the specimens were held in molybdenum trioxide vapor above a bath containing MoO_3 heated to 800°C. This method was also successfully used for the application of molybdenum to niobium and its alloys.

Coatings of the first type on all the materials investigated consisted of two layers, the outer layer on niobium and its alloys consisting of $NbSi_2$, on tantalum of $TaSi_2$, and on the tantalum−tungsten alloy of $TaSi_2$ and some WSi_2. The composition of the inner layers was $Me_{4.5}Si$, where Me was niobium or tantalum. Silicide coatings of the second type consisted of three layers, the outer layer being $MoSi_2$, while the inner layers were similar in composition to the layers comprising the coatings of the first type.

Coatings of the first and second types afforded good protection to the metal against diffusion into it of atmospheric oxygen and nitrogen at a temperature of 1260°C for tens of hours. Thus, no appreciable increase in microhardness was found at a depth of 0.05 mm from the surface, after the metal with a coating of the second type had been kept for 64 hr at 1260°C in air, and after 20 hr for metal with a coating of the first type under the same conditions. Bending tests at room temperature showed that the metal had not been embrittled after being kept for up to 72 hr at 1260°C in air. Despite the fact that in the bending test the coating exfoliated and cracks appeared on it, the original metal was not fractured.

The variation in weight of the specimens during the time they were kept in air at 1260°C to failure of coatings of both types could be described by the equation

$$\Delta P - \alpha = Kt^n,$$

where ΔP is the change in weight at constant temperature, g; t is the time, min; and K, α, and n are constants.

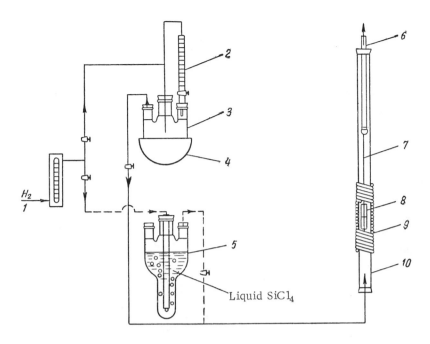

Fig. 36. Diagram of siliconizing apparatus. 1) Flowmeter; 2) buret;
3) evaporating flask; 4) heater; 5) saturation flask; 6) outlet; 7) molybdenum suspension; 8) specimen; 9) inductor; 10) reaction chamber
of Vikor glass (diameter 25.4 mm, length 457 mm).

Since the base metal is not contaminated by diffusing gases, the variation in
weight is mainly due to the formation of oxides on the coating. The commencement of failure of the coating was assumed to be the moment at which there was a
rapid increase in the rate of oxidation, shown by a rapid increase in weight.

The following physical interpretation of the constants was proposed: α ex-
presses the influence of very fine defects in the coating, due to the high initial rate
of oxidation up to the moment at which the defects are healed by the formation of
oxide films; the coefficient K depends on the coefficient of diffusion of the components of the oxide layer, coating, and base; n depends on the rate of decrease in
thickness of the disilicide layer and on the consumption of the silicon reserves. De-
viation from the parabolic oxidation law ($n = \frac{1}{2}$, $\alpha = 0$) is due to the limitation of
the source of silicon, resulting in a variation in the boundary conditions in the oxidation process, since the composition of the disilicide layer varies, and the length
of the diffusion path through the disilicide layer is reduced.

The values of the constants α, K, and n, and also the time to failure of coatings of the first and second types when specimens of the various alloys were heated
in air at 1260°C are given in Table 30.

As will be gathered from Table 30, coatings of the second type have better
protective properties than coatings of the first type.

TABLE 30. Value of α, K, and n and Time to Failure of Coatings of the First and Second Types for Various Alloys

Coated material	Coating	Constants			Time to failure at 1260°C
		α	K	n	
Nb−Ta−W−Zr alloy	Second type (produced by immersion in molten MoO_3)	0	$3.28 \cdot 10^{-5}$	0.704	70
Nb−Ta−W alloy	The same	0	$4.56 \cdot 10^{-5}$	0.758	70
Nb−Ta−W−Zr alloy	First type	0.0002	$9.41 \cdot 10^{-6}$	1.22	40
Nb−Ta−Zr alloy	" "	0.0002	$9.08 \cdot 10^{-6}$	1.30	37
Ta−Zr alloy	" "	0.0013	$1.8 \cdot 10^{-6}$	1.68	15
Niobium	Second type (produced by treatment in MoO_3 vapor)	0.0013	$3.63 \cdot 10^{-7}$	1.74	25
The same	First type	0.0025	$8.03 \cdot 10^{-7}$	1.74	7
Tantalum	Second type (produced by treatment in MoO_3 vapor)	0.0051	$4.86 \cdot 10^{-8}$	2.23	6

A new process of saturating refractory metals with different elements, particularly silicon, has been proposed [96,97]. This process differs from those previously known in that the saturation process is carried out in a hermetically sealed chamber of the furnace with repeated use of the gaseous medium, due to its forced circulation. The proposed process is based on a reaction of the type:

$$HCl + Э \rightarrow Э_m Cl_n + H_2,$$
$$Э_m Cl_n + H_2 + Me \rightarrow Me_x Э_y + HCl,$$

where $Э$ is the coating element (for example, Si, Al, Zr) and Me is the metal to be saturated (Mo, W, Nb, Ta).

The saturation apparatus is a two-stage no-muffle furnace, lined with chloride-resistant refractories, consisting principally of Al_2O_3 or ZrO_2. The articles and the powder of the element with which they are to be saturated are placed on special plates in the furnace. After the furnace has been completely hermetically sealed, hydrogen chloride is led in through a special pipe system and displaces the air. The furnace is heated to the necessary temperature (1000-1200°C), and a fan is then switched on for producing a controlled flow of the gaseous medium, which acts as carrier of the diffusing element of the coating to the metal to be saturated.

A substantial intensification of the process of siliconizing metals from the gas phase may be achieved by using a glow discharge. The apparatus and the first results of experiments on the siliconizing of molybdenum under glow-discharge conditions in a vapor-gas mixture of $SiCl_4 + H_2$ are described in [143]. The principal element of this apparatus is a vacuum reaction chamber with electrodes leading into it, on one of which, the cathode, the specimen to be siliconized is mounted. After evacuation, a mixture of $SiCl_4 + H_2$ is admitted to the chamber and when the pressures is 10-100 mm Hg, a glow discharge is produced between the electrodes by the application of a d.c. voltage of 500-1000 V. Due to bombardment by the ionized gas, the specimen heats up to a temperature of 1000-1200°C (the temperature is regulated by varying the discharge current), at which effective saturation of the molybdenum by silicon takes place. Under optimum conditions, the rate of saturation in a glow-discharge field exceeds the rate of ordinary saturation in a gaseous mixture of $SiCl_4 + H_2$ by several times. Thus, for example, by means of this apparatus, it was possible to produce at 1000°C in 5 min a diffusion layer 25 μ thick. It is stated [143] that the structure of the diffusion layer is similar to that obtained in ordinary gas saturation, and consists mainly of disilicide.

For improving the siliconizing process and the quality of silicide coatings on tantalum and niobium and their alloys with chromium, iron, nickel, zirconium, and others, it is proposed [128] to saturate the surface of parts by the diffusion method with molybdenum or ferromolybdenum before siliconizing. Coating with ferromolybdenum is carried out at a temperature of 870-1540°C for 3-20 hr in a powder mixture consisting of 30-50 parts by weight of ferromolybdenum (55-65% molybdenum, remainder iron), 70-50 parts by weight of inert filler (Al_2O_3, kaolin, ground fireclay, etc.), and 0.02-5 parts by weight of inorganic halides, preferably ammonium halides. Siliconizing is carried out in a mixture of 20-50 parts by weight of Si, 70-45 parts by weight of an inert addition (Al_2O_3), and 0.02-5 parts by weight of an inorganic halide. The entire process is carried out in hermetically sealed boxes or retorts of refractory material provided with a fusible seal, which melts on heating and allows the excess gas to escape to the outside, and on cooling solidifies and prevents air from entering the reaction space.

Specimens of alloys on a niobium base (0.5% Zr, remainder niobium; 0.5% Zr, 39.5% Ta, remainder niobium; 16% Mo, 5.5% Fe, 3.5% Ta, remainder niobium), subjected to the treatment described above, did not show any variation after heating in air to 1300°C for 1.5 hr.

Specimens were treated at 1038°C for 6 hr in a mixture of 35% ferromolybdenum (53.8% Mo and 42.1% Fe), 65% Al_2O_3, and 0.3% NH_4F, while siliconizing was carried out at 1010°C in a mixture of 35% Si, 65% Al_2O_3, and 0.3% NH_4F.

According to [129], silicide coatings can be applied electrolytically to the surface of articles of vanadium, chromium, manganese, iron, cobalt, nickel, niobium, molybdenum, tantalum, tungsten, and other metals, and also alloys containing not less than 90% of one of the above-mentioned metals.

For this purpose, the part is immersed in an electrolyte consisting of an alkali metal fluoride and 5-50% (molar) alkali fluosilicate at a temperature of 600-800°C. The cathode is the article to be coated, and the anode consists of silicon rods. In the electrolysis process, the current density should not exceed 5 A/dm^2, and the time is selected according to the thickness of silicide coating required.

Some examples of the protection of alloys of refractory metals from oxidation are given in [130, 132, 133]. Interesting factual material on the application of carbide, boride,silicide, and nitride coatings on metallic materials is contained in the monograph [131].

Chapter 5

COATINGS ON GRAPHITE

Graphite possesses high thermal conductivity, a low modulus of elasticity, a low coefficient of thermal expansion, and relatively satisfactory strength, increasing with increase in temperature to 2700°C. It is distinguished for its low specific gravity and easy machinability, and is consequently one of the promising high-temperature constructional materials. Its low resistance to oxidation and abrasive wear in a current of hot gases and considerable rate of evaporation at high temperatures, however, make it impossible to use graphite in the pure form, without first providing its surface with protective coatings. It is stated in the literature [98, 99] that graphite and tungsten are the most promising materials for use at temperatures of 1700°C or above, provided, of course, the problem of their protection from oxidation and gas erosion is solved.

The creation of carbide coatings on graphite is possible by thermal diffusion treatment with refractory metals, silicon, or boron. The process may be carried out in the gas phase, using halides, carbonyls, or organic compounds of the above-mentioned saturating elements. A carbide film may also be produced by wetting the surface of the graphite with liquid metal, or flame-spraying it; at a sufficiently high temperature, specific for each metal, the metal coating is converted into a carbide coating [100].

A process of producing metallic layers on graphite articles has been patented [101]. The principle of the process is to apply to the surface of the graphite article a suspension consisting of a solution of polystyrene in an organic solvent and suspended particles of the finely divided metal or its compound. The volatile components of the suspension are then removed by heating the article in a high vacuum. The organic substances are partly evaporated, but are mainly converted into pure spongy carbon, forming an intermediate layer between the graphite and the metallic layer. As a specific example, reference may be made to the following process of applying zirconium to a graphite surface: A suspension of 10 g zirconium powder and 100 ml of a 10% polystyrene solution in benzene is sprayed on the article. After 0.5-1 hr, the article is heated in a high-frequency vacuum furnace at a temperature of 1300°C, and a zirconium coating is produced on its surface. It should be noted that for coating graphite parts with tungsten or molybdenum, heating should be carried out at higher temperatures.

According to [102], a tungsten coating, applied by means of a plasma arc directly to the surface of the graphite nozzles of rocket engines, protects them from the erosion effects of combustion products having high temperatures and velocities. Plasma spraying ensures high density of the coating and its firm bonding to the base. To increase the working temperature of the tungsten coating, it is advisable to apply it to an underlayer of tantalum, previously formed on the graphite, since tungsten forms a eutectic with graphite, melting at about 2480°C, while tantalum forms a eutectic with a melting point of 2800°C. No appreciable improvement in the bonding of the tungsten to the graphite in the presence of a tantalum underlayer has been found. Rhenium is sometimes used instead of tantalum for similar purposes.

A method of protecting graphite elements, the moderators of an atomic reactor, from high-temperature oxidation, has been patented [103]. The protective coating had to have high chemical resistance to superheated water and a small neutron cross section. These requirements were met by a coating on a silicon carbide basis, applied to the surface of the graphite bodies in two stages. First of all, molten silicon powder was applied to the body and formed a film, firmly bonded to the graphite surface. In the second stage of the application, the silicon film was melted by local heating of a portion of the surface of the body without heating the entire graphite mass. The molten silicon spread over the surface and, reacting with the carbon, formed silicon carbide SiC. Local heating may be effected by means of an electric arc produced between a carbon electrode and the treated graphite part. It is also possible to use for this purpose an argon arc-welding apparatus. It is stated that there is no necessity to convert the silicon completely into carbide, since silicon has a sufficiently high resistance to oxidation.

A method has been proposed [104] for applying SiC coatings to various materials, including graphite, comprising the decomposition of silicon organic compounds of the type of methyldichlorosilane or methyltrichlorosilane, in which the molecule contains an equal number of carbon and silicon atoms. Thermal decomposition of these compounds proceeds readily and rapidly on surfaces heated to relatively not very high temperatures (1100-1500°C), dense and homogeneous layers of SiC being formed in a hydrogen atmosphere; these layers do not contain any excess silicon or carbon. The following is the working principle of the apparatus. Hydrogen from a cylinder passes, after purification, into a vessel containing the silicon organic compound at a predetermined temperature, entraps the vapor of the compound, and carries it to the reaction chamber. The reaction chamber is a water-cooled quartz tube or some other hermetically sealed vessel. The part to be treated in the reaction chamber is heated either by high-frequency current or directly by passing current through it.

Before the commencement of the operation, the entire apparatus is purged with hydrogen at a rate of 40-100 liters/hr for 10-20 min; the surface to be treated is then heated to 1000-1500°C, whereupon hydrogen is passed at the required rate through the evaporator, containing methyldi(tri)chlorosilane and controlled thermostatically at a temperature of 25-80°C. The concentration of methylchlorosilane entering the reaction chamber is kept constant in the range 0.01-0.1 g/liter, this being accomplished by selection of the heating temperature of the substance in the evaporator and the rate of flow of the hydrogen. After application of a silicon carbide coating of the required thickness (0.1-1.2 mm), the rate of flow of the hydrogen is increased to 40-100 liters/hr, the hydrogen bypassing the evaporator and entering the chamber directly, where the articles are cooled. The silicon carbide applied in this way is sufficiently pure and contains practically no impurities.

An interesting method of applying a composite coating on carbon articles has been patented [148]. The coating consists of metal carbide and nitride applied in one stage. For producing a high-quality coating, the metal used should form carbides and nitrides, and in addition the carbide of the metal should possess good adhesion to the carbon base. Silicon, titanium, and zirconium satisfy such requirements.

For producing a "carbide-metal" layer on the surface of the article, the latter is heated in an inert gas atmosphere to the carbide-forming temperature. Heating is carried out in the presence of the coating metal, which is partly vaporized, reacts with the surface of the part, and forms a carbide. An unreacted portion of metal remains on the part. Before the actual completion of the carbide-forming process, the inert gas is diluted with nitrogen or a compound of nitrogen. As the result, a nitride layer is deposited on the carbide layer. It is thus possible in one operation to produce a duplex coating, the optimum conditions of carbide and nitride formation being determined separately in each specific case. The patent specification describes the technique of applying the silicon carbide and then nitride to graphite rocket nozzles and gives the results of tests of such nozzles under working conditions. The tests showed that the life of nozzles with a duplex coating was 6-20 times longer than that of nozzles without coating, and 20-150% longer than the service life of nozzles coated with silicon carbide alone.

The conditions for the application of titanium and zirconium carbide coatings on graphite by impregnating the graphite with liquid metal followed by carburization of the metal layer have been studied [149]. Impregnation by the metal was carried out in vacuum furnaces at a temperature 50-100°C above the melting point of the corresponding metal, this temperature being maintained for 20-30 min. Carburization of the metal was effected by heating for 2 hr at temperatures of 1500-1700°C in the case of titanium and 1600-1800°C in the case of silicon. The thickness of the coatings was approximately 50 μ, and their composition was close to the stoichiometric composition for the corresponding carbides.

A study has been made of the diffusion of boron in carbon [105]. The subject for diffusion was spectral graphite in the form of specimens 7 mm in diameter and 250 mm in length. A paste of amorphous boron and starch, in the proportion of 2:1 by weight, was applied to the surface of the specimens in a layer 2 mm thick. The specimens were dried at 150°C, and then placed in a graphite cartridge and heated in a graphite tube furnace to given temperature for 60-80 min. After the temperature had been reached, it was maintained for 15 min, whereupon the cartridges containing the specimens were pushed into the furnace cooler, where they rapidly cooled. The specimens thus obtained were subjected to metallographic examination and chemical and x-ray analysis. It is interesting to note that comparison of the total chemical composition of the specimens, borided with very pure (99%), amorphous boron and boron containing about 70% B (remainder magnesium boride impurity), gave absolutely identical results. This is evidence of the complete elimination of the impurities of the contaminated boron in the boriding process, and shows that boron, highly contaminated with volatile impurities, can be used for saturation.

Investigation of the opposite process of the diffusion of carbon in boron was carried out on specimens of various degrees of porosity, pressed and sintered from boron powder, placed in a cartridge with a packing of carbon black, and heated in a vacuum furnace at 1940°C for 30 min.

Chemical and x-ray analysis showed the rate of diffusion of boron in carbon to be greater than the rate of diffusion of carbon in boron, the process taking place with the formation of intermediate layers of boron carbide, which then decomposed, liberating boron for the formation of solid solutions in carbon.

For calculating the coefficient of diffusion of boron in graphite, the borided specimens of graphite were subjected to chemical analysis by layers; the analytical results are shown in Fig. 37.

The smooth variation of the boron content of the specimens from the surface to the center shows that, in the range of compositions studied (up to 24% B), there are no phase transitions, which in the phase diagram of the boron−carbon system must correspond to the region of solid solutions of boron in carbon. The results of x-ray analysis confirmed the formation of a solid solution of boron in carbon. It was found that an increase in the total boron content produced an increase in the interplanar distances of the graphite lattice, which remains substantially unaltered.

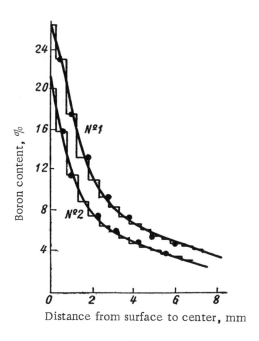

Fig. 37. Variation of boron concentration with depth of its diffusion in graphite.

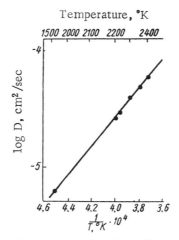

Fig. 38. Temperature dependence of diffusion of boron in graphite.

The coefficient of diffusion of boron in carbon, calculated by means of the Gaussian error integral, was found to be $49.8 \cdot 10^{-6}$ cm^2/sec (for the temperature 2350°C). For other temperatures, the coefficient of diffusion was determined from the mean migration of the diffusing atoms. The relationship found is shown in Fig. 38. The preexponential factor determined from it is 3.02 cm^2/sec, and the energy of activation of the diffusion of boron in carbon Q = 57,250 cal.

In accordance with this, the equation for the diffusion of boron in carbon has the form:

$$D = 3{,}02 \cdot \exp\left(-\,28{,}625/T\right).$$

The fact that the rate of diffusion of boron in carbon is higher than the rate of diffusion of carbon in boron, although the radius of the boron atom is 0.9 Å, while that of the carbon atom is 0.7 Å, may evidently be explained by the lower ionization potential of the boron atoms (8.28 eV) which, as in diffusion in metals [24], ensures high mobility of the boron atoms.

According to [99], protective coatings based on SiC, Cr_3C_2, and ZrC are not very suitable for the protection of graphite articles of complicated shape, since they possess microscopic breaks in continuity, and although they increase the service life of the articles, they fail to protect them to the desired degree from oxidation. Laminated cermet coatings, applied by metallization, are considered to be more suitable [99, 100]. Composite multilayer coatings have higher protective qualities, and evidently will enable considerable progress to be made in solving the problem of graphite protection.

Preliminary experiments showed that laminated coatings, consisting of alternate layers of molybdenum and aluminum oxide, afforded good protection for the graphite linings of rocket engine nozzles. The best properties were found in a coating comprising three layers of molybdenum, each 0.075 mm thick, coated on the

TABLE 31. Composition of Vitreous Binders

Binder	Oxide content, % (wt)										
	SiO_2	Al_2O_3	B_2O_3	TiO_2	ZrO_2	La_2O_3	CoO	BeO	BaO	ZnO	CaO
1	80	2.5	17.5	—	—	—	—	—	—	—	—
2	59	3	20	6	3	2	5	6	—	—	—
3	48.5	31.5	—	—	—	—	20	—	—	—	—
Barium glass	37.6	1.0	6.5	—	2.5	—	—	—	44	5	3.4

top with chromium (0.125 mm). Tests of such a coating applied to siliconized graphite, in an oxyacetylene flame, showed it to be highly resistant to oxidation and to afford graphite articles satisfactory protection from oxidation. No plastic deformation at a temperature of 2200°C, or harmful effect of the coating, was found in the tests.

Final test of the coated articles was carried out in the chamber of a super-sonic uniflow engine (temperature 2200°C, oxidizing atmosphere, 5% oxygen in excess). The tests showed that a purely siliconized layer did not ensure proper pro-tection of the graphite from oxidation, owing to porosity. Once commenced, the oxidation of the siliconized graphite spread under the layer of protective film, re-sulting in the complete destruction of the coating. Multilayer coatings on a basis of $Mo-Al_2O_3-Cr$ and $Mo-ZrO_2-Cr$ melted and ran off the hottest portions, but nevertheless protected the articles from oxidation.

A study has been made of protective vitreous carbide—silicide coatings, pre-pared in the form of aqueous slurries and applied to the graphite by dipping [106]. The starting materials for making the slurries were $MoSi_2$ and SiC, having a particle size of from 50 to 63 μ, and also vitreous binders, the constituents of which are given in Table 31. Bentonite in an amount of 2% was added for stabilizing the suspension. The moisture content of the slurry was 40-45%.

The graphite specimens were first rubbed with water to ensure good wettability by the slurry. The coatings were made from slurries which had not been vacuum treated, since experiments had shown that previous vacuum treatment had no ap-preciable effect on the final properties of the coatings. After application of the slurry, the specimens were dried at a temperature of 100-150°C, and then annealed in an argon atmosphere at 1200-1600°C for 3-4 min, whereupon the three-layer coatings were applied, the total thickness of the protective layer being 0.1-0.2 mm. Increasing the thickness of the protective layer resulted in the formation of cracks and in exfoliation of the coatings.

To assess the quality of the coatings, a study was made of their resistance to high-temperature oxidation, coefficient of linear expansion, microstructure, and resistance to thermal shock. Resistance to high-temperature oxidation was de-termined from the increase in weight of the coated specimens when the latter were heated in air in the temperature range 700-1200°C; the coefficient of linear expan-sion was measured by means of a horizontal quartz dilatometer at temperatures of 20-1000°C. The resistance to thermal shock was determined by the number of

TABLE 32. Composition of Coatings and Their Annealing Temperatures

Coating No.	Content, % (wt)						Maximum annealing temperature, °C
	MoSi$_2$	SiC	Vitreous binders				
			1	2	3	barium glass	
1	20	—	80	—	—	—	1320
2	20	—	—	80	—	—	1270
3	20	—	—	—	80	—	1320
4	30	—	70	—	—	—	1320
5	30	—	—	70	—	—	1280
6	40	—	60	—	—	—	1500
7	40	—	—	60	—	—	1350
8	40	—	—	—	60	—	1500
9	40	—	—	—	—	60	1320
10	50	—	50	—	—	—	1560
11	50	—	—	50	—	—	1370
12	50	—	—	—	50	—	1580
13	50	—	—	—	—	50	1350
14	60	—	40	—	—	—	1580
15	60	—	—	40	—	—	1370
16	80	—	—	—	40	—	1600
17	70	—	30	—	—	—	1580
18	80	—	20	—	—	—	1610
19	80	—	—	20	—	—	1610
20	80	—	—	—	20	—	1610
21	90	—	10	—	—	—	1600
22	90	—	—	10	—	—	1600
23	90	—	—	—	10	—	1600
24	—	40	60	—	—	—	1520
25	—	40	—	60	—	—	1350
26	—	40	—	—	60	—	1500
27	—	40	—	—	—	60	1320
28	—	50	50	—	—	—	1650
29	—	50	—	50	—	—	1370
30	—	50	—	—	50	—	1580
31	—	50	—	—	—	50	1350
32	25	25	50	—	—	—	1560
33	25	25	—	50	—	—	1370
34	25	25	—	—	50	—	1580
35	25	25	—	—	—	50	1350

thermal cycles in the temperature range 20-1200-20°C with air quenching which the coatings withstood without failure.

The composition of the coatings investigated and the optimum annealing temperatures are shown in Table 32.

The properties of coatings Nos. 1-23, containing from 20 to 90% molybdenum disilicide and from 10 to 80% different vitreous binders, varied considerably, according to the composition. Coatings Nos. 1-3 had low fusibility and low resistance to thermal shock, while coatings Nos. 18-23 did not adhere to the graphite and exfoliated readily under the slightest pressure. The addition of 40-60% binders ensured the production of vitreous, porous coatings having a smooth surface. Coating No. 6 showed the best protective properties. Specimens coated with this composition showed no defects when tested in air at a temperature of 1200°C for 125 hr.

The microstructure of this coating (Fig. 39), after test, qualitatively did not differ from the original coating, but the quantitative content of the vitreous phase in the coating had become somewhat higher, while the $MoSi_2$ particles (light inclusions) had diminished both in size and in absolute content in the coating. Apparently, the $MoSi_2$ particles had dissolved in the course of heating and lengthy tests at 1200°C.

Coating No. 6 showed strong adhesion to the graphite and withstood more than 50 thermal cycles in air in the temperature range 20-1200-20°C. Coatings Nos. 10 and 14 also had good properties.

Of the four binders tested, binder No. 1 was the best. With increase in temperature, it softened slowly, and therefore enabled heating of the coatings to be effected in a wide temperature range. Barium glass was the worst binder.

Vitreous carbide coatings Nos. 24-31, containing 40-50% SiC and 50-60% binder, were porous, rough, and did not adhere well to the specimen. None of them were effective against high-temperature oxidation.

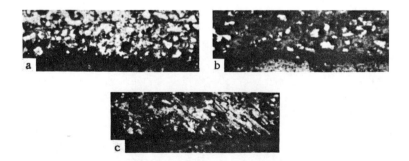

Fig. 39. Microstructure of coating on graphite, × 60. a) After application; b) after heating in air at 1200°C for 20 hr; c) after heating in air at 1200°C for 200 hr.

94

Coatings Nos. 32-35, containing 25% SiC, 25% $MoSi_2$, and 50% binder, occupied an intermediate position between the vitreous silicide coatings and vitreous carbide coatings with regard to their properties. The protected specimens satisfactorily resisted oxidation in air at 1200°C for 20 hr, after which they rapidly decreased in weight.

In the same investigation, a study was made by the spreading drop method of the wettability of graphite, molybdenum disilicide, and silicon carbide by the vitreous binders, and also the influence of wettability on the forming and properties of the coatings. Binders 1, 2, and 3 did not wet graphite, $MoSi_2$, or SiC at all. Barium glass, however, while it did not wet graphite, spread well over the surfaces of $MoSi_2$ and SiC specimens. However, as mentioned above, coatings having the best properties were obtained with binder No. 1, while coatings with a binder of barium glass failed to give satisfactory results. On this basis, it is concluded [106] that spreading drop tests cannot be used for assessing the suitability or otherwise of silicate glasses as binders for heterogeneous coatings. More information is provided by tests to determine the possibility of forming thin films from a powder, previously scattered on the surface and then melted. In this case, binders 1 and 3 were found to wet molybdenum disilicide, silicon carbide, and graphite the best (in an atmosphere of argon and air).

Interest is also afforded by the use of boron silicide (in the form of a fine powder) applied to the article by means of a plasma gun, for protecting graphite from oxidation [107]. Heating in an oxidizing atmosphere results in the formation on the surface of graphite articles of a layer about 0.1 mm thick, consisting of oxides of boron and silicon. Graphite thus protected may be used at temperatures of up to 1400°C and above, depending on the properties of the borosilicate coating.

As shown by tests, a layer of boron silicide adheres well to graphite, partly due to the fact that these materials have very similar coefficients of thermal expansion, do not react with the graphite below a temperature of 1460°C, and are highly resistant to thermal shock (they do not spall when quenched in cold water from a temperature of 1100°C).

Chapter 6

SOME PROPERTIES OF HIGH-TEMPERATURE
COMPOUNDS

It was shown earlier that when the surface of metals and alloys is saturated with carbon, boron, nitrogen, and silicon, the protective diffusion layers formed consist, as a rule, of the corresponding carbides, borides, nitrides, and silicides.

Considerable information on the physicochemical properties of high-temperature compounds is currently available [1-5]. It appears useful to consider only those properties of high-temperature compounds which determine the high qualities of the coatings formed from them, namely: resistance to scaling, corrosion resistance in various corrosive media, hardness, melting point, thermal conductivity, electrical resistance, and coefficient of expansion. In a number of cases, such information may facilitate the choice of the protective coating.

With regard to resistance to scaling, high-temperature compounds may be subdivided into several groups based on different oxidation mechanisms [16]. In the first group may be included the carbides and nitrides of refractory metals, in the second group, their borides, in the third group, tungsten and molybdenum silicides, and in the fourth group, all the remaining silicides.

The protective capacity of an oxide layer may be estimated approximately by what is known as the Pilling-Bedworth ratio, showing by how much the specific volume of the oxide formed is greater or less than the specific volume of the oxidized metal or in the present case the compound

$$\alpha = \frac{M \cdot d}{m \cdot D},$$

where M is the molecular weight of the oxide (or mixture) formed on the oxidation of 1 g-mole of compound, m is the molecular weight of the oxidized compound, and D and d are the densities of the oxide and compound.

For $\alpha < 1$, the film formed is discontinuous, resulting in continuous oxidation (rectilinear law of rate of oxidation), while for $\alpha > 1$, a protective oxide layer is formed, inhibiting the access of oxygen under known conditions (parabolic law of oxidation). For large values of α, the layer has considerable internal stress, spalls, and loses its protective properties; therefore the best protective properties are possessed by layers for which α does not greatly exceed unity.

TABLE 33. Values of the Pilling-Bedworth Ratio (α) for Some High-Temperature Compounds

Carbide	α	Nitride	α	Boride	α
TiC	1.53	TiN	1.57	TiB_2	1.21
ZrC	1.43	ZrN	1.41	ZrB_2	1.16
NbC	2.22	NbN	2.25	NbB_2	1.71
TaC	1.91	TaN	1.84	TaB_2	1.48
Mo_2C	3.56	Mo_2N	2.5	Mo_2B_5	2.19
WC	2.72	WN	2.09	W_2B_5	2.11

Data on the values of α for the carbides, borides, and nitrides of some refractory metals are given in Table 33.

The oxidation of carbides and nitrides, apart from producing the oxides of the corresponding metals, also results in the formation of gaseous oxides of carbon and nitrogen, which disintegrate the oxide films, culminating on the whole in the relatively low resistance of these compounds to scaling.

As will be gathered from the data presented in Table 33, α has the lowest value for the carbides and nitrides of titanium and zirconium, and the highest value for these compounds of tungsten and molybdenum. Accordingly, the carbides and nitrides of titanium and zirconium have the highest resistance to scaling and those of molybdenum and tungsten the lowest resistance to scaling.

The relatively satisfactory resistance to scaling of the carbides and nitrides of titanium and zirconium is also due to the fact that what is known as a pseudomorphous* layer of a solid solution of a lower oxide in the carbide or nitride (TiC – TiO, etc.) is formed at the interface between compound and oxide layer [108]. This pseudomorphous layer is, so to speak, a continuation of the crystal lattice of the carbide or nitride, and is characterized by stresses, due to variation in the lattice constants of compound and oxide. On attaining some critical value, the internal stresses in the layer become effective, and the layer is transformed into the ordinary oxide with its inherent lattice constants and density. The process of the formation and growth of the pseudomorphous layer delays the oxidation process of the compound.

In the oxidation of the carbides and nitrides of molybdenum and tungsten, lower oxides are practically not formed at all, and even if they were formed, they would be unable to form solid solutions with the corresponding high-temperature compounds. In addition, the resistance to oxidation is reduced by the high volatility of the oxides of these metals, which exercises an additional disintegrating effect on the oxide layer.

---

*A pseudomorphous layer is a very thin layer adjacent the underlying matrix, and the lattice of which has orientational correspondence with, and similar lattice constants to, the lattice of the matrix.

In the case of the carbides and nitrides of tantalum and niobium, although lower oxides may be formed, but owing to their nonisomorphous character, and also the very different lattice constants of the respective compounds, the pseudomorphous layers are unstable, resulting in a high rate of oxidation of these compounds, compared with the carbides and nitrides of titanium and zirconium.

In the oxidation of borides, volatile boric anhydride is also formed, in addition to the oxides of the corresponding metals. The solubility of the oxides of most metals in boric anhydride is low, and therefore we cannot expect the formation of pseudomorphous layers with their protective influence on oxidizability. In the oxidation of borides, however, two other processes take place, which determine the rate of oxidation, character of the structure of the oxide film, and also its protective properties: the evaporation of boric anhydride and the formation of borates.

The first of these processes produces a complex form of curves (isotherms) of the oxidation of borides, which is determined at each given temperature by the ratio between the increase in weight, due to the formation of oxides of the metals, and the loss in weight of the specimen, due to partial volatilization of boric anhydride.

At relatively low temperatures, the part played by the high volatility of boric anhydride is fairly considerable, and at temperatures of 1100-1300°C, the process of the formation of borates, or more exactly, as shown by investigations [108, 109], the formation of pyroborates of the refractory metals, begins to predominate, thereby increasing the protective properties of the oxide film. This circumstance, in conjunction with the low value of α, determines the relatively high resistance to scaling of some borides, exceeding in a number of cases the resistance to scaling of carbides and nitrides. Questions of the resistance to scaling of borides have also been considered in [110-112].

The resistance to high-temperature oxidation of silicides of the refractory metals has been much investigated, and a bibliography will be found in the monograph [4]. It is customary to distinguish two main cases A and B (Table 34) of the formation of a protective coating as a function of the volatility and solubility of the oxides of metals and silicon, formed in the high-temperature heating of the silicides [4].

In case A, oxidation of the silicide is accompanied by the formation of an oxide of the metal, which is very volatile at elevated temperatures (for example, MoO_3 begins to volatilize at 850°C, its vapor pressure being 700 mm Hg at 1360°C). At first, the surface layer is very volatile, since it consists of a certain quantity of SiO_2 and oxides of molybdenum or tungsten, but as these oxides are removed, it becomes increasingly viscous and dense, becoming higher in SiO_2. When a film of SiO_2 is formed on the surface of the protective layer, oxidation practically ceases. At temperatures above 1700°C, the quartz film collects in droplets and uncovers the underlying layers of silicide, which commence to oxidize intensely.

In case B, a dense, vitreous layer is formed only at definite temperatures and for definite ratios of the content of SiO_2 and nonvolatile metal oxide (for example, for TiS_2 and VSi_2 at a temperature of 1300-1400°C). A logarithmic or parabolic

TABLE 34. Scheme of Formation of Protective Surface Layer in the Oxidation of Silicides

	Case A		Case B	
Me	$-Si$ ($MoSi_2$, WSi_2)	Me$-$		Si($CrSi_2$, $ZrSi_2$, $TaSi_2$, $TiSi_2$, VSi_2)
$\downarrow$	$\downarrow$	$\downarrow$		$\downarrow$
Volatile oxide of the metal	SiO_2 Surface layer vitreous, applied well to the base, dense, consists mainly of SiO_2	Nonvolatile oxide of the metal		SiO_2 Surface layer porous, not closely applied to the base (Cr_2O_3, ZrO_2, Ta_2O_3, SiO_2). At medium temperatures, coating vitreous, applied closely to the base (TiO_2-SiO_2 and $V_2O_5-SiO_2$)

oxidation law is then found. For $ZrSi_2$, $CrSi_2$, $NbSi_2$, and $TiSi_2$, a porous, loosely attached surface layer is formed, which actually does not retard the oxidation process and itself increases linearly with time.

Microhardness, electrical resistance, thermal conductivity, coefficient of linear expansion, and melting point of high-temperature compounds have been determined in many investigations, a bibliography of which will be found in the monograph [5]. Table 36 gives the characteristics of high-temperature compounds taken from that monograph.

Whereas for borides, carbides, and nitrides, the ratio of their melting point to the melting point of the corresponding metals, as a rule, is greater than unity, it is always less than unity for the silicides (Table 35).

The microhardness of the silicides is much less than the microhardness of the carbides, nitrides, and borides. These differences are due to the difference in the nature of the silicides, on the one hand, and the carbides, nitrides, and borides on the other. As is well known, the first are substitution phases, the substitution of the

TABLE 35. Ratio of Melting Point of High-Temperature Compounds to Melting Point of the Corresponding Metals

Metal	Carbide	Boride	Nitride	Silicide	Metal	Carbide	Boride	Nitride	Silicide
Ti	1.86	1.76	1.89	0.88	Ta	1.29	1.03	1.03	0.71
Zr	1.9	1.63	1.6	0.92	Cr	0.98	1.14	−	0.81
Hf	1.83	1.52	1.55	0.82	Mo	0.98	0.8	−	0.77
V	1.62	1.39	1.37	0.98	W	0.81	0.68	−	0.64
Nb	1.52	1.23	0.94	0.88					

TABLE 36. Some Physical Properties of the Transition Metals and Their High-Temperature Compounds

Metal, compound	Melting point, °C	Micro-hardness, kg/mm^2	Coefficient of linear expansion (0-1200°C), $\alpha \cdot 10^6/°C$	Thermal conductivity, cal/cm·°C·sec	Resistivity, $\mu\Omega \cdot$ cm
Ti	1690	160	8.35	0.0407	48
Zr	1855	97	5.85	0.04	41
Hf	2110	200	~9	–	30
V	1735	65	8.5	0.074	26
Nb	2468	88	7.0	0.125	16
Ta	2996	100	8.6	0.13	14.7
Cr	1930	150	6.2	–	18.9
Mo	2625	190	4.9	0.38	5.2
W	3410	350	4.3	0.31	5.5
TiC	3150	3000	7.74	0.0869	52.5
ZrC	3530	2930	6.73	0.049	50.0
HfC	3890	2900	6.59	0.015	45.0
VC	2810	2090	7.2	0.0587	65.0
NbC	3760	1960	6.5	0.034	51.1
TaC	3880	1599	6.29	0.053	42.1
Cr$_3$C$_2$	1895	1350	11.7	0.0458	75.0
Cr$_7$C$_3$	1665	1336	10.6	0.036	109.0
Mo$_2$C	2565	1499	7.8	0.016	71.0
W$_2$C	2730	1780	3.84	0.07	19.2
WC	2870	923	5.2	0.07	19.2
TiN	3205	1900	9.35	0.046	25
ZrN	2980	1480	7.24	0.049	21.1
HfN	2980	1640	6.9	–	33
VN	2360	1520	8.1	0.027	85
NbN	2300	1400	10.1	0.0191	78
TaN	3090	1060	3.6	0.0205	128.0
CrN	Decomposes at 1500°C	1080	2.3	0.0284	640
MoN	–	–	–	–	–
Mo$_2$N	Decomposes at 600°C	–	4.5	0.427	19.8
WN	The same	–	–	–	–
Cr$_2$N	–	1571	9.41	0.0519	76
TiB$_2$	2980	3370	8.1	0.063	14.4
ZrB$_2$	3040	2250	6.88	0.058	16.6
HfB$_2$	3250	2900	5.73	–	8.8
VB$_2$	2400	2800	7.5	–	19
NbB$_2$	3000	2600	7.9-8.3	0.047	34
NbB	2280	2195	–	–	64.5

TABLE 36. Continued

Metal, compound	Melting point, °C	Micro-hardness, kg/mm^2	Coefficient of linear expansion (0-1200°C), $\alpha \cdot 10^6/°C$	Thermal conductivity, cal/cm · °C · sec	Resistivity, $\mu\Omega \cdot cm$
TaB	2430	3130	–	–	100
TaB$_2$	3100	2500	11.4	0.033	37.4
CrB$_2$	2200	1785	11.1	0.053	84
Mo$_2$B$_5$	2100	2350	–	0.064	18
W$_2$B$_5$	2300	2660	–	0.076	43
TiSi$_2$	1460-1540	890	8.8-8.9	0.111	16.9
ZrSi$_2$	1700	1060	8.6	0.0373	75.8
HfSi$_2$	1750	930	–	–	–
VSi$_2$	1660	960	11.2	0.0383	66.5
NbSi$_2$	2160	1050	11.7	0.0397	50.4
TaSi$_2$	2200	1400	8.8	0.0521	46.1
CrSi$_2$	1500	1130	~10	0.0253	46.1
MoSi$_2$	2030	1200	5.1	0.07-0.093	21.6
WSi$_2$	2165	1070	7.9	0.114	12.5

metal atoms by the smaller silicon atoms facilitating shear deformation, affecting in a decisive manner the hardness and melting point of the silicides. The second are interstitial phases or phases similar to them in type of structure, and in such structures, shear deformation is difficult.

All high-temperature compounds have high chemical stability, principally with regard to the action of acids, their mixtures, and mixtures of acids with oxidizing agents in the cold and hot condition. The chemical stability of high-temperature compounds in powder form has been studied at the Institute of Cermets and Special Alloys of the Academy of Sciences of the Ukrainian SSR [113-117].

The borides of refractory metals resemble the carbides, in their properties, differing from them by their higher chemical stability in various aggresive media [115]. In cold and hot acids of any concentration, tantalum and niobium borides are the most stable; titanium, zirconium, molybdenum, and tungsten borides are stable only in cold acids. The solubility of the nitrides in acids and alkalis of different concentrations was studied in [116].

The behavior of the disilicides of the refractory metals in different chemical agents was studied in [117-119]. The disilicides of the refractory metals have very high chemical stability in most acids and their mixtures and also in weakly concentrated alkalis.

Considerable interest attaches to the properties of high-temperature compounds as refractory materials, i.e., their ability to withstand the action of molten metals, alloys, slags, salts, etc. As yet, there is insufficient published information on these properties of high-temperature compounds. It has been found that the borides have the highest resistance to the action of molten metals. According to

[120], articles based on chromium borides and made by hot pressing are stable to the action of molten salts and metals, including copper, tin, magnesium, silicon, and fluorides. An alloy based on zirconium boride and marketed in America under the name "Borolite I" [121] has high resistance to thermal shock, and does not fracture on contact with molten aluminum, tin, lead, copper, and different brasses.

The reaction of high-temperature compounds, in the form of compact components, with pure metals, cast iron, steel, and slags has been studied [16, 122, 123]. Table 37 gives the results of tests on the reaction of some refractory compounds with the above-mentioned materials in the molten state [16].

As will be seen from the data presented, titanium, zirconium, and chromium borides practically do not react with low-melting nonferrous metals, brass, and slags. Wetting of borides by copper [124] varies, increasing in the following order: TiB_2, VB_2, NbB_2, ZrB_2, TaB_2, CrB_2. Metals of the iron group and alloys based on them wet chromium borides well, but active interaction is rare. Zirconium boride has been found to be particularly resistant in contact with carbon steel and cast iron [125].

The nitrides of refractory metals are less refractory than the borides, but they also react little with molten low-melting metals. Liquid cast iron and basic cupola slag at 1500°C wet and destroy titanium nitride, forming with it an alloy of eutectic character.

The refractory properties of the carbides of refractory metals as a rule are on a lower level than those of the borides. They resist well low-melting nonferrous metals, but react fairly actively with molten steel and cast iron. Chromium carbides Cr_3C_2 and Cr_7C_3, tungsten carbide, zirconium carbide, and titanium carbide do not react with the refractory metals tantalum, molybdenum, and tungsten below temperatures of 1800-2000°C [126].

Of the silicides, maximum interest from the point of view of refractory properties attaches to molybdenum disilicide, since it may be used as material for heat exchangers in power plants (for the abstraction of heat). According to [119], molybdenum disilicide does not react with lead, tin, or sodium below 1000°C. Zinc, when heated to 800°C, may dissolve up to 1% Si, which separates out on cooling; molten silver and mercury also practically do not act on $MoSi_2$. Molten aluminum reacts actively with the latter, forming molybdenum aluminide. Molten iron, copper, chromium, and platinum react with $MoSi_2$, forming binary and ternary silicide phases. A brief review of the refractory properties of refractory compounds is to be found in [127].

Coatings based on high-temperature compounds are currently finding ever increasing application in various branches of industry and technology, above all for the protection components, subjected to high temperatures, from oxidation and gaseous erosion. Further development of aircraft construction, rocket construction, power engineering, and high-temperature engineering is inevitably associated with the creation of protective coatings on vital parts operating under very severe conditions.

The problem of the protection of turbojet engine blades and stationary gas-turbine blades from high-temperature oxidation and gas erosion is most acute. In the opinion of experts, this difficult and pressing problem of modern engineering cannot be solved without the application of coatings, and here multilayer protec-

TABLE 37. Resistance of High-Temperature Compounds to the Action of Inorganic Melts

Composition of melt	Temperature, °C	Duration of contact		Atmosphere	Character of reaction	Content of components of compound passing into the melt, %
		hr	min			

TiB$_2$

Composition of melt	Temperature, °C	hr	min	Atmosphere	Character of reaction	Content, %
Tin	350	10	—	Air	Does not react	Ti-traces
"	350	40	—	"	The same	Ti 0.01
"	350	80	—	"	" "	—
Bismuth	375	10	—	"	" "	Ti-traces
"	375	40	—	"	" "	Ti 0.05
"	375	80	—	"	" "	—
Lead	450	10	—	"	" "	Ti-traces
"	450	40	—	"	" "	Ti 0.06
"	450	80	—	"	" "	—
Cadmium	450	10	—	"	" "	Ti-traces
"	450	40	—	"	" "	Ti 0.026
"	450	80	—	"	" "	Ti 0.026
Zinc	550	80	—	"	" "	Ti not found
"	940	132	—	"	Weak reaction	—
"	940	240	—	"	The same	—
Carbon steel	1600	—	5	CO+N$_2$	Reacts	—
Cast iron	1600	—	5	CO+N$_2$	The same	—

ZrB$_2$

Composition of melt	Temperature, °C	hr	min	Atmosphere	Character of reaction	Content, %
Tin	350	80	—	Air	Does not react	Zr-traces
Bismuth	375	80	—	"	The same	Zr-absent
Lead	450	80	—	"	" "	Zr-traces
Cadmium	450	80	—	"	" "	Zr-absent
Zinc	550	80-	—	"	" "	Zr-traces
"	940	180-200	—	"	Weak reaction	—
Carbon steel	1620	2	—	CO+N$_2$	Does not react	—
Cast iron	1520	12	—	CO+N$_2$	The same	—
Brass	900	86	—	Air	" "	—
Basic slag	1520	12	—	CO+N$_2$	" "	—
Acid slag	1520	12	—	CO+N$_2$	" "	—

CrB$_2$

Composition of melt	Temperature, °C	hr	min	Atmosphere	Character of reaction	Content, %
Tin	350	10	—	Air	Does not react	Cr-traces
"	350	40	—	"	The same	Cr 0.01
"	350	80	—	"	" "	Cr-traces
Bismuth	375	10	—	"	" "	Cr-traces
"	375	40	—	"	" "	Cr 0.01
"	375	80	—	"	" "	Cr-traces
Lead	450	10	—	"	" "	Cr-traces
"	450	40	—	"	" "	Cr 0.01

TABLE 37. Continued

Composition of melt	Temperature, °C	Duration of contact		Atmosphere	Character of reaction	Content of components of compound passing into the melt, %
		hr	min			
Lead	450	80	—	Air	Does not react	Cr-traces
Cadmium	450	10	—	''	The same	Cr-traces
''	450	40	—	''	'' ''	Cr 0.01
''	450	80	—	''	'' ''	Cr-traces
Zinc	940	120	—	''	Weak reaction	—
''	940	156	—	''		—
Steel KhVG	1620	—	5	CO+N$_2$	Reacts	—
Carbon steel	1620	—	30	''	''	—
Cast iron	1520	—	5	''	Does not react	—
Basic slag	1520	—	5	Co+N$_2$	Reacts	—
Acid slag	1520	—	5	''	''	—

TiC

Composition of melt	Temperature, °C	hr	min	Atmosphere	Character of reaction	Content
Tin	350	10	—	Air	Does not react	Ti not found
Bismuth	375	10	—	''	The same	Ti 0.018
Lead	450	10	—	''	'' ''	Ti 0.01
Cadmium	450	10	—	''	'' ''	Ti 0.01
Zinc	550	10	—	''	'' ''	Ti 0.01
Carbon steel	1620	—	5	''	Reacts	—
Cast iron	1520	—	5	''	''	—
Basic slag	1520	—	5	''	Does not react	—
Acid slag	1520	—	5	''	The same	—

ZrC

Composition of melt	Temperature, °C	hr	min	Atmosphere	Character of reaction	Content
Tin	350	10	—	Air	Does not react	Zr not found
Bismuth	375	10	—	''	The same	Zr-traces
Lead	450	10	—	''	'' ''	Zr-traces
Cadmium	450	10	—	''	'' ''	Zr 0.01
Zinc	450	6	—	''	'' ''	Zr 0.02

WC

Composition of melt	Temperature, °C	hr	min	Atmosphere	Character of reaction	Content
Zinc	940	84	—	Air	Does not react	—
Zinc	940	144	—	''	Very weak reaction	—

TiN

Composition of melt	Temperature, °C	hr	min	Atmosphere	Character of reaction	Content
Tin	350	10	—	Air	Does not react	Ti not found
''	350	40	—	''	Weak reaction	Ti 0.26
Bismuth	375	10	—	''	Does not react	Ti-traces
''	375	40	—	''	The same	Ti 0.07
Lead	450	10	—	''	Weak reaction	Ti 0.04
''	450	40	—	''	The same	Ti 0.20
Cadmium	450	10	—	''	'' ''	Ti 0.02

105

TABLE 37. Continued

Composition of melt	Temperature, °C	Duration of contact		Atmosphere	Character of reaction	Content of components of compound passing into the melt, %
		hr	min			
Cadmium	450	40	—	Air		Ti 0.07
Carbon steel	1620	—	5	$CO+N_2$	Wets sligntly, no reaction	—
Cast iron	1520	—	5	$CO+N_2$	The same	—
Basic slag	1520	—	5	$CO+N_2$	Wets, no reaction	—
Acid slag	1520	—	5	$CO+N_2$	The same	—
				$MoSi_2$		
Lead	1000	5	—		Does not react	—
Tin	1000	5	—	—	" " "	—
Sodium	1000	—	—	—	" " "	—
Zinc	800–900	5	—	—	Weak reaction	—
"	940	168	—	—	" "	—
Silver	—	—	—	—	Does not react	—
Mercury	—	—	—	—	" " "	—
Copper Iron	—	—	—	—	Reacts with the formation of silicides	—
Aluminum	1000	5	—	—	Reacts with the formation of aluminide	—

tive coatings, which as a whole ought to combine the best qualities of each of the combined layers, are considered to be the most promising [89].

As already pointed out [18, 122, 125], the application of coatings of high-temperature compounds can substantially increase the service life of some parts of metallurgical equipment. The **high-refractory** properties of the coatings, particularly those based on borides, ought to find application in the metallurgy of nonferrous and noble metals.

The application of boride and carbide layers to machine parts and parts subjected to considerable abrasive wear in service is being widely employed [19, 23].

Parts provided with coatings of refractory compounds may find extensive application in the chemical industry as constructional elements of pumps for pumping cold and hot liquids, in the construction of scrubbers operating with hot corrosive gases, linings of nozzles for spraying hot chemically active liquids, for agitators, etc.

Coatings of high-temperature compounds, possessing a number of valuable electrophysical properties, are also of interest for electrical engineering, radio engineering, electronics. Examples of their application in these branches of engineering will be found in [5].

REFERENCES

1. G. V. Samsonov and Ya. S. Umanskii, Hard Compounds of Refractory Metals, Metallurgizdat, Moscow (1957).
2. R. Kieffer and P. Schwarzkopf, Hard Alloys [Russian translation], Metallurgizdat, Moscow (1957).
3. G. V. Samsonov, L. Ya. Markovskii, A. F. Zhigach, and M. G. Valyashko, Boron, Its Compounds and Alloys, Izd. Akad. Nauk UkrSSR, Kiev (1960).
4. G. V. Samsonov, Silicides and Their Use in Technology, Izd. Akad. Nauk UkrSSR, Kiev (1959).
5. G. V. Samsonov, Refractory Compounds, Metallurgizdat, Moscow (1963).
6. N. P. Chizhevskii, Zh. Russk. Metallurg. Obshch., No. 4: 645 (1915).
7. I. E. Kontorovich and M. Ya. L'vovskii, Metallurg, No. 10-11: 89 (1939).
8. N. S. Gorbunov, Diffusion Coatings on Iron and Steel, Izd. Akad. Nauk SSSR, Moscow (1958).
9. G. V. Samsonov and N. Ya. Tseitina, Fiz. Metal. i Metalloved. 1: 303 (1955).
10. Yu. M. Lakhtin and M. A. Pchelkina, Metalloved. i Term. Obrabotka Metal., No. 7: 40 (1960).
11. V. I. Arkharov et al., Dokl. Akad. Nauk SSSR 89: 269 (1953).
12. M. E. Blanter and N. P. Besedin, Metalloved. i Obrabotka Metal., No. 6: 3 (1955).
13. Yu. M. Lakhtin and M. A. Pchelkina, Metalloved. i Term. Obrabotka Metal., No. 3: 29 (1961).
14. A. F. Zhigach, I. S. Antonov, M. A. Pchelkina, G. I. Yukin, A. S. Dobrodeev, and B. N. Matveev, Metalloved. i.Term. Obrabotka Metal., No. 4: 45 (1959).
15. R. L. Samuel and N. A. Lokington, British Patent No. 861644, March 22, 1961.
16. G. V. Samsonov and K. I. Portnoi, Alloys Based on Refractory Compounds, Oborongiz, Moscow (1961), p. 256.
17. Physical Metallurgy and Heat Treatment (Reference Book), Moscow (1956).
18. P. T. Gorodnov, Metalloved. i Term. Obrabotka Metal., No. 2: 55 (1961).
19. A. V. Orlov, N. I. Sandler, V. V. Kukol', N. P. Aleksandrova, and U. S. Govor, Proceedings of the Ukrainian Scientific Research Institute of Metals, No. 7: 232 (1961).
20. N. N. Nogtev and Yu. M. Rogozin, Metalloved. i Term. Obrabotka Metal., No. 12: 49 (1962).
21. V. D. Taran and A. P. Skugorova, Metalloved. i Term. Obrabotka Metal., No. 1: 2 (1960).

22. A. N. Minkevich and G. N. Ustybin, Metalloved. i Term. Obrabotka Metal., No. 4:48 (1959).

23. I. I. Iskol'dskii and S. L. Cherkinskaya, "Surfacing Alloys Based on Chromium Boride," in collection: Hard Alloys, Vol. I, Metallurgizdat, Moscow (1959).

24. G. V. Samsonov and B. P. Latysheva, Fiz. Metal. i Metalloved. 2: 309 (1956).

25. W. Beck, Metal Ind. (London) 86: 43 (1955).

26. D. R. Stern and L. Linds, Probl. Sovrem. Metallurg. No. 4 (46) (1959).

27. M. P. Asanova, A. F. Gerasimov, and B. N. Konev, Fiz. Metal. i Metalloved. 9: 689 (1960).

28. L. Brewer, D. Sawyer, D. Templeton, and K. Dauben, J. Am. Ceram. Soc. 34: 173 (1951).

29. H. Nowotny, F. Benesovsky, and R. Kieffer, Z. Metallk. 50: 258 (1959).

30. A. N. Minkevich, Metalloved. i Term. Obrabotka Metal., No. 8: 9 (1961).

31. M. L. Rutkovskii, N. A. Anufrieva, O. P. Kop'eva, N. V. Potapova, and I. V. Kazakov, Fiz. Metal. i Metalloved. 12: 217 (1962).

32. T. Neumann and S. Dittrich, Z. Metallk. 50: 584 (1959).

33. G. V. Samsonov and A. P. Epik, Researches on Heat-Resistant Alloys, Vol. X, Izd. Akad. SSSR, Moscow (1964) (in press).

34. G. S. Kreimer, L. D. Éfros, and E. A. Voronkova. Zh. Tekhn. Fiz. 22: 848 (1952).

35. A. N. Minkevich, Chemical Heat Treatment of Steel, Mashgiz, Moscow (1950).

36. Yu. M. Lakhtin, Physical Principles of the Nitriding Process, Mashgiz, Moscow (1948).

37. A. A. Popov, Theoretical Principles of the Chemical Heat Treatment of Steel, Metallurgizdat, Sverdlovsk (1962).

38. G. N. Dubinin, Metalloved. i Obrabotka Metal., No. 9: 21 (1957).

39. H. Wiegand and W. Ruppert, Metalloberflaeche 14 (7-8) (1960).

40. D. S. Plashko, Author's Certificate USSR, No. 621554/22, March 9, 1959.

41. V. I. Arkharov and V. N. Konev, Vestn. Mashinostr., No. 11: 55 (1955).

42. A. Münster and W. Ruppert, J. Electrochem. Soc. 57: 584 (1953).

43. K. Bungardt and K. Rudinger, Z. Metallk. 47: 577 (1956).

44. A. V. Smirnov and A. D. Nachinkov, Metalloved. i Term. Obrabotka Metal., No. 3: 22 (1960).

45. U. S. Patent No. 2892743, June 30, 1959.

46. T. S. Verkhoglyadova, T. V. Dubovnik, and G. V. Samsonov, Poroshkovaya Met., No. 4: 9 (1961).

47. A. N. Minkevich, A. D. Taimer, and Yu. A. Zot'ev, Metalloved. i Obrabotka Metal., No. 7: 39 (1956).

48. E. Guldbransen and K. Andrews, Trans. Am. Inst. Min. Met. Eng., Vol. 185 (1949).

49. A. V. Smirnov and A. D. Nachinkov, Metalloved. i Term. Obrabotka Metal., No. 7: 42 (1960).

50. Y. Takeuchi, R. Komanischi, Y. Morooka, D. Wastanabe, and S. Ogawa, J. Japan. Inst. Met. (Sendai) 23(7) (1959).

51. K. Nakano, S. Yamamoto, H. Kobayaschi, and A. Takamura, J. Japan. Inst. Met. (Sendai) 24(8) (1960).

52. Metal Ind. (London) 97: 87 (1960).

53. E. N. Novikova, Collection: Titanium and Its Alloys, No. III, Izd. Akad. Nauk SSSR, Moscow (1960).

54. Yu. V. Grdina, A. T. Gordeeva, and L. G. Timonina, Izv. Chernaya Met., No. 6: 128 (1962).

55. C. N. Konev, Researches on Heat-Resistant Alloys, Vol. III, Izd. Akad. Nauk SSSR, Moscow (1958).

56. V. I. Arkharov, V. N. Konev, and A. F. Gerasimov, Fiz. Metal. i Metalloved. 9: 659 (1960).

57. A. F. Gerasimov, V. N. Konev, and N. F. Timofeeva, Fiz. Metal. i Metalloved. 11: 596 (1961).

58. W. Ruppert, German Federal Republic Patent No. 1089240, March 1, 1961.

59. O. V. Tolokonnikova, TÉKhSO NKTP SSSR, Series 25, Special Steels, No. 503 (1958).

60. T. Ya. Dueva, Vestn. Metallopromyshlennosti, No. 16-17: 35 (1937).

61. M. G. Butsik, Stal', No. 7-8: 24 (1941).

62. E. Fitzer, Arch. Eisenhuettenw. 25: 455 (1954).

63. N. S. Gorbunov and A. S. Akopdzhanyan, Zh. Prikl. Khim. 29: 655 (19560).

64. A. A. Akopdzhanyan and N. S. Gorbunov, Zh. Prikl. Khim. 29: 659 (1956).

65. Z. G. Ordina, Metalloved. i Term. Obrabotka Metal., No. 6: 46 (1960).

66. G. M. Orlova and V. V. Ignat'ev, Zh. Prikl. Khim. 29: 819 (1956).

67. R. Kieffer, F. Benesovsky, and H. Schroth, Z. Metallk. 44: 437 (1953).

68. N. S. Gorbunov, E. A. Kovalev, and A. G. Latukhova, Researches on Heat-Resistant Alloys, Vol. VII, Izd. Akad. Nauk SSSR, Moscow (1961).

69. G. V. Zemskov and I. V. Kosinskii, Nauchn. Zap. Odessk. Politekhn. Inst. 24: 9 (1960).

70. G. V. Samsonov and L. A. Solonnikova, Fiz. Metal. i Metalloved. 5: 565 (1957).

71. G. V. Samsonov, M. S. Koval'chenko, and T. S. Verkhoglyadova, Dokl. Akad. Nauk UkrSSR, No. 1: 36 (1959).

72. L. F. Verkhorobin, V. E. Ivanov, N. N. Matyushenko, E. P. Nechiporenko, N. S. Pugachev, and A. I. Somov, Fiz. Metal. i Metalloved. 13: 77 (1962).

73. V. E. Ivanov, A. I. Somov, and V. G. Yarovoi, Zh. Prikl. Khim. 35: 1960 (1962).

74. A. W. Searcy and A. G. Thorp, J. Phys. Chem. 64(10) (1960).

75. N. M. Arzhanyi, R. M. Volkova, and D. A. Prokoshkin, Researches on Heat-Resistant Alloys, Vol. VI (1960)· Vol. VII (1961), Izd. Akad. Nauk SSSR.

76. A. I. Borisenko, Protection of Niobium from High-Temperature Gaseous Corrosion, Izd. Akad. Nauk SSSR, Moscow—Leningrad (1961).

77. S. T. Wlodek, J. Electrochem. Soc. 108: 67 (1961).

78. E. Beidler, C. Powell, J. Campbell, and L. Intema, Electrochem. Soc. 98: 21 (1951).

79. R. Kieffer and F. Nachtigal, Heraues-Festschrift, 186, Hanau (1950).

80. Metal Progr. 68: 109 (1955).

81. P. Chao, D. Priest, and J. Myers, J. Less-Common Metals 2: 426 (1960).

82. G. Miller and F. Cox, J. Less-Common Metals 2: 207 (1960).

83. R. Long, U.S. Patent No. 2878554, March 24, 1958.

84. J. Moor and P. Clough, U.S. Patent No. 2857297, October 21, 1959.

85. P. Clough and P. Raymond, Am. Ceram. Soc. Bull. 40: 314 (1961).

86. K. Sedlatschek and H. I. Stadler, Planseeber. Pulvermet. 9.40 (1961).

87. R. Kieffer and P. Sedlatschek, Austrian Patent No. 203312, May 11, 1959.

88. G. Oxx and L. Coffin, Trans. Metallurg. Soc. AIME, No. 218: 541 (1960).

89. A. I. Borisenko, Protection of Molybdenum from High-Temperature Gaseous Corrosion, Izd. Akad. Nauk SSSR, Moscow—Leningrad (1960).

90. R. Runck, J. Electrochem. Soc. 104:74 (1957).

91. D. Couch, H. Schapiro, J. Taylor, and A. Brenner, J. Electrochem. Soc. 105:450 (1958).

92. D. Couch, H. Schapiro, and A. Brenner, J. Electrochem. Soc. 105:48 (1958).

93. C. Goetzel and P. Landler, Planseeber. Pulvermet. 9:36 (1961).

94. P. Schwarzkopf, Austrian Patent No. 215761, June 26, 1961.

95. R. Lorenz and A. B. Michall, Oxidation-Resistant Silicide Coating for Columbium and Tantalum Alloys by Vapor Phase Reaction, Fansteel Metallurgical Corp., North Chicago.

96. B. N. Arzamasov and D. A. Prokoshkin, Author's Certificate USSR, No. 148318, June 21, 1962.

97. B. N. Arzamasov and D. A. Prokoshkin, Researches on Heat-Resistant Alloys, Vol. IX, Izd. Akad. Nauk SSSR, Moscow (1962).

98. Missiles and Rockets, No. 32:17 (1959).

99. W. Aves, Metal Finishing J. (London) 7:139 (1961).

100. A. Levy, Metal Progr. 79:81 (1961).

101. J. Janko and T. Filipek, Czechoslovak Patent No. 97550, December 15, 1960.

102. Ind. Heating 27:1936 (1960).

103. British Patent No. 866818, May 3, 1961.

104. N. G. Slavina, A. A. Pletyushkin, S. N. Gorin, and A. I. Ivanova, Author's Certificate USSR, No. 145106, February 26, 1962.

105. P. S. Kislyi and G. V. Samsonov, Fiz. Tverd. Tela 2:1729 (1960).

106. M. V. Sazonova, L. Ya. Sitnikova, and A. A. Appen. Zh. Prikl. Khim. 34:505 (1961).

107. B. Cross, Prod. Eng. 32:18 (1961).

108. G. V. Samsonov and N. K. Golubeva, Zh. Fiz. Khim. 30:1258 (1956).

109. V. S. Neshpor and G. V. Samsonov, Zh. Prikl. Khim. 30:1584 (1957).

110. J. Campbell, C. Powell, D. Nowicki, and B. Gonser, J. Electrochem. Soc. 96:318 (1949).

111. G. V. Samsonov, Izv. Sektora Fiz.-Khim. Analiza Inst. Obshch. Neorgan. Khim. Akad. Nauk 27:97 (1956).

112. K. I. Portnoi and G. V. Samsonov, Boride Alloys, Izd. Filiala VINITI GNTK and Akad. Nauk SSSR, Moscow (1959).

113. Analysis of Refractory Compounds (Collection), Metallurgizdat, Moscow (1962).

114. V. P. Kopylova, Zh. Prikl. Khim. 34:1936 (1961).

115. D. K. Modylevskaya and G. V. Samsonov, Ukr. Khim. Zh. 25:55 (1959).

116. O. I. Popova and G. T. Kabannik, Zh. Neorgan. Khim. 5:930 (1960).

117. T. Ya. Kosolapova and E. E. Kotlyar, Zh. Neorgan. Khim. 3:1241 (1958).

118. M. Diesen and G. Hüttig, Planseeber. Pulvermet. 4:10 (1956).

119. E. Fitzer and J. Schwab, Metall. 9:1062 (1955).

120. I. Everhart, Mater. Methods 40:90 (1954).

121. Iron Age 173:138 (1954).

122. G. V. Samsonov, G. A. Yasinskaya, and T'ai Shou-wei, Ogneupory, No. 1:35 (1960).

123. V. N. Eremenko and Yu. V. Naidich, Wetting of the Surface of Refractory Compounds by Rare Metals, Vid. Akad. Nauk UkrSSR, Kiev (1958).

124. E. Reed, J. Am. Ceram. Soc. 37:146 (1954).

125. G. V. Samsonov, P. S. Kislyi, A. D. Panasyuk, A. G. Strel'chenko, I. G. Khav-runyak, and G. N. Serikova, Ogneupory, No. 2:72 (1961).

126. Yu. B. Paderno, G. V. Samsonov, and L. M. Khrenova, Élektronika, No. 4:165 (1959).

127. G. V. Samsonov, Ogneupory, No. 3:122 (1956).

128. M. R. Commanday and J. R. Darnele, U. S. Patent No. 3015579, January 2, 1962.

129. N. C. Cook, U.S. Patent No. 3024177, March 6, 1962.

130. Protection of Refractory Metals from Oxidation (Proceedings of International Conference on Refractory Metals and Alloys, 1960, Sheffield, England) [Russian translation] IL, Moscow (1962).

131. C. Powell, J. C. Campbell, and B. Gonser, Vapour-Plating, New York (1955).

132. Mater. Design Eng. 54:129 (1961).

133. R. F. Voitovich, V. A. Lavrenko, and I. N. Frantsevich. High-Temperature Oxidation of Metals and Alloys, Gostekhizdat UkrSSR, Kiev (1963).

134. C. Agte and K. Moers, Z. Anorg. Allgem. Chem. 198:233 (1931).

135. S. Susman, R. S. Spriggs, and H. S. Weber, Proceedings of the Conference on Silicon Carbide, Pergamon Press, New York (1960).

136. V. P. Elyutin, G. I. Pepekin, and B. S. Lysov, Izv. VUZov, Chernaya Met., No. 3:124 (1964).

137. A. D. Macquillen and M. K. Macquillen, Titanium [Russian translation], Izd. Inostr. Lit., Moscow (1958).

138. Yu. V. Grdina, L. T. Fordeeva, and L. G. Timonina, Izv. VUZov, Chernaya Met., No. 4:129 (1963).

139. B. H. Ekstein and R. Forman, J. Appl. Phys. 33(1):82 (1962).

140. V. N. Konev, A. F. Nesterov, and I. P. Glazkova, Fiz. Mctal. i Metalloved. 16:86 (1963).

141. V. E. Ivanov, E. P. Nechiperenko, V. M. Krivoruchko, and A. S. Mitrofanov, Fiz. Metal. i. Metalloved. 17:862 (1964).

142. V. E. Ivanov, E. P. Nechiperenko, and V. I. Zmii, Fiz. Metal. i Metalloved. 17:94 (1964).

143. D. A. Prokoshkin, B. N. Arzamasov, and E. V. Ryabchenko, in collection: Diffusion Coatings on Metals, Izd. Naukova Dumka (in press).

144. H. Colan, A. Domsa, A. Palfalvi, V. Nicolae, and L. Botha, Stud. sí Cer. de Metallurg. 4(8):397 (1963).

145. E. Fitzer, Pulvermetallurgie, I. Planseeseminar, Vienna (1953).

146. A. R. Cox and R. Brown, J. Less-Common Metals 6(1):51 (1964).

147. C. D. Dickinson, M. G. Nicholas, A. L. Pranatis, and C. L. Whitman, J. Metals 15(10):787 (1963).

148. U.S. Patent No. 2972556.

149. A. L. Burykina and T. M. Evtushok, Izv. Akad. Nauk SSSR, Metal. i Gornoe Delo, No. 5 (1964).

PART 2

Properties of Coated Refractory Metals

W. A. Gibeaut and E. S. Bartlett

SUMMARY

This report summarizes the information generated since the middle of 1961 on the chemical, physical, and mechanical properties of refractory metals that are coated with oxidation-resistant coatings of advanced-experimental or commercial status. It is a supplement to DMIC Report 162, "Coatings for the Protection of Refractory Metals from Oxidation", dated November 24, 1961. Recent data on specific silicide- and aluminide-type coatings for columbium, molybdenum, tantalum, and tungsten and their alloys reflect general advances in coating quality and performance, understanding of the behavior of coated systems, and more complete realization of the problems associated with the use of coated hardware.

Programs to provide comparative evaluations of coatings on columbium and molybdenum alloys have pointed up some of the relative merits and deficiencies of the various coatings. Properties that have been studied and evaluated in recent investigations have included the following:

(1) Oxidation lives at various temperatures and pressures

(2) Degradation in low-temperature ductility of substrates by coatings or coating processes.

(3) Degradation of mechanical properties by oxidation exposure (thermal stability)

(4) Effects of strain at low and high temperatures on protectiveness of coatings

(5) Stress rupture and creep data of coated systems

(6) Fatigue properties of coated systems

(7) Emittance of coatings.

Although there is no "ideal" coating for a given application, the data now available may permit selection of a coating or coatings based on a balance of performance features such as those listed above. Continued detailed evaluation and general comparative programs are expected to greatly improve the ability to select a coating-substrate system best suited for given design requirements.

Generally, the areas involving coated tantalum and tungsten alloy substrates are not so well developed; there are fewer coatings available and data are more limited.

INTRODUCTION

This report presents chemical, physical, and mechanical properties of refractory metals that are coated with advanced experimental or commercial oxidation-resistant coatings, and supplements the second half of DMIC Report 162, "Coatings for Protection of Refractory Metals From Oxidation", which dealt with the characteristics of coating systems. The information presented covers the period from the middle of 1961 to date. The coatings considered are silicides, aluminides, and the liquid tin-aluminum system. Because they represent a different class of thermal protection system, thin oxide coatings and thicker metal-reinforced oxide layers are not covered. The report is divided into four sections, covering coatings for columbium, molybdenum, tantalum, tungsten, and their alloys. Coating processes are described summarily for those systems for which information is available.

The primary intention is to present performance data on coated refractory metal systems. Interpretations, summarizations, or conclusions have been added where warranted. Frequently, however, the interpretation of the data is complicated by factors such as the scatter of data in test results, the tentative nature of data obtained from progress reports, and lack of supporting information in references; in these instances evaluation of data has been left to the reader.

Strength data, such as yield, tensile, and stress-rupture strengths, of coated specimens generally are calculated using the thickness of the uncoated sheet. The actual thickness of substrate remaining after a coating is applied may be reduced by up to 1 mil per side for diffusion interaction with the coating, which is equivalent to a 5 to 20 per cent reduction in actual substrate thickness when considering sheets up to 30 mils thick. Hence, apparent strength losses of from 5 to 20 per cent (depending on sheet thickness) for coated versus uncoated thin sheet may not be significant when considering only the effect of the coating on the substrate. Unless the method of calculating strength is described it can be assumed that it is based on sheet thickness prior to coating.

COATINGS FOR COLUMBIUM AND COLUMBIUM-BASE ALLOYS

Numerous columbium-base alloys have been developed to a commercial status. Those with which coatings investigations have been concerned and for which data are described in this report include:

B66	Cb-5Mo-5V-1Zr
Cb-1Zr	Cb-1Zr
C103	Cb-10Hf-1Ti
C129	Cb-10W-10Hf
Cb752	Cb-10W-2.5Zr
D14	Cb-5Zr
D31	Cb-10Mo-10Ti
D36	Cb-10Ti-5Zr
D43 (X110)	Cb-10W-1Zr
F48	Cb-15W-5Mo-1Zr
FS82	Cb-33Ta-1Zr
FS85	Cb-27Ta-10W-1Zr

Interest is increasing in coated columbium alloys because alloys higher in strength and more fabricable than former ones are being made available. Research and development on the coating of columbium alloys now equals or exceeds that for molybdenum alloys. The competitiveness of columbium alloys for applications in the temperature range originally dominated by molybdenum alloys makes it necessary to compare the performance of coated high-strength alloys of both types.

Although much information is available concerning oxidation resistance and mechanical properties of coated columbium alloys, there is a lack of emittance data for even the better coatings.

Data for Individual Coatings

TRW Cr-Ti-Si Coating

During the past 2 years Thompson Ramo Wooldridge has endeavored to make its process for applying the Cr-Ti-Si coating more amenable to coating large pieces of hardware and to improve coating performance. They have conducted extensive evaluations of the coating on a variety of columbium alloys.[1] The conditions reported most recently for applying the coating are given below in chronological order.[1,2]

(1) Titanium precoat - 6 hours at 1900 F under 10^{-2} mm pressure in a titanium-sponge pack containing KF activator

(2) Cr-Ti codeposition - 8 hours at 2300 F under 1.5 mm pressure in a 50Cr-50Ti metal pack containing KF activator

(3) Siliconizing - 4 hours at 2000 F under 10^{-2} or 1.5 mm pressure in a silicon pack containing KF activator.

The chief attribute of the titanium precoat is that it maximizes oxidation life of the coating in the temperature range from 1200 to 1800 F. It frequently is eliminated if 25 to 100 hours' protection is all that is needed in this low-temperature range. Siliconizing can be done under 150 mm argon pressure but preliminary data indicate that the oxidation resistance of the resulting system at 1800 F is less than that achieved by siliconizing at the lower pressures.[3] The Cr-Ti-Si coating is 3 to 4 mils thick.

Oxidation life of the coating on unalloyed columbium, FS82, Cb752, D43, D31, D36, and B66 alloys in cyclic furnace oxidation tests is given in Figure 1 and Table 1. The coating generally was protective for greater than 150 hours at temperatures up to 2500 F, except for the shorter lives exhibited at low temperatures by specimens that were not precoated with titanium. Note that the titanium precoat increased coating life on even the titanium-bearing alloys (D31 and D36) at low temperatures. Coating life dropped sharply at 2800 F, but it still afforded 1 to 4 hours' protection to B66 alloy at 3000 F.

The coating system also has been oxidation tested at reduced pressures to ascertain its propensity for failure under the conditions of high temperature and low pressure encountered during re-entry.[3] Coated D14 specimens were exposed in the static

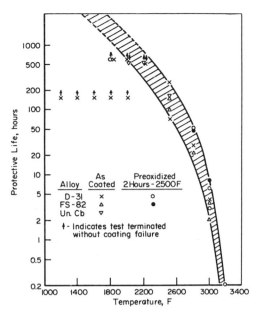

FIGURE 1. PROTECTIVE LIFE OF Cr-Ti-Si COATING IN CYCLIC
FURNACE OXIDATION TESTS[1]

TABLE 1. OXIDATION LIFE OF Cr-Ti-Si COATING ON COLUMBIUM ALLOYS IN STILL AIR[a][1]

Alloy	Alloy Composition	Protective Life, hours, at Indicated Temperature							
		1200 F	1800 F	2000 F	2300 F	2500 F	2600 F	2800 F	3000 F
Cb752	Cb-10W-4Zr[b]	>150	>150	92 to >150	>150	>150	--	--	--
D43	Cb-10W-1Zr	>150	>150	>150	>150	>150	--	--	--
D14	Cb-5Zr	>150	85 to >150	>150	>150	>150	--	--	--
D31	Cb-10Ti-10Mo	>150	>150	>150	>150	>150	--	--	--
D31[c]	Cb-10Ti-10Mo	24	53	92 to >150	>150	>150	--	--	--
D36	Cb-10Ti-5Zr	>150	>150	>150	>150	>150	--	--	--
D36[c]	Cb-10Ti-5Zr	24	53	92-150	>150	>150	--	--	--
B66	Cb-5Mo-5V-1Zr	>150	>150	>150	>150	>150	>100	3-9	1-4[d]

(a) Cycling procedure: Up to 2600 F − once each hour for 8 hours, then a 16-hour cycle in each 24-hour period.
        2800 F − approximately once each 0.5 hour.
        3000 F − approximately once each 0.3 hour.
   Specimens were sheet materials, 30 to 60 mils thick. Values are range of oxidation lives for four specimens.
(b) Obsolete composition. Cb752 is now Cb-10W-2.5Zr.
(c) Not precoated with titanium; all others precoated.
(d) Preoxidized 2 hours in air at 2500 F.

atmosphere of a vacuum furnace under air pressures of 10^{-2}, 1, or 5 mm at 2500 F for times ranging up to 4 hours. The coating lost about 6 mg/cm^2/hour during the exposure at 10^{-2} mm pressure. Microstructural changes and a green deposit on the retort walls which accompanied the weight loss has led TRW to conclude that chromium evaporated from the coating. The results of the subsequent oxidation tests at 2500 F under atmospheric air pressure are presented in Table 2. The low-pressure pre-exposure did not impair the oxidation resistance of the coating at 1800 F, but it did reduce coating life at 2500 F, especially after the pre-exposure treatment of 4 hours at 10^{-2} mm pressure. The outer coating region which underwent microstructural changes during the vacuum treatment oxidized rapidly during the atmospheric-pressure oxidation exposure. Future tests are planned to elucidate the oxidation characteristics of the coating over a range of pressures and temperatures.

TABLE 2. PROTECTIVENESS OF Cr-Ti-Si COATING ON D14 ALLOY AT ATMOSPHERIC PRESSURE AFTER PRE-EXPOSURE AT REDUCED PRESSURE[3]

Pre-Exposure at 2500 F at Reduced Pressure		Subsequent Oxidation Life of Coating at 1 Atmosphere Air Pressure	
Air Pressure, mm	Time, hr	1800 F	2500 F
No pre-exposure		>200, >200	>104, >104
10^{-2}	1	>200, >200	63
10^{-2}	2	>200, >200	81
10^{-2}	4	>200, >200	6
1	1	>24[a]	>24[a]
5	1	>24[a]	>24[a]

(a) Postoxidation test not completed.

Recrystallized 0.032-inch thick, B66 alloy sheet coated with Cr-Ti-Si has been evaluated in several tests by TRW. Thermal-shock and erosion-test specimens were 1 by 2 by 0.032-inch sheet bent over a 3/16-inch radius before coating. Specimens were tested in three conditions:

(1) As coated

(2) Preoxidized 24 hours at 1800 F

(3) Preoxidized 24 hours at 2500 F.

The test consisted of heating the convex surface with an oxidizing oxyacetylene flame to 2500 F at an average rate of 100 F/sec, followed immediately by cooling with an air jet at the rate of 200 F/sec. The coated specimens were unfailed after 250 such thermal cycles.

B66 specimens were bend tested (4T radius) to ascertain the effects of the coating thermal treatment, the coating, and subsequent oxidation exposure on the ductile-to-brittle transition temperature. The bend-test results are shown in Figure 2. The coating and subsequent thermal exposures in argon or air at 1800 or 2500 F increased the transition temperature by from 300 to 550 F.

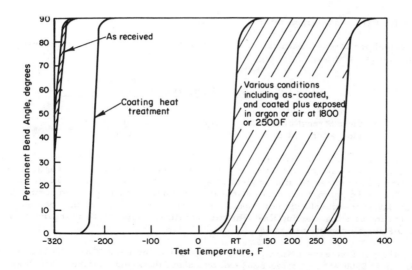

FIGURE 2. BEND TRANSITION TEMPERATURES OF UNCOATED AND
Cr-Ti-Si-COATED B66 ALLOY AFTER VARIOUS HEAT
TREATMENTS AND CYCLIC OXIDATION EXPOSURES[1]

The coated B66 alloy sheet was also tensile tested. As-coated specimens exhibited only 3 per cent elongation (in 1 inch) at room temperature, so the balance of the tests were conducted at 200 F to compare tensile properties of heat-treated specimens with ductile as-coated specimens. The prior histories of the tensile specimens are given below:

Bare Substrate

(1) As-received, recrystallized condition.

(2) Subjected to coating thermal treatment.

Coated Substrate

(1) As coated.

(2) Oxidized 100 hours in still air at 1800 F while under tensile stresses of
10, 20, and 40 per cent of yield strength. Creep was 0, 0.1, and 0.7 per
cent, respectively.

(3) Heated in argon for 100 hours at 1800 F.

(4) Oxidized in still air at 2500 F while under tensile stress: (a) 24 hours,
10 per cent of yield strength and (b) 8 hours, 20 per cent of yield strength.
Creep ranged from 4 to 7 per cent.

(5) Heat treated in argon for 8 and 24 hours at 2500 F.

These thermal and stress treatments had only slight effects on the tensile properties at 200 F, as indicated below:

	Bare Substrate	All Coated Conditions
Tensile Strength	93,000 psi	80,000-90,000 psi
Yield Strength	67,000 psi	56,000-66,000 psi
Elongation in 1 Inch	28 per cent	20-26 per cent

The various treatments lowered the ductility slightly at 200 F. Because the original sheet thickness was used to calculate the cross-sectional areas for all strength values, no real variation in either tensile or yield strengths of the substrate at 200 F is apparent. The creep (up to 7 per cent permanent deformation) that occurred during the stress-oxidation treatments did not impair the oxidation resistance of the coating. These tests indicate that the ductile-to-brittle transition temperature in tension was below 200 F for all conditions tested.

Figure 3 is a stress-rupture plot for Cr-Ti-Si-coated FS82 (Cb-33Ta-1Zr) sheet tested in air at 2500 F[4]. Coated FS82 exhibits about the same rupture strength as bare FS82.

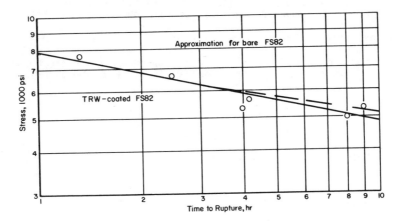

FIGURE 3.   2500 F STRESS-RUPTURE STRENGTH OF 20-MIL FS82 SHEET COATED WITH TAPCO Ti-Cr-Si COATING TESTED IN AIR[4]

Boeing Straight Silicide and Si-(SiC + SiO_2)
Coatings

Boeing has done extensive work on applying and testing straight silicide coatings, sometimes referred to as Disil coatings, and an improved-emittance silicide coating on

FS82 (Cb-33Ta-1Zr) and D36 (Cb-10Ti-5Zr) alloys.[5] The coatings also have been applied to other alloys. The straight silicide coatings, usually about 1.5 mils thick, are applied by the fluidized-bed process, which has been described elsewhere[5,6], at temperatures below 2000 F. The emittance-improved coating, designated Si-(SiC + SiO_2) is produced by applying an overlay of silicon carbide dispersed in silicon dioxide sol on a straight silicide coating and firing at 2000 F.

Results of oxyacetylene torch tests of the straight silicide coating on sheet specimens 12 to 50 mils thick and 2 inches square are shown in Figure 4. Maximum temperature variation of the sheet specimen was 500 F from the 3/4-inch hot zone to the edges. The minimum protective life of the coating on D36 was 4 hours at 2700 F and 2.5 hours at 3000 F (uncorrected optical temperatures), whereas it was only 1.5 and 1 hours on FS82 at the respective temperatures.

Emittance of the straight silicide coating is shown in Figure 5. The higher emittance of coated D36 relative to FS82 has been attributed to the influence of the titanium in D36[7]. Emittance has been increased further with the Si-(SiC + SiO_2) coating on D36 to values between 0.80 and 0.96 under the conditions of temperature and ambient air pressure encountered in a typical Dyna-Soar re-entry profile.[5]

Vought II and Vought IV Modified Silicide Coatings[8]

Chance Vought has optimized the pack-cementation process parameters for applying its Vought II (Si-Cr-Al) and Vought IV (Si-Cr-B) coatings on columbium alloys, as described below:

First Cycle - Siliconizing

Pack composition: 60 per cent Si, 6 to 10 per cent halide, balance 325-mesh Al_2O_3

Furnacing: 16 hours, 2100 F

Second Cycle for Vought II - Codeposition of Cr + Al

Pack composition: 35 per cent Cr, 20 per cent Al, 4 per cent halide, balance 325-mesh Al_2O_3

Furnacing: 16 hours, 2300 F

Second Cycle for Vought IV - Codeposition of Cr + B

Pack composition: 30 per cent Cr, 30 per cent ferroboron, 4 per cent halide, balance 325-mesh Al_2O_3

Furnacing: 16 hours, 2200 F

The inner region of coatings applied in this manner is $CbSi_2$ while the outer coating region contains a variety of phases, which have been identified by X-ray techniques as:

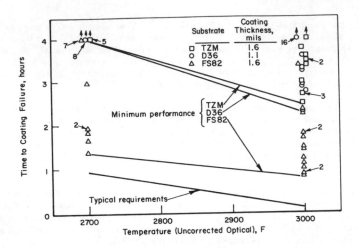

FIGURE 4.   OXIDATION LIFE OF BOEING'S STRAIGHT SILICIDE COATING ON
D36, FS82, AND TZM IN OXYACETYLENE TORCH TESTS[5]

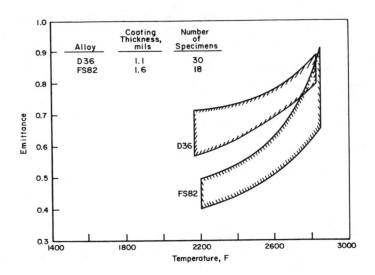

FIGURE 5.   EMITTANCE OF BOEING'S STRAIGHT SILICIDE COATING ON
D36 AND FS82 ALLOYS[5]

(1) In Vought II coating - $CbAl_3$, $CbCr_2$, Cr_3Si, Al_5Cr, and $CbSi_2$

(2) In Vought IV coating - CrB, FeB, $CbCr_2$, Cr_3Si, CbB_2, and $CbSi_2$.

These coatings are typically about 2 mils thick.

Oxidation resistance of the two coatings on Cb-1Zr, D31, and C103 (Cb-10Hf-1Ti) alloys is given in Table 3. In cyclic furnace tests at 2600 F, average coating life was 9 to 12 hours, with Vought IV exhibiting slightly better performance. Propensity for low-temperature pest failure was investigated by exposing specimens successively for 1 hour at 2400, 1000, 1200, 1400, 1600, 1800, 2000, and 2400 F. The Vought IV coating displayed superior resistance to failure in this test (Table 3).

TABLE 3. OXIDATION RESISTANCE OF VOUGHT COATINGS ON 20-MIL COLUMBIUM ALLOY SHEET[8]

Alloy	Coating	2600 F Test Results[a]	
		Time to Coating Failure, hr	
		Minimum – Maximum	Average
		(3 specimens)	
Cb-1Zr	Vought II	7-12	8.8
Cb-1Zr	Vought IV	9-14	11.2
C103	Vought II	7-13	9.0
C103	Vought IV	8-15	11.4
D31	Vought II	8-12	10.9
D31	Vought IV	8-15	11.5

Alloy	Coating	Low-Temperature Oxidation-Test Results[b]
		Failure Temperatures, F[c]
Cb-1Zr	Vought II	1400
Cb-1Zr	Vought IV	Full cycle (5), 1600 (1)
C103	Vought II	1400 (5), 2000 (1)
C103	Vought IV	Full cycle (5), 1800 (1)
D31	Vought II	1800 (4), 2000 (1), 1600 (1)
D31	Vought IV	Full cycle

(a) Specimens exposed in air furnace; cooled to room temperature once each hour.
(b) Test consisted of successive 1-hour exposures in a furnace at the following temperatures: 2400, 1000, 1200, 1400, 1600, 1800, 2000, and 2400 F. Specimens were cooled to room temperature after exposure at each temperature.
(c) Failure temperatures for six specimens are given, if they are different. Full cycle means specimen survived entire test without failure of the coating.

Coated bend specimens were bent at room temperature in 0.5 per cent strain increments (outer fiber strain) and oxidized 1 hour in air at 2000 F after each straining increment to determine the resistance of the coatings to oxidation failure after straining. On the Cb-1Zr and C103 alloys, the Vought IV coating withstood 2 per cent deformation and Vought II 1 per cent without loss of short-time oxidation protection. The as-coated D31 specimens (both coatings) fractured after only 0.7 to 1.4 per cent elongation, indicating severe embrittlement due to the coating or the coating process.

Figure 6 shows that the spectral emittance (λ = 0.65 micron) of the Vought IV coating on unalloyed columbium in vacuum is greater than 0.9 at temperatures up to 2500 F[9].

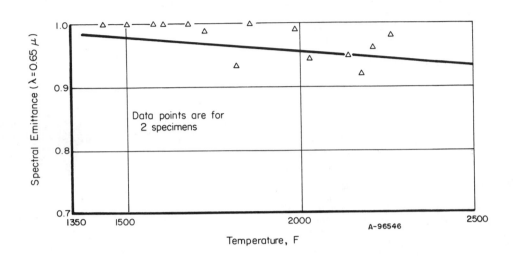

FIGURE 6.   SPECTRAL EMITTANCE OF VOUGHT IV COATING ON
COLUMBIUM MEASURED IN VACUUM[9]

Pfaudler Modified Silicide Coatings

Pfaudler has a series of proprietary modified silicide coatings for columbium alloys that are applied by the pack-cementation process.[10] In the first cycle, a layer of chromium alloy is formed. Silicon and other modifying elements are deposited during a second coating cycle. The thickness of coatings applied usually are from 1.5 to 2 mils. Typical coating lives over various substrates in an oxyacetylene torch test are given in Table 4. At 2600 F, where all the coating-substrate systems were tested, the coatings exhibited the longest oxidation lives on D31 alloy (Cb-10Ti-10Mo).

The oxidation performance of Pfaudler's PFR-1M and PFR-2M coatings on sheet coupons of Cb-1Zr and F48 also has been investigated by McDonnell.[11] The specimens were heated in air with oxyacetylene and plasma arc torches. As shown in Table 5, the coatings were protective for at least 10 to 15 minutes at 3000 F and 5 minutes at 3200 F.

126

TABLE 4. OXIDATION LIVES OF PFAUDLER MODIFIED SILICIDE COATINGS ON COLUMBIUM ALLOYS IN OXYACETYLENE TORCH TEST[10]

Substrate	Coating	Oxidation Life, hours, at Indicated Temperatures		
		2600 F	2800 F	3000 F
Cb	PFR-2M	3-6		0.5-1
D31	PFR-3A	5-28		
D31	PFR-4A	2-14		
D31	PFR-1	5-14		
D31	PFR-1M	16-26	5-11	2-4
FS82	PFR-1M	2-6		0.5-0.8
Cb-1Zr	PFR-1M	3-4	1-4	0.5-4
C103	PFR-2M	>3	0.5-1	
F48	PFR-2M			0.3-1

TABLE 5. TORCH-OXIDATION TESTS OF PFAUDLER PFR-1M AND PFR-2M COATINGS ON COLUMBIUM ALLOYS[11]

Substrate	Coating	Type of Torch	Test Temperature, F	Test Time, minutes	Coating Performance
Cb-1Zr	PFR-1M	Oxyacetylene	2800	15	No coating failure
Cb-1Zr	PFR-1M	Oxyacetylene	3000	15	Edge failure at 10 minutes
Cb-1Zr	PFR-1M	Oxyacetylene	3000	15	No coating failure
Cb-1Zr	PFR-1M	Oxyacetylene	3200	5	No coating failure
Cb-1Zr	PFR-1M	Plasma arc	3000	5	No coating failure
F48	PFR-2M	Oxyacetylene	3000	15	No coating failure

127

LB-2 Aluminide Coating

The LB-2 aluminide coating, originally developed by General Electric Corporation in conjunction with McDonnell Aircraft Company, now is being used extensively by McDonnell to coat columbium alloy components of the ASSET vehicle. The coating is applied by the slurry process* using a slurry of Al-10Cr-2Si alloy powder suspended in a mixture of several organic vehicles. The coating is dried in air at 150 F and a second coat is similarly applied. The "green" coating is diffusion annealed at 1700 to 1900 F in argon to form primarily CbAl₃.[12] The resulting coating is 2 to 5 mils thick. (McDonnell has observed that using the Al-10Cr-2Si alloy powder for the second coat instead of unalloyed aluminum, as was the practice in earlier work[13], improves the coating's oxidation performance of low temperatures without degrading performance at high temperatures.) The LB-2 coating is normally protective for a minimum of 2 hours at 2500 F or 1/2 hour at 2700 F at atmospheric pressure.[14]

McDonnell has tensile tested 36-mil Cb-5Zr sheet coated with LB-2 at room temperature after short postcoating exposures in argon or air at 1900 F.[15] The purpose was to investigate the effects of an "oxidation proof test" on the tensile properties of the substrate by isolating the effects of temperature and oxidation. The tensile test results for bare and coated specimens are given in Table 6. The coating and subsequent thermal treatments for up to 4 hours in argon or air had little effect on the tensile properties of the Cb-5Zr sheet. The maximum decrease in room-temperature yield and tensile strength and elongation was 10 per cent; the reduction in strength might be expected since the reported strength values are based on the original sheet thickness.

TABLE 6. ROOM-TEMPERATURE TENSILE PROPERTIES[a] OF 36-MIL Cb-5Zr SHEET COATED WITH LB-2[15]

Thermal Treatment of Coated Test Specimens	Yield Strength, psi	Ultimate Strength, psi	Elongation in 1 Inch, per cent
Uncoated sheet	51,000–53,000	67,000–68,000	24–26
1 hr, 1900 F, in argon	47,000–49,000	64,000–65,000	20–22
2 hr, 1900 F, in argon	49,000–51,000	62,000–65,000	24–27
4 hr, 1900 F, in argon	47,000–48,000	64,000	22–23
2 hr, 1900 F, in argon; plus 1/2 hr at 1900 F in air	53,000–54,000	64,000–67,000	19–24

(a) Range of values obtained with three specimens is reported. Strength values are based on original sheet thickness.

Table 7 presents some room-temperature tensile-test data for LB-2-coated FS82 alloy. The yield and tensile strength in the as-coated condition and after oxidation exposure at 2500 F were midway between that for stress-relieved and recrystallized bare FS82 (recrystallization temperature is between 2100 and 2400 F). Elongation increased to the level of recrystallized material during the oxidation exposures.

*Slurry processes comprise application of the active coating material in powder form suspended in a vehicle, by brushing, dipping, or spraying.

TABLE 7. ROOM-TEMPERATURE TENSILE PROPERTIES OF FS82 COLUMBIUM ALLOY COATED WITH LB-2[16]

Condition of Test Specimen	Room-Temperature Strength, 1000 psi		Elongation in 2 Inches, per cent
	Ultimate	0.2% Yield	
As coated	65	45	17
Oxidized 1 hr at 1800 F + 1.5 hr at 2540 F	64	49	22
Oxidized 2 hr at 2500 F	63	49	27
Bare stress-relieved sheet	80	70	11
Bare recrystallized sheet	55	37	25

General Telephone and Electronics
Tin-Aluminum Coating

General Telephone and Electronics has developed a family of tin-aluminum coatings applied by the slurry process. Although developed originally for tantalum alloys, their (Sn-25Al)-10TaAl$_3$ coating composition also protects columbium.[17] The coating system and process are described in the section on coatings for tantalum.

The oxidation-performance data of the (Sn-25Al)-10TaAl$_3$ coating on Cb-5Zr alloy are given in Table 8. The coating protected the substrate for about 90 hours at 1400 and 2000 F, 40 hours at 2200 F, and 20 hours at 2400 F. Oxidation life increased with coating thickness which depended on the number of coating layers applied. Coating thickness was more than doubled by applying a second layer of the coating. In general, coatings ranged from about 1 to 4 mils thick.

TABLE 8. OXIDATION LIFE OF (Sn-25Al)-10TaAl$_3$ COATING ON 20-MIL Cb-5Zr ALLOY SHEET[a][17]

Oxidation Temperature, F	Number of Coats Applied	Weight Gain During Coating, mg/cm^2[b]	Oxidation Life, hr	
			Range	Average
1400	1	16-28	5-17	9
1400	2	44-54	40-100	88
2000	2	42-50	75-100	95
2200	1	19-36	9-19	14
2200	2	43-55	18-54	45
2400	1	18-32	1-6	4
2400	2	43-55	14-27	21

(a) Tests conducted in still air in a furnace. Specimens generally cycled to room temperature ten times each 24 hours.

Tensile and creep properties of Cb-5Zr sheet coated with the (Sn-25Al)-10TaAl₃ system are given in Table 9 and Figure 7. Strength values were calculated using the original thickness of the sheet. Yield, tensile, and stress-rupture strengths of coated specimens were only slightly lower than those of bare Cb-5Zr sheet, in accord with the reduction of sheet thickness effected by the coating. Tensile elongation compared favorably with that for bare substrate, except at 2400 F where the excessive plastic deformation may have triggered a coating failure and attendant failure of the specimen.

NAA-85 Aluminide Coating

North American Aviation has developed an aluminide coating, designated NAA-85, primarily for columbium alloys.[6,18] It is applied by the slurry process using a slurry consisting of aluminum and unidentified ceramic powders in an organic vehicle. The "green" coating is diffusion annealed for 1 hour at 1900 F in argon during which the aluminum reacts with the substrate to form columbium aluminides.

The coating is capable of protecting FS82 alloy from oxidation for 5 hours at 2600 F in static air.[18] No pest-failure problem has been encountered by North American in oxidation tests at temperatures ranging from 1800 to 2600 F. Low-pressure testing has indicated that NAA-85 remains protective on Cb752 and C129 alloys for more than 15 minutes at 2250 F in air at 10^{-5} mm of mercury[18].

The total normal emittance of the coating on FS82 alloy is tabulated below:[18]

Temperature, F	Emittance
1000	0.90
1500	0.88
1850	0.85
2300	0.80

The tensile properties at 2600 F of FS82 coated with NAA-85 are given in Table 10. The structure of the FS82 sheet when it was tested at 2600 F is not known. The low tensile strength of coated specimens versus the strengths reported for uncoated sheet (16,000 versus 23,000 psi) could be rationalized by assuming that the coated substrate was completely recrystallized whereas the 30-second heat-up time for the bare substrate allowed only partial recrystallization. Some 2600 F creep data for FS82 coated with NAA-85 are presented in Figure 8.

Other Coatings

There are a few coatings for columbium for which little or no information has been published by the coating developer, but which have been tested in the various comparative evaluation programs presented in the next section. These coatings include:

Chromalloy W-2 - pack-cementation silicide developed for molybdenum

Chromizing Durak Cb ⎱ pack cementation,
          Durak KP ⎰ modified silicides

130

TABLE 9. TENSILE PROPERTIES OF 20-MIL Cb-5Zr SHEET COATED WITH (Sn-25Al)-10TaAl₃ AND TESTED IN AIR[17]

Condition of Test Specimen	Test Temperature, F	Yield Strength[a], psi	Tensile Strength[a], psi	Elongation, per cent	Gage Length, in.
		Coated Specimens			
As coated	RT	53,000	69,000	23	2
As coated	2000	31,000	39,000	21	1
As coated	2200	20,000	28,000	31	1
As coated	2400	15,000	19,000	47	1
Coated + oxidized 1 hour at 2000 F	RT	44,000	60,000	19	1
Coated + oxidized 1 hour at 2400 F	RT	27,000	50,000	24	1
		Typical Properties for Uncoated Stress-Relieved Cb-5Zr Sheet			
Uncoated	RT	61,000	75,000	15	--
Uncoated	2000	28,000	40,000	32	--
Uncoated	2400	12,000	17,000	90	--

(a) Strengths of coated specimens based on substrate thickness prior to application of coating.

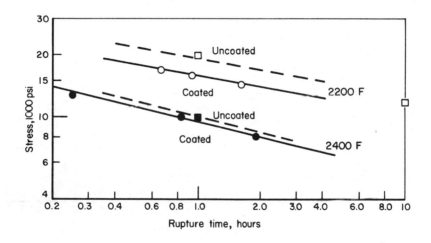

FIGURE 7. STRESS-RUPTURE PROPERTIES FOR 20-MIL Cb-5Zr COATED WITH (Sn-25Al)-10TaAl₃ AND TESTED IN AIR[17]

Note: uncoated specimens tested in argon.

131

TABLE 10. 2600 F TENSILE PROPERTIES OF FS82 COLUMBIUM ALLOY COATED WITH NAA-85[19]

Ultimate Tensile Strength, psi	0.2% Offset Yield Strength, psi	Elongation in 2 Inches, per cent
12,700	7,900	25
15,800[a]	12,300	20
15,500[a]	10,900	21
17,700[a]	15,300	18
17,600	13,100	27
16,500	--	17
23,000[b]	13,000[b]	--

(a) After 1 per cent strain for creep test at 2600 F.
(b) Uncoated sheet data for comparison. Heat-up time to test temperature was 30 seconds.

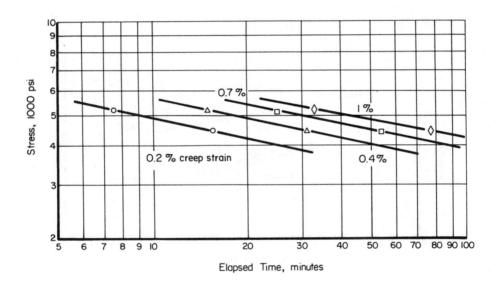

FIGURE 8. CREEP STRAIN AT 2600 F OF FS82 ALLOY COATED WITH NAA-85 ALUMINIDE COATING[19]

132

General Technology Corp. - pack cementation, modified silicide

General Telephone and Electronics - pack titanizing, followed by either:

(a) Hot dip in Al-Cr-Si bath, or

(b) Pack siliconizing.

Pratt & Whitney, CANEL - pack cementation, modified silicide.

Comparative Evaluations of Coatings

Comparative Evaluation of Coatings on Columbium, D31 and F48 Alloys[20]

In 1961 Thompson Ramo Wooldridge (TRW) conducted a comparative evaluation of several of the more promising coating systems for columbium alloys. The substrates coated were 60-mil sheet of unalloyed columbium, D31 (Cb-10Ti-10Mo) and F48 (Cb-15W-5Mo-1Zr) alloys. These are representative low-, medium- and high-strength columbium-base materials, respectively. Test specimens were coated by Sylcor (a subsidiary of GT&E), General Electric, Vought, Chromalloy, TRW, and Chromizing; the coatings are described in Table 11. Coated specimens were evaluated by oxidation, bend, and tension tests.

The protectiveness of the coating systems in cyclic furnace oxidation tests at 2300 and 2500 F is illustrated on Figures 9 and 10. The TRW coating exhibited superior oxidation life; it was protective for greater than 300 hours at 2300 F and for about 200 hours at 2500 F. The Sylcor and GE coatings lasted for up to 300 hours at 2300 F and 20 hours at 2500 F. The thickest coatings (i. e. , Sylcor, GE, and TRW) provided the longest oxidation lives at 2300 F. In general, the coatings exhibited greater than average life on the titanium-bearing D31 alloy and less than average life on unalloyed columbium.

The ductile-to-brittle bend transition temperatures of the coated substrates were estimated by bend testing three specimens over a 1.5T bend radius at various temperatures. Figures 11 and 12 show the bend transition temperatures of the coated D31 and F48 alloys in the following conditions:

(1) As coated

(2) Coated and oxidized 2 hours at 2500 F

(3) Coated and heat treated in vacuum for 2 hours at 2500 F.

The transition temperatures for coated columbium specimens in these three conditions were below room temperature with one expection; the Chromizing coating embrittled columbium in the as-coated condition, but not after either of the thermal treatments. As can be seen in Figure 11, the coatings applied to D31 alloy by Chromalloy, Chromizing, and TRW resulted in the largest increase in transition temperature in the as-coated condition. The Vought coating was moderately detrimental, and the degradation of

133

TABLE 11. COATING SYSTEMS EVALUATED BY THOMPSON RAMO WOOLDRIDGE
ON UNALLOYED COLUMBIUM, D31, AND F48 ALLOYS[20]

Organization That Applied Coating	Coating	Average Coating Thickness, mils	Coating Process
Sylcor[a]	--	5	F48 and columbium were titanized in titanium sponge in a vacuum, then hot dipped in Al-Cr-Si bath; D31 was only hot dipped in Al-Cr-Ti bath; all specimens diffusion annealed 1 hour at 1900 F in argon
General Electric	LB-2	8	Two-layer paint-and-sinter coating; Al-Cr-Si layer painted on followed by unalloyed Al top coat; sintered at 1900 F under argon
Vought	--	2	Two 16-hour pack-cementation cycles at 1900 F followed by preoxidation consisting of 32 hours at 1900 F
Chromalloy	W-2	1.8	Chromium modified silicide coating applied by pack cementation
TRW	Cr-Ti-Si	3.7	Three-cycle vacuum pack cementation: (1) Titanized in KF-activated Ti pack, 8 hours at 2100 F (2) Cr-Ti deposited in KF-activated 50Cr-50Ti pack, 8 hours at 2300 F (3) Siliconized 5 hours at 2150 F
Chromizing	Durak Cb	1.5	Unspecified; believed to be a pack-cementation silicide coating, perhaps modified with boron

(a) A subsidiary of General Telephone and Electronics.

134

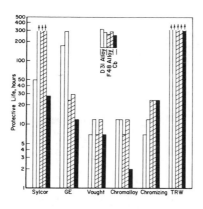

FIGURE 9.   PROTECTIVE LIFE OF COATINGS ON COLUMBIUM, D31, AND F48
ALLOYS IN OXIDATION TESTS IN STILL AIR AT 2300 F[20]

Specimens cycled to room temperature each hour for 24 hours; thereafter cycled nine times each 24-hour period.   Each bar represents
one test specimen.

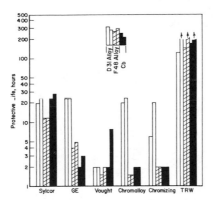

FIGURE 10.   PROTECTIVE LIFE OF COATINGS ON COLUMBIUM, D31, AND F48
ALLOYS IN OXIDATION TESTS IN STILL AIR AT 2500 F[20]

Specimens cycled to room temperature once each hour for 24 hours;
thereafter cycled nine times each 24-hour period.   Each bar
represents one test specimen.

135

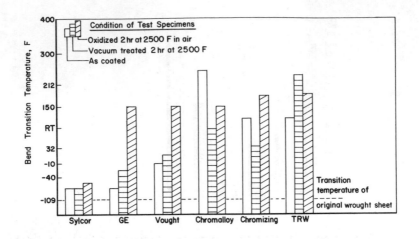

FIGURE 11. BEND TRANSITION TEMPERATURE OF COATED D31 ALLOY[20]

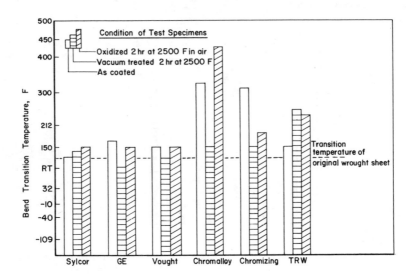

FIGURE 12. BEND TRANSITION TEMPERATURE OF COATED F48 ALLOY[20]

low-temperature ductility by the Sylcor and GE coatings was negligible. Vacuum heat treatment beneficially lowered the transition temperature of Chromalloy- and Chromizing-coated D31, suggesting that degradation in the as-coated condition may have been partially due to interstitial (hydrogen) contamination; for other coatings vacuum treatment had little effect or was detrimental (e. g. , TRW coating). Postcoating oxidation exposures were markedly detrimental to transition behavior of the GE- and Vought-coated D31; other coated systems were affected less by this parameter.

Over F48, only the Chromalloy and Chromizing coatings increased the transition temperature appreciably, and as was true for these coatings over columbium and D31, vacuum heat treatment greatly reduced this degradation. Only the TRW coating exhibited substantial increase in transition temperature as a result of the vacuum treatment. Except for Chromalloy-coated F48, the transition behavior of the various systems was affected little by the oxidation exposure, in contrast to the general behavior of coated D31.

Over all, the Sylcor coating and/or process exhibited the best low-temperature mechanical compatibility with columbium and the two alloys.

Table 12 presents tensile properties for coated specimens which were tested in the following conditions:

(1) As coated

(2) Heat treated in vacuum for 2 hours at 2500 F

(3) Oxidized in furnace for 2 hours at 2500 F while under a tensile stress equal to 20 per cent of the yield strength of the base metal. Specimens underwent 1 to 2 per cent creep.

Unalloyed columbium was tensile tested at room temperature; D31 was tested at room temperature and 1000 F, and F48 was tested at 1000 F. The F48 alloy (and probably the D31 and unalloyed columbium) was in the wrought condition prior to application of the coatings. Some of the coatings were applied within the recrystallization-temperature range of unalloyed columbium (1600 to 2000 F) and D31 alloy (the same or slightly higher temperature range than for columbium), and F48 (2200 to 3000 F), so varying amounts of recrystallization could be expected to occur during coating. The 2500 F vacuum anneal would recrystallize pure columbium and restore the 21,000-psi tensile strength that was characteristic of the recrystallized material. Unalloyed columbium coated by Sylcor, GE, and TRW had about the expected tensile properties in the as-coated condition. The unusually high strength of columbium coated by Vought, Chromalloy, and Chromizing in the as-coated and vacuum-annealed conditions suggests that the substrate was contaminated during the coating process. The Chromizing coating embrittled the columbium, but the Vought and Chromalloy coatings did not. The coated D31 specimens exhibited adequate ductility for design purposes (7 to 18 per cent) with the exception of coatings applied by Chromalloy and TRW which embrittled the substrate at room temperature. Tensile strengths were as expected, assuming that the substrates were mostly recrystallized. (Tensile strength of recrystallized D31 is about 95,000 and 65,000 psi, respectively, at room temperature and 1000 F.) D31 specimens coated by GE had the lowest strength, perhaps due to exceptional diffusion consumption of the substrate. The strengths of F48 specimens reflected the combined effects of retained cold work, substrate consumption, and substrate contamination. Vacuum annealing at 2500 F

Coating	As Coated			Vacuum Annealed 2 Hr at 2500 F			Oxidized 2 Hr at 2500 F in Air		
	Tensile Strength, psi	0.2 Per Cent Offset Yield Strength, psi	Elongation in 1 Inch, per cent	Tensile Strength, psi	0.2 Per Cent Offset Yield Strength, psi	Elongation in 1 Inch, per cent	Tensile Strength, psi	0.2 Per Cent Offset Yield Strength, psi	Elongation in 1 Inch, per cent
Unalloyed Columbium, Tensile Tested at Room Temperature[a]									
Sylcor	19,620	10,750	28.4	20,200	8,670	19.6	19,100	8,460	17.4
GE	22,000	9,260	39.2	21,000	11,800	22.0	(b)	--	--
Vought	47,200	28,900	25.4	33,900	23,700	24.8	32,200	23,500	16.4
Chromalloy	42,800	32,500	28.4	36,800	20,750	25.0	25,500(c)	--	0(c)
Chromizing	43,800	--	0	38,000	37,800	1.6	28,900	28,400	1.8
TRW	25,300	13,500	20.2	20,150	11,660	19.2	23,400	13,700	15.1
D31 Alloy, Tensile Tested at Room Temperature[d]									
Sylcor	91,600	85,400	20.6	88,000	76,000	22.2	92,000	83,400	18.2
GE	81,400	75,000	19.6	80,000	69,400	21.4	80,400	74,000	14.6
Vought	92,000	82,600	13.8	85,400	73,400	20.6	95,400	86,000	16.4
Chromalloy	(e)	--	--	91,500	78,600	25.6	(e)	--	--
Chromizing	94,000	85,400	10.2	91,500	78,600	10.2	98,000	89,400	8.4
TRW	80,000	--	0	(e)	--	--	(e)	--	--
D31 Alloy, Tensile Tested at 1000 F[f]									
Sylcor	64,000	49,300	12.6	64,000	40,600	13.0	68,000	48,000	8.0
GE	56,600	42,000	12.6	57,300	36,000	12.7	60,000	43,400	7.3
Vought	68,700	45,200	14.8	65,400	38,000	12.6	67,400	48,600	8.2
Chromalloy	62,600	43,400	14.1	65,400	40,600	13.4	69,400	50,000	9.6
Chromizing	62,000	44,600	13.5	64,000	40,000	13.0	68,000	50,000	9.3
TRW	64,600	43,400	12.6	69,400	43,400	14.0	67,400	44,000	11.0
F48 Alloy, Tensile Tested at 1000 F[g]									
Sylcor	70,600	66,000	11.0	55,400	40,600	7.9	57,300	40,300	5.8
GE	66,700	63,000	3.2	52,000	38,000	5.9	55,700	48,300	0.14
Vought	70,600	66,000	3.8	55,400	42,000	5.3	62,600	46,300	6.0
Chromalloy	62,600	58,700	1.3	57,900	40,000	8.5	66,000	52,000	2.8
Chromizing	76,700	72,400	2.8	62,600	47,400	9.2	65,300	48,000	4.2
TRW	55,000	44,000	7.2	59,300	40,000	7.3	57,300	41,300	7.4

(a) Tensile strength of bare columbium = 62,000 psi in cold-rolled condition and 21,000 psi in recrystallized condition.
(b) Substrate oxidized too extensively to provide meaningful tensile data. Specimen not tested.
(c) Localized substrate oxidation may have affected tensile properties.
(d) Tensile strength of bare D31 = 105,000 psi in wrought condition and 95,000 psi in recrystallized condition.
(e) Specimen broke at loading-pin hole.
(f) Tensile strength of bare recrystallized D31 at 1000 F = 65,000 psi.
(g) Tensile strength of bare F48 = 100,000 psi in as-rolled condition and 60,000 psi in recrystallized condition. Ductility of F48 is about 10 per cent at 1000 F.

reduced strength from that of the as-coated condition while oxidation exposure increased the strength compared to the vacuum-annealed condition. The ductility of F48 specimens generally was low compared to that for uncoated material at 1000 F, which is about 10 per cent.

Comparative Evaluation of Coatings on D14 and FS85 Alloys[3,21]

Thompson Ramo Wooldridge has conducted a screening evaluation of the seven coatings described in Table 13 on D14 alloy and a design-data study with FS85 alloy coated by Pfaudler and TRW. All available commercial coatings were tested on D14 alloy sheet, a readily available low-strength columbium alloy, to select the best coatings for the more extensive evaluation.

TABLE 13. COATINGS EVALUATED BY THOMPSON RAMO WOOLDRIDGE ON
D14 AND FS85 COLUMBIUM ALLOYS[21]

Coating	Organization That Applied Coating	Description of Coating and Coating Process
W-2	Chromalloy	Modified silicide applied by pack cementation
LB-2	McDonnell	Cr-Si-modified aluminide coating applied by paint-and-sinter technique
--	Pfaudler	Cr-Mo-modified silicide applied by 2-cycle pack cementation at 2050 F
--	Pratt & Whitney – CANEL	Two-cycle pack cementation coating: (Cycle 1) 23 hours at 1800 F in 80 vol % alumina, 15 vol % Si powder, 5 vol % Ti powder, plus some $CuCl_2$ activator, under argon; (Cycle 2) 16 hours at 1800 F in Cr power pack, under argon
R-506	General Telephone & Electronics (GT&E)	Two-cycle pack-cementation process consisting of titanizing under vacuum followed by siliconizing under argon
Cr-Ti-Si	Thompson Ramo Wooldridge (TRW)	Vacuum pack-cementation process: (Cycle 1) Cr-Ti deposited in 50Cr-50Ti pack in 8 hours at 2300 F using KF activator; (Cycle 2) Si applied over Cr-Ti layer in 4 hours at 2000 F in silicon pack activated with KF; D14 specimens were pretitanized at 1900 F as the first of 3 coating cycles.
Vought IV	Chance Vought	Two-cycle pack-cementation process: (Cycle 1) Si applied in 10 hours at 2100 F, (Cycle 2) Cr, B, and Fe codeposited in 16 hours at 2200 F

139

Screening Tests of Coated D14 Alloy. The performances of the seven coatings on 30-mil D14 alloy sheet were compared in the following screening tests:

(1) Oxidation

(2) Bend ductility

(3) Oxidation exposure following prestraining by bending.

The oxidation data for the coatings tested at temperatures of from 1600 to 2600 F are given in Table 14. The TRW coating afforded the most reproducible and longest oxidation life.

TABLE 14. PROTECTIVE LIFE OF VARIOUS COATINGS ON D14 ALLOY IN CYCLIC FURNACE
OXIDATION TESTS[21]

| Coating | Protective Life, hours[a] | | | |
Organization	1600 F	2000 F	2300 F	2600 F
Chromalloy	4, 150, 150	5, 18, 43	5, 6, 16	1, 1, 9
McDonnell	4, 4, 5	16, 16, 17	5, 5, 16	2, 2, 2
Pfaudler	67, 150, 150	5, 66, 69	1, 1, 17	9, 11, 11
Pratt & Whitney	150, 150, 150	17, 39, 44	3, 3, 19	1, 2, 2
GT&E	5, 61, 82	6, 21, 39	43, 62, 150	17, 19, 24
TRW	150, 150, 150	150, 150, 150	150, 150, 150	21, 27, 37
Vought	1, 150, 150	130, 150, 150	17, 18, 18	6, 13, 13

(a) Oxidation exposure terminated at 150 hours at 1600, 2000, and 2300 F. At 1600, 2000, and 2300 F, specimens were cycled to room temperature once each hour during the first 24 hours of testing. Thereafter specimens were cycled nine times in each 24-hour period. Specimens were cycled once each hour at 2600 F until failure.

Coated D14 specimens were bend tested at room temperature in the as-coated condition, after 50 hours' preoxidation at 2000 F, and after 10 hours at 2600 F (unless coatings failed in shorter times). The bend tests followed procedures recommended by the Refractory Metal Sheet Rolling Panel of the Materials Advisory Board[22]. The bend radius was 4T. The bend transition temperature of bare D14 in the stress-relieved condition was -320 F. In the as-coated condition, specimens coated by McDonnell, Pfaudler, GT & E, and TRW, were ductile (90-degree bend) at room temperature. On the other hand, the coatings applied by Chromalloy, Pratt & Whitney, and Vought, embrittled the substrate, indicating an increase in the bend transition temperature of D14 to above room temperature. The TRW coating alone was both protective and passed 90-degree bends after the long preoxidation treatments. The bend-test results for the other coating systems that were preoxidized were complicated by the high frequency of coating oxidation failures and attendant substrate contamination that occurred. Table 14 shows clearly that 50 hours at 2000 F or 10 hours at 2600 F approach the protective life of many of the coating systems. However, it is significant that most coated specimens that resisted oxidation failure passed the 90-degree bend test; the exception was the GT & E coating which embrittled the substrate even though the coating did not appear to have failed.

140

The effect of prestrain on the oxidation resistance of the coating systems was investigated by bending coated D14 specimens 2, 5, and 10 degrees with the 4T bend fixture and oxidation testing them at 2000 and 2600 F. The 2-degree bend was within the elastic range, but the specimens deformed plastically during the 5- and 10-degree bends. The coatings did not crack on specimen deflected 2 or 5 degrees, however all the coatings cracked and some spalled along the edges of the specimens during the 10-degree bends. Coating failures in the subsequent oxidation tests did not occur preferentially in the deformed region of specimens bent only 2 or 5 degrees, but the 10-degree bend did cause premature localized failure of most of the coatings.

Design Data Study of Coated FS85 Alloy. Based on the performance of the seven coating systems in the screening tests, the Pfaudler, TRW, and Vought coatings were selected for advanced evaluation on recrystallized 30-mil FS85 alloy, a medium-strength columbium alloy. The Vought coating was dropped from further consideration when it was observed that it provided less than 1-hour protection to FS85 at 2600 F (furnace oxidation test). Failure was accompanied by a molten oxide slag which destroyed the specimen. This was in marked contrast to the 6 to 13 hours' protection afforded by the coating on D14 at 2600 F (Table 14), suggesting that the difference may be due to substrate effects.

FS85 alloy sheet coated by TRW and Pfaudler was subjected to the following tests:

(1) Oxidation

(2) Combined thermal-shock and erosion test

(3) Prestrain followed by oxidation

(4) Tensile

(5) Stress rupture.

The oxidation data for the two coatings in cyclic furnace tests are given in Table 15. Both coatings were protective for greater than 50 hours at 1600, 1800, 2000, and 2300 F, but the Pfaudler coating had only 4 hours' average life at 2500 and 2600 F whereas the TRW coating exhibited 130 and 50 hours' average life at the respective temperatures. The performance of the TRW coating was reproducible at all temperatures, but the Pfaudler coating had inconsistent life at 1800 F.

TABLE 15. PROTECTIVE LIVES OF PFAUDLER AND TRW COATINGS ON FS85 ALLOY IN CYCLIC OXIDATION TESTS[21]

Oxidation Temperature, F	Lives of Replicate Specimens, hr[a]	
	Pfaudler	TRW
1600	>150, >150, >150	>150, >150, >150, >150
1800	21, 125, >150, >150	>150, >150, >150, >150
2000	>150, >150, >150, >150	>150, >150, >150, >150
2300	48, 48, 48, 56	>150, >150, >150, >150
2500	3, 3, 3, 5	117, 117, >150, >150
2600	1, 5, 5, 6	45, 51, 51, 51

(a) Specimens cycled to room temperature once each hour for 8 hours followed by 16 hours of static exposure in each 24-hour period. Tests stopped after 150 hours if specimens were unfailed.

141

Both coatings performed similarly in a test combining thermal shock and erosion
Curved sheet specimens were heated with an oxyacetylene torch to 2600 F in 20 seconds
and cooled immediately to 250 F with an air jet at an average rate of 100 F/second.
The Pfaudler and TRW coatings were protective during 500 of these thermal cycles.
However, gross coating failure occurred in the maximum-temperature zone of specimens cycled 100, 250, and 500 times when the specimens subsequently were oxidized
for 2 hours at 1600 F in a furnace. A lone exception was one TRW-coated specimen
which resisted gross coating failure at 1600 F after 100 thermal cycles to 2600 F.
Although both coating systems appeared resistant to thermal-shock failures, deficiencies in the thermal stability of coating protectiveness were defined.

Coated FS85 sheet was bent 2 degrees (elastic strain) and 5 degrees (plastic
deformation) and oxidation tested at 2000 and 2600 F. Neither level of strain caused
premature oxidation failure of either coating.

The deformation tolerance of the two coatings also was investigated by straining
coated FS85 tensile specimens varying amounts at temperatures up to 2600 F, removing
the load, and oxidation testing the strained specimens for 2 hours at 1600 or 2600 F.
The test results are presented in Table 16. With only one exception in the entire series
of tests, both coating systems withstood substantial plastic prestrains (greater than the
proportional limit) without loss of subsequent 2-hour oxidation protection at 1600 or
2600 F.

TABLE 16. TOLERANCE OF PFAUDLER AND TRW COATINGS ON FS85 ALLOY TO DEFORMATION
AT VARIOUS TEMPERATURES WITHOUT LOSS OF 2-HOUR OXIDATION PROTECTION
AT 1600 AND 2600 F[21]

Prestrain Temperature, F	Proportional Limit, per cent strain	Limit of Tensile Prestrain Without Loss of 2-Hour Protection, per cent strain			
		TRW		Pfaudler	
		1600 F	2600 F	1600 F	2600 F
RT	2.2	6.4	4.5	3.3	3.0
400	1.8	4.1	5.5	3.1	2.7
800	1.6	>8.5	4.6	2.7	1.3
1200	1.4	>4.1	>4.1	2.1	2.3
1600	1.1	>2.0	>2.0	2.0	1.4
2000	1.1	7.0	>4.0	4.2	5.?
2300	1.1	25.8	18.0	<5.7	12.1
2600	1.1	>34.5	>37.3	<23.8	>38.5

Results of tensile tests of uncoated and coated FS85 sheet at temperatures up to
2600 F are presented in Figures 13, 14, and 15. The alloy was recrystallized prior to
coating or testing in the uncoated condition. Coated specimens were tested in air;
uncoated specimens were tested in vacuum at elevated temperatures. Both substrate-
coating systems exhibited similar tensile properties. The yield and tensile strengths
of coated specimens were less than those of uncoated specimens; however, only in the
temperature range from 800 to 1600 F was this differential more than 5 to 10 per cent.
The coatings eliminated the strain-aging peak of the substrate at 1200 F (Figure 13 and
14), but appeared to effect a phenomenon similar to strain aging at somewhat higher
temperatures (1600 to 1800 F). (This anomaly has been reported to occur in Cb-1Zr
alloy.) Ductility of coated specimens was somewhat lower than uncoated specimens;

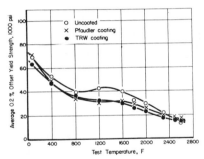

FIGURE 13. YIELD STRENGTH OF UNCOATED AND COATED 30-MIL
FS85-ALLOY SHEET[21]

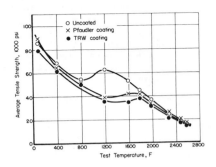

FIGURE 14. ULTIMATE TENSILE STRENGTH OF UNCOATED AND
COATED 30-MIL FS85-ALLOY SHEET[21]

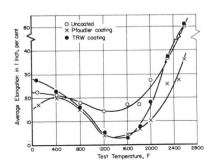

FIGURE 15. TENSILE ELONGATION OF UNCOATED AND COATED
30-MIL FS85-ALLOY SHEET[21]

143

this was most serious at temperatures of from 800 to 1800 F. Other tensile tests at 1200 F of specimens which had the Pfaudler and TRW coatings stripped off resulted in restoration of the ductility obtained with the bare substrate (15 per cent). Hence the brittle coatings and/or diffusion zones, rather than the coating heat treatments caused the sharp drop in ductility at around 1200 F.

Tensile tests were repeated at 1200 F using another heat of FS85 that was lower in interstitial content (oxygen = 60 versus 150 ppm in original heat; carbon = 40 versus 250 ppm), because it was believed that the higher interstitial level of the first heat was responsible for the embrittlement of coated sheet at around 1200 F. The embrittlement persisted in spite of the reduction of the interstitial content in the second heat of FS85.

Stress-rupture data for coated specimens tested in air at temperatures of from 1600 to 2600 F are presented in Figures 16 and 17. The calculated stress to rupture in 10 or 100 hours, based on these data, is given in Table 17. Specimens coated by TRW had higher stress-rupture strength than those coated by Pfaudler at 1600, 1800, 2500, and 2600 F, but the converse was true at 2000 and 2300 F (for times less than 75 hours at 2300 F). The stress-rupture strengths of coated specimens and bare FS85 sheet appear similar at 2000 and 2600 F although data for the base alloy are meager. Considerable elongation occurred during the tests without causing oxidation failures of either system. For instance, some specimens elongated 100 per cent at 2300 F without evidence of substrate oxidation. A significant side light is that coating oxidation life was considerably longer in the noncyclic exposures of the stress-rupture tests than it was in the cyclic oxidation tests described earlier. Both coatings exhibited lives of up to 100 hours at 2600 F in the stress-rupture tests.

TABLE 17. STRESS TO RUPTURE IN 10 AND 100 HOURS FOR PFAUDLER- AND TRW-COATED FS85 ALLOY TESTED IN AIR[21]

Test Temperature, F	Stress to Rupture, psi			
	Coated by Pfaudler		Coated by TRW	
	10 Hours	100 Hours	10 Hours	100 Hours
1600	26100	24200	30500	29300
1800	26700	25900	28400	23300
2000	24500	18300	22300	17600
2300	16000	9500	13800	9800
2500	8900	3400	11600	6800
2600	8600	3100	9300	6250

Screening Evaluation of Coated D36 and B66 Foil[23]

Solar has conducted an extensive screening evaluation of coated 6-mil foils of D36 (Cb-10Ti-5Zr) and B66 (Cb-5Mo-5V-1Zr) alloys. Coated TZM foil also is included in the program; these results are presented in the section on molybdenum. The immediate purpose was to ascertain the state of the art of coated foils. The long-range objective of this and other related programs is to be able to incorporate coated foils in honeycomb sandwich or monocoque construction for hot radiating surfaces of re-entry vehicles. The low-strength D36 alloy was chosen because it is readily available and can be rolled easily to foil. B66 was selected because it is fabricable, weldable, and has fairly high strength at elevated temperatures.

144

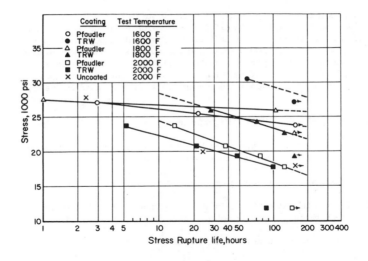

FIGURE 16.   STRESS RUPTURE LIFE OF FS85 ALLOY COATED WITH PFAUDLER
AND TRW COATINGS AND TESTED IN AIR AT 1600 TO 2000 F[21]

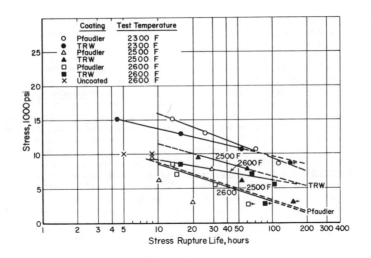

FIGURE 17.   STRESS RUPTURE LIFE OF FS85 ALLOY COATED WITH PFAUDLER
AND TRW COATINGS AND TESTED IN AIR AT 2300 TO 2600 F[21]

The coatings that were applied to the foils by outside organizations are described in Table 18. The coatings applied by GT & E were aluminum and tin base, and the balance of the coatings were modified silicides. The coating organizations were asked to apply coatings which would provide the best compromise between good oxidation resistance and mechanical properties. Only the D36 specimens coated by Vought were warped; the B66 specimens coated by Vought were not. Other coated specimens underwent little or no distortion. The coated specimens were evaluated by the following methods:

(1) Weight and thickness of coating applied

(2) Decrease in substrate thickness by diffusion interaction with coating during the coating process and oxidation tests

(3) Cyclic oxidation of as-coated specimens at 2000 and 2500 F

(4) Cyclic oxidation at 2000 and 2500 F of specimens previously bent over a 4T radius to a little below the outer fiber yield point

(5) Plasma-torch oxidation tests at 2000 and 2500 F

(6) Tensile tests of as-coated specimens

(7) Bend tests of specimens in the as-coated condition and after static oxidation exposure at 2000 or 2500 F for about 85 per cent of the oxidation life in the cyclic tests [(3) above].

The weight of coating applied becomes increasingly important as sheet thickness is reduced to foil gages when considering strength-to-weight ratios. The coating weight ranged from 7 (GT & E coating on B66) to 52 per cent (GT & E coating on D36) of the weight of the substrate (Table 19). Another important consideration for foils is the reduction in substrate thickness by diffusion during coating and oxidation exposure, for this reduces load-carrying capacity. The data on residual substrate thickness are to be accepted with reservation, because they are single-value measurements and the diffusion fronts between the coating and/or diffusion zones and the substrate occasionally are jagged and therefore difficult to measure. In other instances the measurement of substrate thickness is an incomplete description of the structural effect of the coating on the substrate. Intergranular diffusion and formation of an intergranular phase also may adversely affect strength. The TRW coating effected substantial substrate consumption during coating (1.6 mils per side) but not during subsequent oxidation exposure at 2000 or 2500 F (Table 19). An intergranular phase formed throughout the D36 foil coated by TRW after being oxidized for 42 hours at 2500 F, but it did not occur in coated B66 that was oxidized for only 5 hours. The thick Sn-Al-Ta coating of GT & E reacted so extensively with the D36 substrate that the foil was consumed completely in 11 hours at 2500 F. In general, the other coatings consumed about 1 to 1.5 mils per side of the foil as a result of the coating process plus 5 to 10 hours' oxidation exposure at 2500 F.

The results of cyclic oxidation tests of as-coated specimens and specimens prestrained in bending are presented in Figures 18 and 19. Coating failures of unstrained specimens started predominantly at edges. Coating failures of prestrained specimens started in the bend area on about two-thirds of the specimens; the remaining failures were random. The TRW coating demonstrated superior oxidation resistance, protecting

146

Organization That Applied Coating	Average Coating Thickness, mils	Coating Process
		Coatings for D36 Alloy
Vought	2.0	Vought IV applied by 2-cycle pack-cementation process: (Cycle 1) siliconized 6 hr at 1950 F. (Cycle 2) Cr and B codeposited in 4 hours at 1950 F
General Telephone and Electronics (GT&E)	5.1	Painted with 95 (Sn-25Al)-5Ta metal powder in lacquer carrier and vacuum sintered 1/2 hour at 1900 F; coated and sintered twice
Chromizing	1.8	Durak KP; modified silicide coating applied by pack cementation in 12 hours at 1850 F
Thompson Ramo Wooldridge (TRW)	3.8	Two-cycle (Cr, Ti)-Si coating applied by vacuum pack cementation: (Cycle 1) Packed in Cr-Ti alloy powder and KF and heated for 4 hr at 2300 F, (Cycle 2) Siliconized in Si powder + KF for 4 hours at 2000 F
General Technology Corporation (GTC)	3.3 (Lot A) 1.6 (Lot B)	Three-cycle vacuum pack cementation: (Cycle 1) 20(Cr-Ti)-80 Al_2O_3 pack for 10 hours at 2200 F, (Cycle 2) Si-Cb-Cr-B-W pack for 3 hours at 2000 F, (Cycle 3); repeat (2)
		Coatings for B66 Alloy
Vought	1.5	Vought IV applied by 2-cycle pack cementation: (Cycle 1) Si pack, 3-1/2 hr at 2000 F, (Cycle 2) Cr-B pack for 3-1/2 hr at 2000 F, specimens preoxidized 10 minutes at 2000 F
GT&E	2.3	(1) Vacuum pack titanized 16 hr at 2000 F, (2) hot dipped in aluminum alloy for 15 seconds at 1900 F, and (3) diffusion annealed 1 hr at 1900 F in argon
Chromizing	1.5	Durak KA
TRW	3.3	Same as for D-36
GTC	2.6	Three-cycle vacuum pack cementation: (Cycle 1) 20Ti, 80Al_2O_3 for 10 hours at 2100 F, (Cycle 2) 20Cr, 80Al_2O_3 pack for 10 hr at 2200 F, (Cycle 3) Si-Cb-Cr-B-W pack for 6 hr at 2000 F
Pfaudler	1.8	Two-cycle pack cementation: (Cycle 1) chromized 7 hr at 2050 F, (Cycle 2) modifier + silicon for 5 hr at 2050 F

TABLE 19. THICKNESS OF COATINGS AND D36 AND B66 FOIL IN AS-COATED AND OXIDIZED CONDITIONS[23]

Coating	Coating Thickness as Coated, mils	Coating Weight, per cent of foil weight	Residual Substrate Thickness				
			As Coated, mils	After 2000 F Oxidation		After 2500 F Oxidation	
				Hours	Thickness, mils	Hours	Thickness, mils
D36 Foil (5.75 ± 0.4 Mils, Prior to Coating)							
Chromizing	1.8	14	4.7	72	4.0	6	3.7
Vought	2.0	27	4.5	75	4.2	14	3.6
GT & E	5.1	52	5.0	75	1.4	11	0
TRW	3.8	35	2.4	75	1.8	42	2.7
GTC	1.6	25	4.2	--	--	--	--
B66 Foil (6.6 ± 0.4 Mils, Prior to Coating)							
Chomizing	1.5	12	5.3	57	5.0	6	4.3
Vought	1.5	14	5.0	33	4.5	6	4.5
GT & E	2.3	26	5.7	74	4.3	2	3.5
TRW	3.3	44	3.3	43	4.1	5	3.1
GTC	2.6	7	3.6	--	--	--	--
Pfaudler	1.8	16	5.2	75	5.3	6	4.1

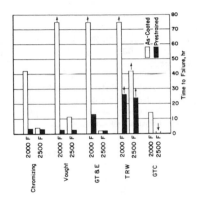

FIGURE 18. AVERAGE CYCLIC OXIDATION LIVES OF AS-COATED AND
PRESTRAINED COATED D36 FOIL AT 2000 AND 2500 F[23]

Furnace oxidation tests: specimens cycled to room temperature about once each hour; average of three specimens is
reported.

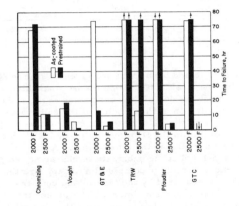

FIGURE 19. AVERAGE CYCLIC OXIDATION LIVES OF AS-COATED AND
PRESTRAINED COATED B66 FOIL AT 2000 AND 2500 F[23]

Furnace oxidation tests: specimens cycled to room temperature once each hour; average of three specimens is reported.

D36 and B66 for greater than 75 and 13 hours at 2000 and 2500 F, respectively, in both test conditions. Several coatings provided 75 hours' protection at 2000 F, but they were protective for only a few hours at 2500 F. The prestraining treatment effected greater reduction of oxidation life at 2000 F than it did at 2500 F, perhaps due to self-healing at the higher temperature.

The results of the plasma-torch oxidation tests at 2000 and 2500 F are given in Table 20. All the coatings except the one applied by Chromizing on D36 survived the 1-hour exposure at 2000 F. The 2-hour test at 2500 F approached the oxidation life of several of the coatings (Figures 18 and 19) and they (understandably) failed.

TABLE 20. RESULTS OF PLASMA-TORCH OXIDATION TESTS[a][23]

Coating	2000 F	2500 F
	D36 Foil	
Chromizing	Failed by pest	Failed by pest in low-temperature zone
Vought	Passed	Passed
GT & E	Passed	Failed (burned through)
TRW	Passed	Passed
GTC	Passed	Failed (burned through)
	B66 Foil	
Chromizing	Passed	Passed (some pits)
Vought	Passed	Failed (two of three specimens burned through)
GT & E	Passed	Failed (burned through)
TRW	Passed	Passed
GTC	Passed	Failed (burned through)
Pfaudler	Passed	Passed

(a) Specimens positioned at 35 degrees to arc effluent of simulated air having velocity of 200 feet per second. Tests consisted of 4 to 15-minute cycles at 2000 F or 8 to 15-minute cycles at 2500 F.

The results of the tensile and bend tests are given in Figure 20 and Table 21. The yield and tensile strengths were calculated using the original thickness of the foil, so the reported values reflect effects due to the coating and to the reduction in substrate thickness effected by the coating operation. Some of the substrate-coating systems exhibited 90-degree bend angles in the 4T bend test and yet had very low ductility in the tension test. An example of this is the D36 foil coated by TRW which passed the 90-degree bend test but had nil ductility in the tensile test. A photomicrograph showed a crack extending through one-third of the substrate thickness of one of the bent specimens, but the specimen did not fracture completely. It appears that part of the discrepancy between ductilities measured by the tensile and bend tests is attributable to the method of defining failure in the bend specimens. The procedure recommended by the Materials Advisory Board for bend tests[22] specifies that initiation of a surface crack (not complete fracture) is the failure criterion. Undoubtedly it is difficult to distinguish a coating crack from a shallow substrate crack. The two GT & E coatings provided the best combination of strength and tensile elongation, but their extreme diffusion instability prognosticates sharply reduced strength after exposure at about 2500 F. The strengths of other substrate-coating systems generally were 80 per cent of those of the bare substrate, commensurate with the reduced substrate thickness and perhaps substrate strengthening. Tensile elongation was only 0 to 25 per cent of the bare foil.

150

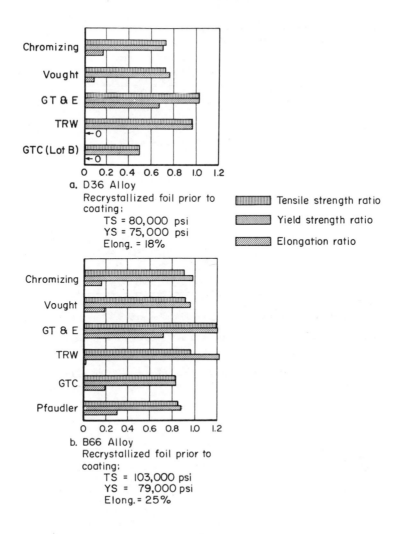

FIGURE 20. ROOM-TEMPERATURE TENSILE PROPERTIES OF
AS-COATED D36 AND B66 FOIL[23]

Strength values based on foil thickness prior to
coating.

TABLE 21. ROOM-TEMPERATURE BEND TESTS OF COATED D36 AND B66 FOIL IN AS-COATED CONDITION AND AFTER OXIDATION EXPOSURE[a] [23]

| Coating | Bend Angle in As-Coated Condition, degrees | Bend Angle After Oxidation Exposure at Indicated Temperature | | | |
| | | 2000 F | | 2500 F | |
		Oxidation Time, hr	Bend Angle, degrees	Oxidation Time, hr	Bend Angle, degrees
		D36 Foil			
Bare substrate	90, 90	--	--	--	--
Chromizing	90, 90	42	90, 90, 90	7.0	90, 90
Vought	90, 90	64	90, 90, 90	7.0	90, 90
GT & E	90, 90	64	20, 28, 30	1.7	90, 90
TRW	90, 90	64	90, 90, 90	7.0	20, 20
GTC	36, 45	--	--	--	--
		B66 Foil			
Bare substrate	90, 90	--	-- --	--	--
Chromizing	90, 90	22	90, 90, 90	4.5	90, 90, 90
Vought	44, 45	32	90, 90, 90	4.5	90, 90, 90
GT & E	90, 90	55	90, 90, 90	1.7	82, 85, 62
TRW	90, 90	29	90, 90, 90	1.7	90, 90, 90
GTC	42, 48	55	90, 90, 60	--	--
Pfaudler	42, 53	30	90, 90, 90	1.7	90, 90, 90

(a) Test Procedure:

(1) Specimens preoxidized in static furnace exposure (no cycling) for about 85 per cent of cyclic life of coating system.

(2) Bend radius = 0.024 inch, nominal 4T bend radius. Tested according to procedure recommended by the Refractory Metals Sheet Rolling Panel of the MAB. Bend angle is the angle at which fracture occurred, or 90 degrees if specimen did not fracture.

Based on their performance in these screening tests, the following coatings currently are undergoing process optimization and advanced evaluation using 6-mil B66 foil:

(1) Chromizing

(2) GT & E

(3) Pfaudler

(4) TRW.

COATINGS FOR MOLYBDENUM AND MOLYBDENUM-BASE ALLOYS

The following three molybdenum-base alloys are available commercially and they, along with unalloyed molybdenum, are the substrates that have been coated:

TZM - Mo-0.5Ti-0.08Zr
TZC - Mo-1.25Ti-0.15Zr-0.15C
Mo-0.5Ti

There is no indication that oxidation performance of the various coatings is affected by these low alloy additions. Mechanical tests (and oxidation tests) of coated molybdenum alloys are conducted at temperatures up to 3000 F because it is in the 2700 to 3000 F temperature range where the attractive strength-to-density ratio of molybdenum is particularly attractive. Most of the recent work on testing coatings for molybdenum alloys has been done with TZM, because it is readily available in sheet form and because of its favorable rating in considerations such as strength, fabricability, transition temperature, and recrystallization temperature.

Test Data for Individual Coatings

W-3 Coating

The W-3 coatings is Chromalloy's latest and best modified silicide coating[10], and is applied by a proprietary pack-cementation process. Oxidation life of the W-3 coating on 35-mil Mo-0.5Ti sheet coupons in cyclic furnace tests has been reported by Chromalloy[10] as follows:

Test Temperature, F	Coating Thickness, mils	Time to Coating Failure, hr		
		Minimum	Maximum	Average
2500	3.5	732	931	812
2700	3.4	26	395	268
3000	1.2	1.25	3.75	2.85

The 3.5-mil coating tested at 2500 and 2700 F were abnormally thick compared to the 2-mil W-3 coatings being applied for vehicle applications such as ASSET. The 3000 F test results may not be representative of the W-3 coating, because a reaction between the specimens and ceramic supports caused localized failures. McDonnell has reported that a 1.3-mil-thick W-3 coating protects TZM substrate from oxidation for a minimum of 2 hours at 3100 F at atmospheric pressure or 30 minutes at 3000 F under 0.07 mm air pressure[24]. A comparison of the oxidation lives of W-3 and W-2 (an earlier commercial variety) coatings on Mo-0.5Ti substrate at atmospheric pressure is shown in Figure 21[10]. While there was little practical difference in the minimum coating life, about 60 per cent of the W-3-coated samples exhibited lives of from 6 to 8 times longer than the W-2 coating.

The W-3 coating has been oxidation tested at low air pressures by resistance heating of coated 25-mil molybdenum wires in a vacuum chamber[25]. The test results are shown in Figure 22. The reported temperatures are uncorrected optical values, so the true temperatures probably were somewhat higher. The W-3 coating resisted failure at 1 mm air pressure for 15, 30, and 100 minutes at optical temperatures of 3000, 2900, and 2800 F, respectively. For comparison, under atmospheric pressure the average life of similarly tested specimens was 3.8 hours at 3000 F.

Results of tensile tests of W-3-coated TZM sheet conducted in air at temperatures up to 3000 F[26] are given in Table 22. Some specimens were uncoated (tested in inert atmosphere); others were coated twice. Still others were coated, oxidation proof tested for 1/2 hour at 2000 F, and finally coated again. Tensile properties at room temperature were not degraded significantly by either coating sequence. Elongation

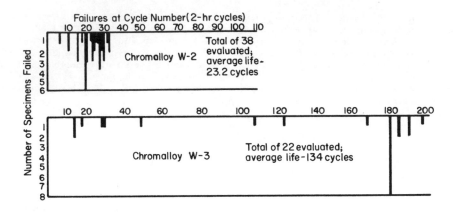

FIGURE 21. 2700 F CYCLIC OXIDATION LIVES OF CHROMALLOY'S W-2 AND W-3
COATINGS ON Mo-0.5Ti ALLOY IN SLOWLY MOVING AIR[10]

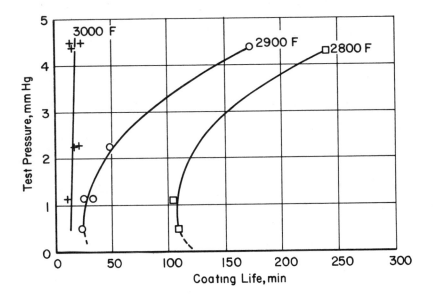

FIGURE 22. PROTECTIVE LIFE OF W-3 COATING ON MOLYBDENUM IN
LOW-PRESSURE OXIDATION TESTS[25]

Temperatures are uncorrected optical values.

decreased as test temperature was increased, perhaps due to strain-induced coating failures. The relatively high strengths obtained indicate that the wrought structure of TZM was retained during the coating process. At 2500 F, where some recrystallization during testing is probable, strength values were most erratic; at lower or higher temperatures strengths were more reproducible. The coating was not significantly detrimental to the tensile behavior of TZM in these tests. The very low ductility at 1800 F (1 per cent) is not understood, but it may be a response to an equicohesive temperature condition that is accentuated by the coating.

TABLE 22. TENSILE PROPERTIES OF 20-MIL TZM SHEET COATED WITH 2-MIL W-3 COATING AND TESTED IN AIR[a][26]

Condition of Specimen[b]	Test Temperature, F	Yield Strength, psi	Ultimate Strength, psi	Elongation in 2 Inches, per cent
Uncoated	RT	118,000	135,000	9
"	RT	122,000	135,000	8
"	RT	121,500	135,000	7[c]
"	RT	124,500	138,000	8[c]
C-O-C	RT	110,500	124,000	8[c]
C-O-C	RT	119,500	122,500	(c)
C-C	RT	119,000	127,000	7[c]
C-C	RT	117,000	127,000	7
C-O-C	400	94,000	105,000	4
C-O-C	400	93,000	107,000	6[c]
C-C	400	90,500	105,000	5
C-C	400	90,000	103,500	4
C-O-C	1800	76,000	82,000	1
C-O-C	1800	73,000	79,500	--
C-C	1800	74,000	85,500	1[c]
C-C	1800	72,500	78,500	1
C-O-C	2500	18,500	22,000	(d)
C-O-C	2500	35,000	39,000	(d)
C-C	2500	17,000	22,500	(d)
C-C	2500	23,000	27,500	(d)
C-O-C	3000	8,500	9,500	(d)
C-O-C	3000	9,000	11,500	(d)
C-C	3000	12,500	--	(d)

(a) Specimens soaked 30 minutes at test temperature before testing. Strengths based on area before coating.

(b) C-O-C = coated, then oxidation check tested 30 minutes at 2000 F, then coated again; C-C = coated twice without intermediate oxidation check.

(c) Specimen failed outside gage length.

(d) Oxidation in failure area was too extensive to measure elongation.

W-2 Coating

Chromalloy has been granted a patent covering its W-2 coating[27] which has been applied predominantly to molybdenum and its alloys. The coating is applied by the pack-cementation process using the following pack composition;

6 per cent chromium
11 per cent silicon

0. 25 per cent NH$_4$I

83 per cent Al$_2$O$_3$.

Parts to be coated are placed in the particulate mix in a metal retort. The retort becomes sealed with a fusible silicate as it is heated to 1400 F in a furnace. A typical coating temperature is 2000 F. X-ray diffraction analysis of the coating indicates that the major coating phase is MoSi$_2$, and there are thin diffusion layers of Mo$_5$Si$_3$ and Mo$_3$Si between the MoSi$_2$ layer and the substrate[28]. The chemical analysis of the coating[27], in atomic per cent is

Molybdenum = 30. 5

Silicon = 69

Chromium = 0. 5 ,

which approximates MoSi$_2$.

The Douglas Aircraft Company[29] has conducted preliminary studies concerning the effect of a 0. 001-inch-thick W-2 coating on the crack propagation and residual strength of cracked molybdenum sheet. Fatigue cracks were grown in 2 by 6-inch panels of 0. 050-inch-thick sheet with a 0. 40 by 0. 010-inch slot cut into the center of the specimen. Typical fatigue-crack growth curves for coated and uncoated specimens of the same lot are illustrated in Figure 23. The uncoated specimens were cycled at a stress level of 40,000 psi, whereas the coated specimens were cycled at 25,000 psi. Figure 24 shows that variations in crack growth characteristics among the several sheets examined were considerably larger for the coated specimens. The scatter was attributable largely to variations in the crack nucleation period rather than to variations in the growth rates of the cracks. Figure 24 also shows that the lower limit of the scatter band for coated panels merges with the upper limit of the scatter band for uncoated panels in spite of the fact that the coated panels were cycled at 15,000-psi lower stress. This observation indicates that the application of an oxidation-resistant coating may make crack nucleation and propagation considerably easier and thereby tends to embrittle the material. In this connection, it was reported that coated panels tended to shatter when accidentally struck with light impact loads at room temperature.

Figure 25 illustrates the effect of degree of cracking on the residual strength of coated molybdenum panels tested in air at high temperatures. The Douglas interpretation that the strength decreases with increasing crack length is as would be expected due to reduction of the cross-sectional area supporting the load. The scatter, which is particularly great at 1600 F, makes interpretation difficult, and tends to impugn the effect of soak time (at 2000 F) cited in Figure 25.

PFR-6 Coating

Pfaudler's PFR-6 coating is applied in a one-cycle pack-cementation process in a pack containing particulate silicon and columbium. Thickness of the coating can be varied by altering coating time, temperature, or pack composition. Pfaudler has evaluated the high-temperature oxidation resistance of the coating on Mo-0. 5Ti sheet in oxyacetylene-torch tests[30]. Coated specimens 1. 5 by 3 inch were heated to 3000 F with the flame and then quenched to room temperature with an air jet after every 0. 5-hour exposure period. Coating weight gain was proportional to coating thickness (5 to 6 mg/cm^2 is equivalent to 1 mil of silicide coating), and Figure 26 shows that coating life increased with coating thickness.

156

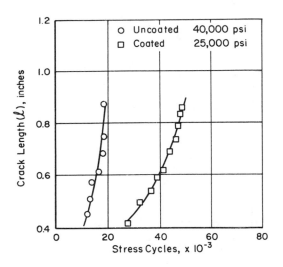

FIGURE 23. TYPICAL FATIGUE-CRACK GROWTH IN SPECIFIC PANELS OF
COATED AND UNCOATED MOLYBDENUM AT 80 F[29]

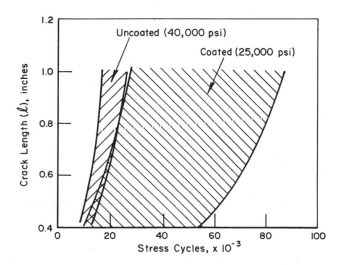

FIGURE 24. SCATTER IN THE CRACK-GROWTH CHARACTERISTICS OF SEVERAL
COATED AND UNCOATED MOLYBDENUM SHEETS AT 80 F[29]

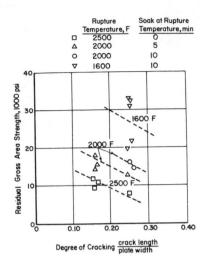

FIGURE 25. RESIDUAL STRENGTH OF COATED PANELS VERSUS DEGREE
OF CRACKING[29]

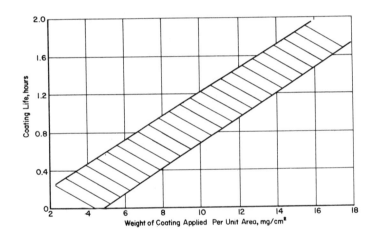

FIGURE 26. OXIDATION LIFE OF PFR-6 COATING ON 30-MIL Mo-0.5Ti
SHEET IN 3000 F OXYACETYLENE-TORCH TEST[30]

5 to 6 mg/cm^2 ≈ 1 mil of disilicide coating.

The PFR-6 coating also was tested on Mo-0.5Ti and TZM sheet at low temperatures to check for the occurrence of pest failure[30]. Pest was not observed when coated Mo-0.5Ti specimens were exposed consecutively for periods of 3 hours each at 50 F temperature increments from 1100 to 1650 F (total exposure = 36 hours). Coated TZM sheet also was exposed for 24-hour periods at temperatures ranging from 800 to 1300 F. Only the specimen exposed 24 hours at 1100 F had irregular oxidation performance. A large weight gain and increase in thickness accompanied formation of a white oxide on the coating. This phenomenon was not duplicated in even 100 hours on coated Mo-0.5Ti or other TZM specimens in another oxidation test at 1100 F. Other noncyclic furnace oxidation tests of the PFR-6 coating on Mo-0.5Ti sheet showed that it resisted pest failure for more than 50 hours at 1500 F, but pinhole coating failures occurred on 6 out of 16 specimens during the 50-hour exposure period[4]. The oxidation life of PFR-6 coating as determined in furnace oxidation tests at 2400, 2600, and 2800 F is given in Table 23. There is appreciable scatter in the coating-life data. The coating failed most frequently at edges, and edge failures generally occurred earlier than failures on flat surfaces.

TABLE 23. OXIDATION LIFE OF PFR-6 COATING ON Mo-0.5Ti SHEET
IN CYCLIC FURNACE OXIDATION TESTS [a] [4]

Temperature, F	Sheet Thickness, mils	Coating Life, hr	Failure Location
2400	50	>50, >50, >50,	No failure
2400	50	28	Edge
2400	10	40	Flat surface
2400	10	7, 10, 10	Edge
2600	50	48	Flat surface
2600	50	2[b], 2[b], 14, 15, 22	Edge
2600	10	14, 22[b], 32	Flat surface
2600	10	12, 12[b], 14	Edge
2800	50	12,	Flat surface
2800	50	1[b], 2[b], 2, 6, 12	Edge
2800	10	2[b]	Flat surface
2800	10	1, 1, 2, 2, 2[b]	Edge

(a) Specimens cycled to room temperature at 1-hour intervals.
(b) Preoxidized 50 hours at 1500 F without failure.

General Dynamics ascertained the stress-rupture strength of Mo-0.5Ti sheet coated with PFR-6[24]. Test specimens were resistance heated and optical pyrometer temperature was corrected assuming emittance to be 0.9. The 30-minute stress-rupture strength at 2800 F was about 7,400 psi. The coating demonstrated capability for protecting the substrate from oxidation for greater than 30 minutes at 2800 F while undergoing 1.5 to 4 per cent creep. Stress-rupture data for 20- and 50-mil Mo-0.5Ti sheet coated with PFR-6 and tested in air at 2400, 2500, and 2600 F as shown in Figure 27.

159

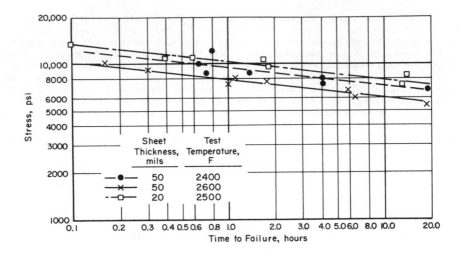

FIGURE 27.   STRESS-RUPTURE STRENGTHS OF 50-MIL Mo-0. 5Ti COATED
WITH PFR-6 TESTED IN AIR[4]

Durak-B Coating

    Durak-B is a modified silicide pack-cementation coating of the Chromizing
Corporation.   Table 24 gives some room-temperature tensile properties of TZM alloy
coated with Durak-B.   Elongation dropped from 20 to 2 per cent as a result of applying
the coating[16].   The yield and tensile strength decreased only slightly in the as-coated
condition, but they dropped about 35 per cent after oxidation exposure at 2750 F, as a
consequence of recrystallization.

TABLE 24.   ROOM-TEMPERATURE TENSILE PROPERTIES OF TZM
MOLYBDENUM ALLOY COATED WITH DURAK-B[16]

Condition of Test Specimen	Room-Temperature Strength, 1000 psi		Elongation in 2 Inches, per cent
	Ultimate	0.2% Yield	
Uncoated	117	104	20
As coated	105	100	2
Coated and oxidized 2 hr at 2750 F	74	66	5

Boeing Silicide Coating[5]

Boeing's straight silicide coating, sometimes called Disil, is applied by a fluidized-bed process. The oxidation protection afforded by the coating in oxyacetylene-torch tests was presented in Figure 4. Minimum coating life is 4 hours at 2700 F or 2.5 hours at 3000 F (uncorrected optical temperatures).

Vitro Nickel-Modified Silicide Coating[31]

Vitro has a coating for molybdenum that is applied by electrophoretic deposition. Particulate material having the composition $94MoSi_2$-6Ni is applied to the substrate by this process, and then the coated parts are pressed isostatically under pressures of 10 to 30 tons/in.^{2} to densify the coating. Further densification and bonding occur in a subsequent sintering treatment at about 2300 F. The coating has protected 1/4-20 TZC bolts from oxidation for up to 40 hours at 2500 F.

Other Coatings

The coatings for molybdenum for which little or no recent information is available from the producer, but which have been tested in the comparative evaluation programs presented in the next section, are as follows:

American Machine & Foundry, AMFKOTE-2 - pack cementation, modified silicide

Chance Vought, Vought IX (now obsolete) - pack cementation, modified silicide

Chromizing, Durak-MG - pack cementation, modified silicide

General Technologies Corp. - pack cementation, modified silicide

General Telephone & Electronics - Sn-Al slurry coating, modified with molybdenum

Pfaudler, PFR-5 - pack cementation, modified silicide.

Comparative Evaluations of Coatings

Comparative Evaluation of Coatings on Mo-0.5Ti Sheet[32,33]

Langley Research Center (NASA) has conducted a comparative screening evaluation of 6 coating systems on 12-mil stress-relieved Mo-0.5Ti sheet as part of an overall program to define the utility of coated thin-gage refractory-metal sheet for hot surfaces of aerospace vehicles. Sheet specimens were tumbled in an abrasive mixture to round the edges in preparation for applying the coatings. The coatings that were tested are described in Table 25. The coatings were fairly thin, ranging from 1.2 to 2.3 mils, and the substrate thickness was decreased from 10 to 25 per cent by the various coating processes.

161

TABLE 25. COATING SYSTEMS EVALUATED ON 12-MIL Mo-0.5Ti SHEET BY LANGLEY RESEARCH CENTER[32,33]

Organization That Applied Coating	Coating Designation	Constituent Elements	Method of Application	Metallographic Coating Thickness, mils	Metallographic Substrate Thickness			Weight Change During Coating, per cent
					Before Coating, mils	After Coating, mils	Decrease, per cent	
American Machine & Foundry	AMFKOTE-2 (preoxidized[a])	Si, B, Cr, Cb, Al, C	Two-cycle pack cementation	1.7	12.2	9.2	24	2.2
American Machine & Foundry	AMFKOTE-2	Ditto	Ditto	1.7	12.2	9.9	18	2.2
Boeing	Disil	Si	Fluidized bed	1.5	10.8	8.1	25	-3.8[b]
Chance Vought	IX[c]	Si, Cr, B, C, Al, Ti, Cb	Two-cycle pack cementation	1.4	12.0	10.6	12	3.4
Chromalloy	W-2	Si, Cr	Two-cycle pack cementation	1.2	12.1	10.9	10	4.4
Pfaudler	PFR-5	Si, Cr	Two-cycle pack cementation	2.3	11.8	9.1	23	13.7
Pfaudler	PFR-6	Si, Cb	One-cycle pack cementation	1.9	11.6	9.7	16	7.9

(a) Preoxidized 1 hour at 2800 F to form glassy oxide.
(b) Weight loss apparently due to removal of substrate by Boeing during cleaning operation in preparation for coating.
(c) Vought IX coating now is obsolete.

The oxidation life of the coatings in cyclic and noncyclic furnace oxidation tests at 2300 F is shown in Figure 28. The data are reported in terms of oxidation time to 10 per cent weight loss (due to molybdenum oxide volatilization) as an expedient in establishing coating failure time. Cycling to room temperature at 1.0- and 0.1-hour intervals decreased coating life considerably compared to that obtained in noncyclic exposure. AMFKOTE-2 exhibited superior oxidation resistance, followed by the Pfaudler coatings.

Room-temperature tensile properties of as-coated specimens are compared to those of the bare substrate in Figure 29. Yield and tensile strengths were calculated using the thickness of the uncoated sheet. Considering that the substrate thickness was reduced by applying the coatings (Table 25) only the AMFKOTE and probably the Pfaudler coatings reduced the strength of the residual substrate. Substrate ductility was retained in Disil-, Vought-, and Pfaudler-coated specimens, but was degraded by the W-2 coating and even more seriously by AMFKOTE-2.

The reduction in substrate thickness by diffusion interaction with the coatings during oxidation exposure at 2500 F is given in Figure 30. As each point represents only one observation, full reliance on the data shown is hazardous. Generally, assuming that coatings were applied at temperatures appreciably less than 2500 F, the expected effects of both temperature and time were approximated, although there are discrepancies that are best rationalized by assuming that specific data points are not representative. From the data shown one might conclude that the Vought and perhaps the AMFKOTE coatings have somewhat superior diffusional stability.

Screening Evaluation of Coated TZM Foil[23]

The program at Solar to evaluate coated foils, which was outlined in the section on columbium, also included 6-mil TZM foil. Test procedures were the same as those described earlier. Table 26 describes the coating systems that were investigated.

The TZM foil was in the stress-relieved condition prior to coating. None of the coating processes brought about significant recrystallization, with the exception of the Vitro coating. The sintering operation at 2300 F for this coating resulted in partial recrystallization in the TZM adjacent to the coating, apparently due to depression of the recrystallization temperature by inward diffusion of nickel from the coating.

Only the GT & E tin-aluminum coating effected a large increase in the weight (47 per cent). The weight of the silicide coatings ranged from 6 to 19 per cent of the weight of the foil as shown in Table 27. The reduction in the foil thickness by diffusion during application of the coatings and during subsequent oxidation exposures is also given in Table 27, and indicates superior diffusional stability for the Vitro, Chromalloy, and Chromizing coatings compared to the other silicide coatings. The GT & E coating effected relatively rapid diffusion consumption of the foil substrate, based on these data.

The results of cyclic furnace oxidation tests of as-coated and prestrained (specimens bent over 4T radius at room temperature to just below the outer fiber yield point) specimens are shown in Figure 31. All coatings except GT & E and AMF protected unstrained specimens for 50 hours at 2000 F. Protective life was reduced to only a few hours at 2500 F, with the exception of the 50 hours' life exhibited by the Vitro coating. Most coating failures of prestrained specimens occurred preferentially in the bend

163

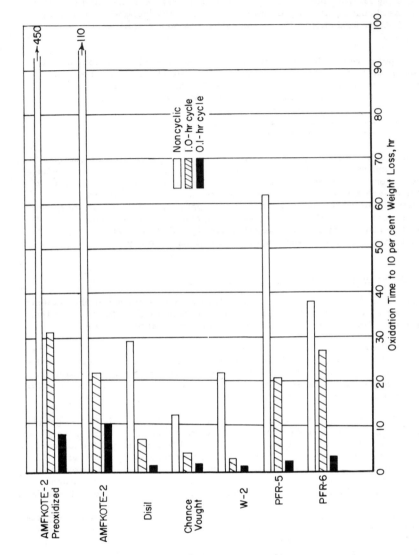

FIGURE 28. OXIDATION LIFE OF COATINGS ON 12-MIL Mo-0.5Ti SHEET IN CYCLIC AND NONCYCLIC FURNACE TESTS[33] AT 2500 F

Failure time arbitrarily selected as time at which 3/4 x 1-1/2 inch specimen lost 10 per cent weight.

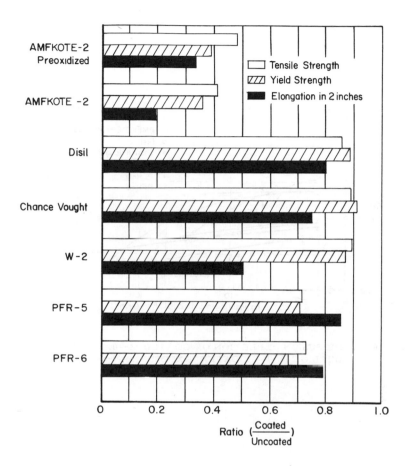

FIGURE 29.   ROOM-TEMPERATURE TENSILE PROPERTIES OF
AS-COATED Mo-0.5Ti SHEET[33]

Strength values based on foil thickness prior to
coating.

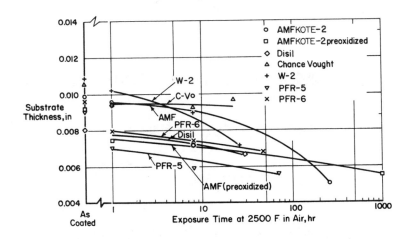

FIGURE 30.   DIFFUSION DEPLETION OF COATED Mo-0.5Ti SUBSTRATE
DURING 2500 F OXIDATION EXPOSURE[33]

166

TABLE 26. COATING SYSTEMS EVALUATED BY SOLAR ON 6-MIL TZM FOIL[23]

Organization That Applied Coating	Average Coating Thickness, mils	Coating Process
Chromizing	1.4	Durak B
Vought	2.1	Vought IV, applied by 2-cycle pack cementation: (Cycle 1) siliconized 5 hr at 1900 F; (Cycle 2) Cr-B applied in 5 hr at 1900 F
General Telephone & Electronics (GT&E)	3.2	Painted with Sn-25Al-5Mo-2Si metal powder in lacquer carrier and vacuum sintered 1/2 hr at 1900 F
General Technologies Corporation (GTC)	2.0	Pack-cementation process using pack containing Si, Cr, Cb, W, and Al_2O_3 for 6 and 4 hr (2 cycles) at 2000 F
Pfaudler	2.0	PFR-6 applied by pack cementation, pack contains Si, Cb, Al_2O_3, and halide carrier; 1 hr at 1850 F and 7 hr at 2050 F
Chromalloy	1.1	W-3 which is a modified silicide coating applied by pack cementation
AMF	1.4	AMFKOTE-2 which is a modified silicide coating applied at 1975 F
Vitro	3.1	$94MoSi_2$-6Ni composition applied by electrophoretic deposition; coating is isostatically pressed at 15,000 psi and then sintered in argon for 1 hr at 2300 F

TABLE 27. THICKNESS OF COATINGS AND TZM FOIL[a] IN AS-COATED AND OXIDIZED CONDITIONS[23]

Coating	Coating Thickness As Coated, mils	Coating Weight, per cent of foil weight	Residual Substrate Thickness				
			As Coated, mils	After 2000 F Oxidation		After 2500 F Oxidation	
				Hours	Thickness, mils	Hours	Thickness, mils
Chromizing	1.4	--	4.7	75	4.6	15	3.9
Vought	2.1	19	3.8	75	3.2	31	1.9
GT&E	3.2	47	5.5	18	4.6	6	3.0
GTC	2.0	15	4.3	75	2.6	6	3.4
Pfaudler	2.0	15	4.7	59	4.1	11	3.2
Chromalloy	1.1	6	5.1	72	4.4	7	4.6
AMF	1.4	11	4.6	3	4.4	1	4.5
Vitro	3.1	--	4.5	75	4.5	56	3.1

(a) TZM foil was 6 ± 0.6 mils thick prior to coating.

167

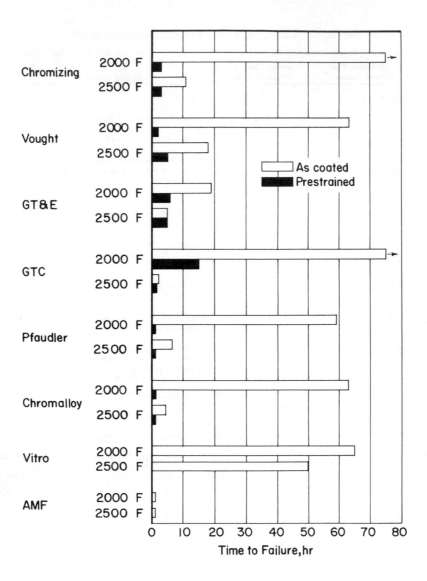

FIGURE 31. AVERAGE CYCLIC OXIDATION LIVES OF AS-COATED AND
PRESTRAINED COATED TZM FOIL AT 2000 AND 2500 F[23]

Furnace oxidation tests: specimens cycled to room temperature about once each hour. Average of three specimens
reported.

area. All the coatings passed the 1- and 2-hour cyclic plasma-arc tests at 2000 and 2500 F, respectively, except the Chromalloy and AMF coatings which developed pin holes at 2500 F. The Vitro coating was not tested.

All as-coated specimens passed the 90-degree 4T bend test at room temperature with the exception of those coated by AMF. Bend ductility of some systems decreased after oxidation exposure at 2000 and 2500 F as shown in Table 28, although some ductility was retained by all specimens. Tensile-test results are shown in Figure 32 in comparison to initial substrate values. The original foil thickness was used for calculating strength values. Elongation was reduced considerably by all coatings; this may account for lower retained ultimate strength relative to the yield strength (because of reduced strain hardening).

The over-all performance of the coatings applied by Vought, GT & E, Pfaudler, and Chromalloy was considered better than that of the others, so they were selected for advanced evaluation in a program that is currently under way.

Oxidation Performance of Silicide Coatings at Low Pressures[34]

Lockheed has investigated the oxidation protection afforded by silicide coatings on molybdenum at low oxygen pressures to gain some information about the capabilities of the coatings for resisting failure during re-entry. Coated molybdenum rods were resistance heated in a vacuum chamber. Oxygen pressure was controlled by balancing an oxygen leak against the vacuum pump. Specimens were exposed at a given oxygen pressure and temperature for 30 minutes.

The maximum temperatures for 30 minutes' life for the four coatings tested are shown in Figure 33. The Disil II, PFR-6, and Durak-B coatings suffered a reduction of about 450 F in their 30-minute life at 0.2 mm oxygen pressure in comparison to 760 mm air pressure. The Chance Vought coating, which is more limited in maximum temperature capability at atmospheric pressure, was actually superior to the other coatings in these tests as it did not show the extreme sensitivity to low-pressure deterioration.

The coatings failed in the low-pressure tests by localized attack at coating cracks, causing substrate oxidation. A gaseous oxidation product that condensed on the furnace walls was found to be amorphous and rich in silicon. This gaseous transport of silicon plus thermodynamic considerations has led Lockheed to believe that the failure mechanism for the silicide coatings at reduced pressure involves stabilization and volatilization of SiO.

Oxidation Tests of Silicide Coatings on Mo-0.5Ti[35]

The University of Dayton has reported on the oxidation performance of five silicide coatings on 30-mil Mo-0.5Ti sheet in the following tests:

(1) Coating life at 3000 F - specimens heated at 3000 F with oxyacetylene or plasma-arc torch

TABLE 28. ROOM-TEMPERATURE BEND TESTS OF COATED TZM FOIL IN AS-COATED CONDITION AND AFTER OXIDATION EXPOSURE[a][23]

Coating	Bend Angle in As-Coated Condition, degrees	Bend Angle After Oxidation Exposure at Indicated Temperature			
		2000 F		2500 F	
		Oxidation Time, hr	Bend Angle, degrees	Oxidation Time, hr	Bend Angle, degrees
Bare substrate	90, 90	--	---	--	--
Chromizing	90, 90	9	30, 90, 20	5	68, 90, 90
Vought	90, 90	38	90, 19, 15	18	80, 72, 76
GT&E	90, 90	15	90, 90, 90	2	90, 90, 90
GTC	90, 90	--	--	--	--
Pfaudler	90, 90	30	19, 90, 21	7	90, 90, 90
Chromalloy	90, 90	36	12, 22, 21	3	19, 90, 79
AMF	19, 19	--	--	--	--
Vitro	90, 90	35	90, 90, 90	50	31, 34, 40

(a) Test procedure:

    (1) Specimens preoxidized in static furnace exposure (no cycling) for about 85 per cent of the cyclic life of the coating system.

    (2) Bend radius = 0.024, nominal at bend radius. Tested according to procedure recommended by the Refractory Metals Sheet Rolling Panel of MAB. Bend angle is that angle at which fracture occurred, or 90 degrees if specimen did not fracture.

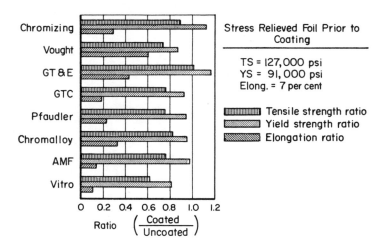

FIGURE 32. ROOM-TEMPERATURE TENSILE PROPERTIES OF AS-COATED TZM FOIL

Strength values based on foil thickness prior to coating.[23]

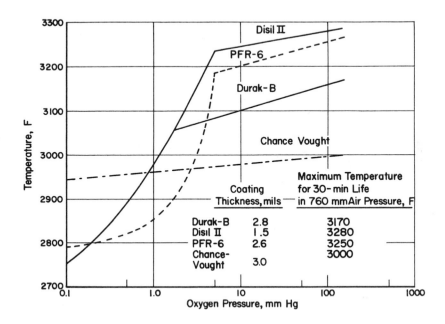

FIGURE 33. MAXIMUM TEMPERATURE FOR 30-MINUTE LIFE OF COATINGS ON
MOLYBDENUM IN PURE OXYGEN ATMOSPHERE[34]

171

(2) Maximum useful temperature - specimens heated for consecutive 5-minute periods at 2500, 2700, 2900, 3000, 3100, 3200, 3300, and 3400 F, or until coating failure

(3) Check for pest occurrence - specimens exposed for 50 hours at 2000 F*

The test results are given in Table 29. Coating lines were erratic in the plasma-arc test at 3000 F, but they were fairly uniform for duplicate specimens in the oxyacetylene-torch test. The PFR-6 coating displayed the best over-all performance; its oxidation life at 3000 F varied from 1 to more than 4 hours, and it had a maximum temperature capability of 3400 F. None of the coatings failed by the pest phenomenon at 2000 F.

TABLE 29. OXIDATION PERFORMANCE OF COATED 30-MIL Mo-0.5Ti SHEET[a][35]

| Coating | 3000 F Oxyacetylene-Torch-Test[b] Coating Life, min | 3000 F Plasma-Arc Torch-Test[c,d] Coating Life, min | Plasma-Arc Test at Increasing Temperatures[d,e] | | | Coating Performance in 50 Hr, 2000 F, Furnace Oxidation Test |
			Coating Failure Temperature, F	Total Exposure Time, min	Time at Failure Temperature, min	
Boeing Fluidized Bed Silicide	--	223, 90	3300	32	2	Edge failure at 25 hours; no pest
			3300	34	4	
Boeing Disil 1	22, 24, 25	2, 105	3300	34	4	Good; no pest
			3400	37	2	
PFR-6	64, 66, 82	>240, >240	3400	35	<1	Good; no pest
			3400	39	4	
W-2	21, 24, 25	25, >240	3200	26	1	Good; no pest
			3200	29	4	
Vought II & IV	60, 67, 84	28, 96	3200	26	1	Good; no pest
			3300	31	1	

(a) Test specimens were 2 by 2-inch sheet.
(b) Specimens cooled to room temperature once each 30 minutes.
(c) Specimens cooled to room temperature once each 15 minutes.
(d) Arc effluent was simulated air at a mass flow rate of 0.0082 lb/sec.
(e) Each specimen exposed for consecutive 5-minute periods at 2500, 2700, 2900, 3000, 3100, 3200, 3300, and 3400 F, or until coating failed.

Dynamic Oxidation Tests of Durak-MG and W-2 Coatings[36]

Simulated leading-edge components (Figure 34) of Mo-0.5Ti alloy machined from solid stock and coated with W-2 and Durak-MG have been tested in a dynamic air environment by NASA. One test facility was a 6-inch subsonic arc-powered tunnel

*2000 F is above the temperature range in which pest has been reported to occur in $MoSi_2$. No reason for selection of this temperature was given.

operated at a reduced air pressure of 2 psi. The other test facility was a subsonic arc jet operating in the open atmosphere with the effluent consisting of air plus CO and CO_2 from the carbon electrodes. Surface temperature of the leading-edge specimens was 3000 F during the tests.

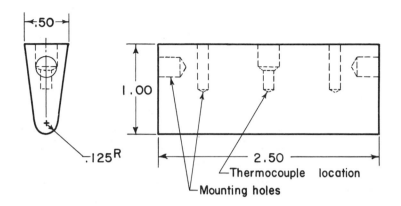

FIGURE 34. DESIGN OF COATED Mo-0.5Ti LEADING-EDGE SPECIMEN[36]

The test results are summarized in Table 30. Both coatings protected the substrate from oxidation for the duration of the tests, which lasted 70 seconds in the low-pressure tunnel and 5 and 10 minutes in the atmospheric-pressure jet. Weight changes of the specimens were fairly low, ranging from -6 to +4 mg/cm^2, except for 20 mg/cm^2 gained by one specimen coated with W-2.

Tensile-Shear Tests of Coated Riveted
Mo-0.5Ti Sheet[37,38]

Bell Aerosystems Company has conducted tensile shear tests of riveted Mo-0.5Ti sheet specimens coated with Durak-B and W-2 silicide coatings. Stress-relieved sheet specimens (10, 30, and 50 mils thick) and rivets were coated, and then the test specimens (Figure 35) were riveted at about 1500 F. Finally, the assembled test specimens were coated again. Prior to tensile testing the specimens were subjected to various pretreatments consisting of oxidation exposure at 2000 and 2500 F and low tensile loads (considerably below the elastic limit) at room temperature and 2500 F. These treatments are described in the footnotes in Table 31. The oxidation exposures at 2500 F recrystallized the Mo-0.5Ti and rivets.

The tensile-shear strengths of the coated specimens are compared with calculated failure loads for uncoated specimens in Table 31. With only a few exceptions the strengths of the coated specimens were in fair agreement with the values that were calculated for uncoated specimens.

TABLE 30. TEST DATA FOR COATED Mo-0.5Ti LEADING-EDGE SPECIMENS TESTED BY NASA IN TWO ARC-POWERED FACILITIES[36]

| Coating | Test Time, min | Characteristics of Test Facility[a] | | | Surface Tempera- ture, F | Weight Change of Specimen, mg/cm^2 |
		Air Flow, lb/sec	Heat Input Btu/ft^2-sec	Static Pressure, psia		
Tests Conducted With Arc Jet						
W-2	5.0	0.24	210	14.7	3000	+3.4
Durak MG	2.4	0.24	210	14.7	3000	+0.2
Durak MG	5.0	0.24	210	14.7	3000	-0.8
W-2	10.0	0.08	170	14.7	3000	+20.0
Durak MG	9.5	0.08	170	14.7	3000	-5.8
Tests Conducted in Low-Pressure Arc-Powered Tunnel						
W-2	1.16	0.08	220	2	3000	+1.0
Durak MG	1.16	0.08	220	2	3000	+0.4

(a) Additional characteristics of test facilities used for these tests:

	6-Inch Subsonic Low-Pressure Arc-Powered Tunnel	Subsonic Arc Jet
Test Section Diameter, in.	6	6
Test Atmosphere	2-psia air	Air + 4% carbon as CO and CO$_2$ from carbon electrodes
Stagnation Temperature, F	7200	3200-8500 (two values refer to low- and high-arc-power tests)
Enthalpy, Btu/lb	3900	1000-4500
Velocity, ft/sec	720	40-300
Dynamic Pressure, lb/ft^2	4.7	0.25-6.0
Mach Number	0.17	0.01-0.06
Reynolds Number Per Foot	6,500	6,000 to 30,000

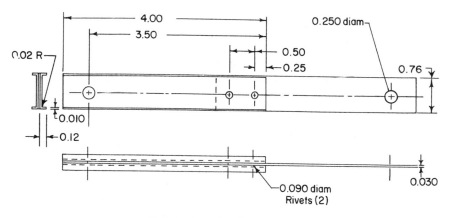

a. Double Shear Specimen

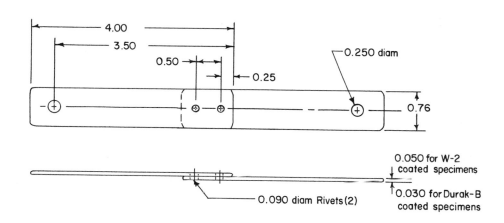

b. Single Shear Specimen

FIGURE 35. CONFIGURATION OF COATED RIVETED Mo-0.5Ti SHEET SPECIMENS[37]

All dimensions are in inches.

TABLE 31. TENSILE-SHEAR STRENGTH OF COATED RIVETED Mo-0.5Ti SPECIMENS TESTED IN AIR[37, 38]

Type Specimen[a]	Prior History[b]	Test Temperature, F	Failure Load[c], pounds	Failure Location	Calculated Failure Load[d], pounds
Specimens Coated With W-2					
Double shear	A	RT	564-1020 (836)	1/4-inch loading-pin holes	800
Single shear	A	RT	925-1065 (973)	Rivets and base metal	935-1470
Double shear	B	RT	406-673 (517)	Base metal at rivets	540
Single shear	C	RT	935-1020 (970)	Rivets sheared	625
Double shear	B	2500	190-297 (235)	Base metal at rivets	135
Single shear	C	2500	200-253 (228)	Rivets sheared	155
Specimens Coated With Durak-B					
Double shear	A	RT	440-546 (493)	1/4-inch loading-pin holes	800
Single shear	A	RT	785-1005 (895)	Rivets and sheet adjacent to rivets	880-935
Double shear	B	RT	465-520 (496)	Base metal at rivets	540
Single shear	C	RT	725-850 (785)	Rivets sheared	625
Double shear	A	2500	180-215 (198)	Base metal at rivets	135
Single shear	A	2500	190-200 (195)	Rivets sheared	155
Double shear	B	2500	215-229 (222)	Base metal at rivets	135
Single shear	C	2500	195-213 (205)	Rivets sheared	155

Footnotes appear on the following page.

(a) See specimen designs in Figure 38.

(b) Prior history of test specimens:

   A = Oxidized in air for 10 minutes at 2000 F

   B = A+ cyclic load of 115 to 210 pounds applied 10 times at room temperature; followed by heating in air at 2500 F for 4 minutes under a 6.5-pound load

   C = A + cyclic load of 290 to 315 pounds applied 10 times at room temperature; followed by heating in air at 2500 F for 4 minutes under 16-pound load.

(c) Failure load range is followed by average value in parentheses where applicable.

(d) Calculated failure loads:

	Calculated Failure Load for Uncoated Material, pounds		
	at 80 F for As-Received Material	at 80 F for Recrystallized Material	at 2500 F for Recrystallized Material
2 rivets, 0.090-inch diameter			
Single shear	935	625	155
Double shear	1870	1250	310
2 channels 0.010 inch thick			
Loading-pin hole (stress-concentration factor of 2.25 assumed)	800	535	--
Rivet hole, tension (stress-concentration factor of 2.70 assumed)	810	540	135
Rivet hole, bearing	765	510	125
1 sheet 0.050 inch thick			
Loading-pin hole	1330	885	--
Rivet hole, tension	1470	980	245
Rivet hole, bearing	1910	1270	320
1 sheet 0.030 inch thick; rivet hole, tension	880	590	--

Tensile and Fatigue Tests of Coated
Threaded Fasteners[39]

Republic Aviation is engaged in a program to design and manufacture refractory-
metal fasteners that can be used in the coated condition. Bolts having a rounded thread
form for the root and crest have been made in the 1/4-20 size from TZC and TZM
molybdenum alloys. The limited amount of test data available for these fasteners is a
premonition of some of the problems that can be anticipated with other coated refractory-
metal threaded fasteners.

The tensile-failure loads of the uncoated and coated 1/4-20 TZC and TZM
fasteners are given in Table 32. Room-temperature failure loads were reduced 50 to 70
per cent by the PFR-6 and W-3 coatings, but only 20 per cent by the Vitro coating.
Bolts coated with PFR-6 and W-3 had higher strength at 2000 F than at room temperature, suggesting increased notch sensitivity effected by the coating. TZM as the substrate was somewhat superior to TZC at both test temperatures.

TABLE 32. TENSION-FAILURE LOADS OF COATED 1/4-20 TZC AND TZM BOLTS
AT ROOM TEMPERATURE AND 2000 F[39]

Condition	Test Temperature, F	Failure Load, pounds[a]
TZC Bolts		
Uncoated	RT	4440-4595 (4528)
Coated with PFR-6	RT	950-1850 (1312)
Ditto	2000	2595 (2595)
Coated with W-3	RT	1550-1820 (1685)
Ditto	2000	2200
Coated with Vitro 94MoSi$_2$-6Ni	RT[b]	3245-3965 (3605)
Ditto	RT	2565
"	2000	2500
TZM Bolts		
Uncoated	RT	4850-5340 (5072)
Coated with PFR-6	RT	1560-2725 (2111)
Ditto	2000	2830-2840 (2835)
Coated with W-3	RT	2860
Ditto	2000	3010

(a) Range is followed by average in parentheses where more than 1 specimen was tested.
(b) Specimens previously oxidized for 24 hours at 2500 F.

PFR-6 is the only coating for which fatigue data are available at this time. The
tension-tension fatigue lives of PFR-6 coated bolts at room temperature are given in
Table 33. The fatigue life of the bolts dropped precipitously upon being coated. In

178

TABLE 33. RESULTS OF ROOM-TEMPERATURE TENSION-TENSION FATIGUE TESTS OF 1/4-20 TZC AND TZM BOLTS[39]

Maximum Tensile Load, pounds[a]	Cycles to Failure	Failure Location[b]
	Uncoated TZC	
3400	9,000	Threads
3400	24,000	"
2945	57,000	"
2945	18,000	"
2265	2,000,000	No failure
2265	2,000,000	No failure
	PFR-6-Coated TZC[c]	
1200	2,000	Head
1200	320,000	Threads
1200	--	Broke on loading; threads
1000	--	Broke on loading; head
1000	112,000	Head
975	1,258,000	Threads
975	1,000	Head
975	38,000	Head
800	2,000,000	No failure
800	2,000,000	No failure
800	4,000	Head
800	6,000	Head
800	2,000,000	No failure
750	16,000	Head
750	12,000,000	No failure
400	2,000,000	No failure
	Uncoated TZM	
2945	434,000	Threads
2945	1,953,000	Threads
2945	622,000	Threads
	PFR-6-Coated TZM[c]	
1800	--	Broke on loading; threads (two specimens)
1700	496,000	Head
1600	417,000	Threads
1600	400,000	No failure
1500	240,000	Head
1500	--	Broke on loading
1500	322,000	Threads
1500	1,500,000	Threads

(a) Ratio of minimum load to maximum load was 0.1.
(b) Threads = failed in threads; head = failed in head-to-shank fillet radius.
(c) PFR-6 coating applied by Republic with technique recommended by Pfaudler.

179

addition, the fatigue life of coated bolts under a given load was erratic. The maximum tensile load for 2 million cycles' life with TZC bolts was 2200 pounds for uncoated specimens, but only 800 pounds for coated bolts. Yet three coated bolts tested at 750 or 800 pounds' load failed in less than 20,000 cycles, two orders of magnitude below the maximum fatigue life at this load. The fatigue life of a coated TZC bolt at 2000 F was 515,000 cycles under 1300 pounds' load, whereas the longest life at room temperature with a 1200-pound load was 312,000 cycles. TZM, both uncoated and coated, was superior to the TZC alloy.

Apparently the presence of a coating such as PFR-6 or W-3 and the notched-thread form synergistically embrittle the bolts at room temperature.

Emittance of Silicide Coatings

Emittance data obtained by several investigators for silicide coatings on molybdenum or molybdenum alloys are summarized in Table 34 and Figures 36 to 40. The spectral normal emittance (0.65μ) and the total normal emittance of the PFR-6 coating in a vacuum were above 0.80 (Table 33), and the total hemispherical emittance in air varied between 0.6 and 0.7 (Figure 36). The total hemispherical emittance of Durak-B coating in air ranged from 0.40 to 0.55 at temperatures up to 3200 F (Figure 37). The emittance of Boeing's straight silicide coating on TZM increased from about 0.65 to about 0.9 as temperature increased from 2200 to 2800 F (Figure 38). The total hemispherical emittance of Vought IV coating varied from 0.6 to 0.7 at temperatures up to 3000 F (Figure 39). The spectral normal emittance of AMFKOTE-2 and AMFKOTE-2 which was modified to improve its emittance is compared with that of bulk $MoSi_2$ in Figure 40. Emittances of the standard AMFKOTE-2 and $MoSi_2$ are similar, but the modified coating exhibits higher emittance.

COATINGS FOR TANTALUM AND TANTALUM-BASE ALLOYS

Activity in developing and testing coatings for tantalum and its alloys is not nearly so extensive as it is for columbium and molybdenum alloys. The tantalum alloys for which advanced experimental coatings are available are Ta-10W and Ta-30Cb-7.5V. The performance of the GT & E tin-aluminum coatings on Ta-10W and Ta-30Cb-7.5V and the Battelle straight silicide coating on Ta-30Cb-7.5V alloy has been well characterized with regard to oxidation performance at atmospheric pressure and mechanical properties. Information is lacking on the emittance of both coating systems and low-pressure oxidation performance of the silicide coating system.

General Telephone & Electronics Tin-Aluminum Coatings[17]

The family of tin-aluminum coatings developed for tantalum alloys by General Telephone and Electronics (GT & E) has undergone a transition in their chemical composition within the past 2 years to provide better over-all performance. The earlier coatings had compositions prior to sintering of Sn-25Al (designated 40S) or Sn-50Al

180

TABLE 34. EMITTANCE OF PFR-6 COATING ON MOLYBDENUM IN
A VACUUM

Temperature, F	Spectral Normal Emittance (0. 65 μ)[40]
1449	0.98
1674	0.95
1679	0.92
1920	0.93
1920	0.92
2066	0.91
2071	0.88
2242	0.88
2248	0.89
2584	0.82
2601	0.79
Temperature, F	Total Normal Emittance[41]
1562	0.88
1742	0.84
1922	0.83
2102	0.83
2282	0.84
2462	0.85
2642	0.89
2822	0.93
3002	0.96

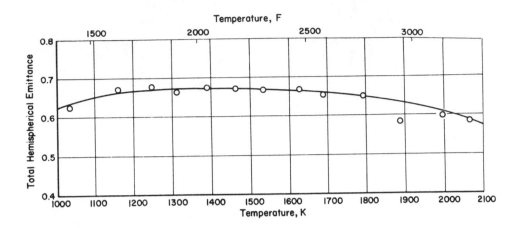

FIGURE 36.   TOTAL HEMISPHERICAL EMITTANCE OF PFR-6 COATING
ON MOLYBDENUM MEASURED IN AIR[9]

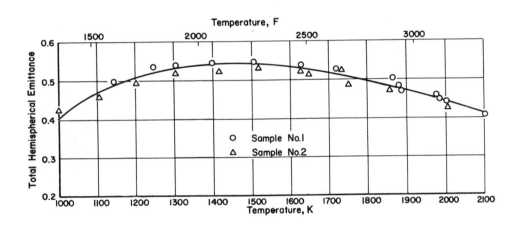

FIGURE 37.   TOTAL HEMISPHERICAL EMITTANCE OF DURAK-B COATING
ON MOLYBDENUM IN AIR[9]

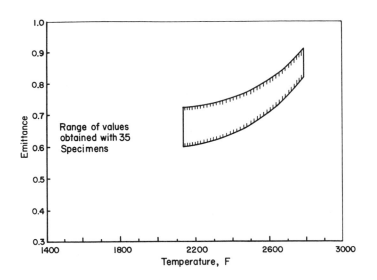

FIGURE 38.   EMITTANCE OF BOEING'S STRAIGHT SILICIDE COATING
ON TZM ALLOY[5]

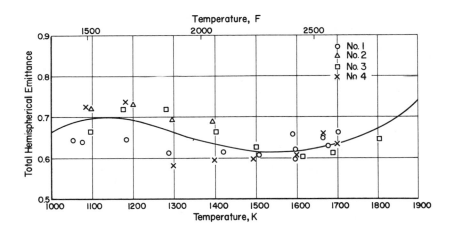

FIGURE 39.   TOTAL HEMISPHERICAL EMITTANCE OF VOUGHT IV COATING
ON MOLYBDENUM IN AIR[9]

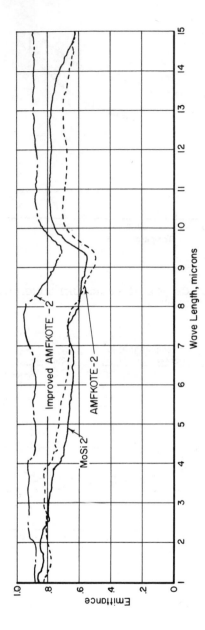

FIGURE 40. SPECTRAL NORMAL EMITTANCE OF A SINTERED SAMPLE OF MoSi$_2$ AND AMFKOTE-2 COATING ON MOLYBDENUM AT 1832 F[42, 43]

(34S). A distracting feature of these first-generation coatings was that a lump of Sn-Al formed at the drain-off end of specimens during the sintering heat treatments. Retention of the lump resulted in excessive diffusion interaction of the lump with the substrate during service, and its removal resulted in reduced oxidation life. The problem was minimized by adding a refractory powder such as tantalum or molybdenum to the slurry to support the coating during sintering and thereby prevent runoff.

GT & E has conducted extensive evaluations of the following substrate-coating systems:

Substrate	Applied Coating Composition, weight per cent
Ta-10W	(Sn-25Al)-10TaAl$_3$
Ta-10W	(Sn-50Al)-10TaAl$_3$
Ta-10W	(Sn-25Al)-10MoAl$_3$
Ta-30Cb-7.5V	[Sn-50(Al-11Si)]-10TaAl$_3$, identified hereafter as (Sn-50Al-Si)-10TaAl$_3$
Ta-30Cb-7.5V	[Sn-50(Al-11Si)]-10MoAl$_3$, identified hereafter as (Sn-50Al-Si)-10MoAl$_3$

To clarify the compositions, (Sn-25Al)-10TaAl$_3$ is 90 weight per cent (Sn-25Al) and 10 per cent TaAl$_3$. The elemental powders (Sn, Al, Ta, etc.) are mixed in a 1 to 1 volume ratio with lacquer. The slurry is sprayed on specimens, and then the specimens are dried and sintered in a vacuum for 1/2 hour at 1900 F. Thicker coatings are obtained by repeating the paint and sinter sequence a second time. The coatings range in thickness up to 6 mils. During sintering the molten aluminum reacts with the substrate and the tantalum or molybdenum powder in the coating to form MAl$_3$ aluminides. The unreacted Sn-Al phase is molten in service at temperatures above 1200 F.

Typical lives of the coatings in cyclic furnace oxidation tests are presented in Table 35 and Figure 41. Average coating life was 50 to 100 hours at temperatures up to 2000 F. At temperatures from 2500 to 3000 F, coating life increased with increasing coating thickness and length of oxidation cycle (Figure 41). For instance, oxidation life of the (Sn-25Al)-10MoAl$_3$ coating on Ta-10W at 2800 F was tripled by increasing the length of oxidation cycles from 1 to 12 hours. Doubling the coating thickness approximately doubled the oxidation life at 2500 F. The (Sn-25Al)-10TaAl$_3$ coating on Ta-10W resisted failure for 1 hour at 3300 F in oxyacetylene-torch tests.

Preliminary low-pressure oxidation tests indicated that the tin-aluminum coatings are susceptible to early failure due to volatilization of the liquid Sn-Al phase. About 70 weight per cent of a (Sn-25Al)-10TaAl$_3$ coating was lost in 30 minutes at 2600 F under 1.5 mm air pressure. The coating was depleted similarly in 1 hour at 2450 F. On the other hand, the coating was stable under 3 mm pressure at 2600 F and under 6 mm at 2800 F.

The tensile and stress-rupture properties of the coated alloys are shown in Figures 42 to 46. Figure 42 to 44 show similar tensile properties of coated and uncoated Ta-10W. The loss in strength depicted in Figure 44 resulting from oxidation at 2500 and 3000 F probably reflects both recrystallization and diffusion consumption of the

185

TABLE 35. OXIDATION LIVES OF Sn-Al COATINGS ON Ta-10W AND Ta-30Cb-7.5V ALLOYS[a][17]

Substrate	Coating	Oxidation Temperature, F	Coating Life, hr[b]
Ta-10W	(Sn-25Al)-10TaAl$_3$	1100	21-162
Ta-10W	(Sn-50Al)-10TaAl$_3$	1100	44-63
Ta-30Cb-7.5V	(Sn-50Al-Si)-10TaAl$_3$	1100	>100
Ta-10W	(Sn-25Al)-10TaAl$_3$	1400	23-157
Ta-30Cb-7.5V	(Sn-50Al-Si)-10TaAl$_3$	1400	>100
Ta-10W	(Sn-25Al)-10TaAl$_3$	2000	>100
Ta-10W	(Sn-50Al)-10TaAl$_3$	2000	71-96
Ta-30Cb-7.5V	(Sn-50Al-Si)-10TaAl$_3$	2000	>100
Ta-10W	(Sn-25Al)-10TaAl$_3$	2500	16-77
Ta-30Cb-7.5V	(Sn-50Al-Si)-10TaAl$_3$	2500	43-87
Ta-30Cb-7.5V	(Sn-50Al-Si)-10MoAl$_3$	2500	>100
Ta-10W	(Sn-25Al)-10TaAl$_3$	2800	3-15
Ta-10W	(Sn-25Al)-10MoAl$_3$	2800	21-51
Ta-10W	(Sn-50Al)-10TaAl$_3$	2800	6-7
Ta-30Cb-7.5V	(Sn-50Al-Si)-10TaAl$_3$	2800	7-31
Ta-30Cb-7.5V	(Sn-50Al-Si)-10MoAl$_3$	2800	24-40
Ta-10W	(Sn-25Al)-10TaAl$_3$	3000	3-10

(a) Tests conducted in still air in a furnace. Specimens generally cycled to room temperature ten times each 24 hours at and below 2500 F, and once each hour above 2500 F.

(b) Range of coating lives obtained with coatings of varying thickness in multiple tests.

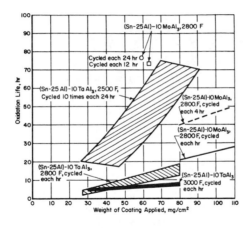

FIGURE 41. EFFECT OF COATING THICKNESS AND CYCLING ON LIFE OF
(Sn-25Al)-10TaAl₃ AND (Sn-25Al)-10MoAl₃ COATINGS ON
Ta-10W IN FURNACE OXIDATION TESTS[17]

25 mg/cm² = 2-mil coating; 90 mg/cm² = 5-mil coating.

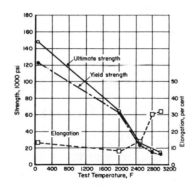

FIGURE 42. TENSILE PROPERTIES OF 40-MIL Ta-10W SHEET COATED WITH
(Sn-25Al)-10TaAl₃, TESTED IN AIR[17]

Alloy apparently was in wrought or stress-relieved condition prior
to coating.

187

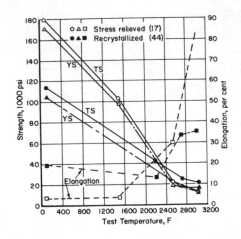

FIGURE 43. TENSILE PROPERTIES OF UNCOATED Ta-10W SHEET
            TESTED IN VACUUM

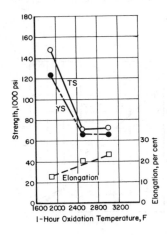

FIGURE 44. ROOM-TEMPERATURE TENSILE PROPERTIES OF Ta-10W SHEET
            COATED WITH (Sn-25Al)-10TaAl$_3$ AFTER OXIDATION FOR 1 HOUR
            AT VARIOUS TEMPERATURES

Alloy apparently was in the wrought or stress-relieved condition
prior to coating.

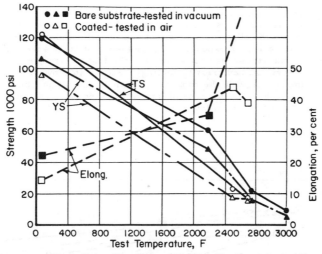

a. Tensile Properties of Bare (Recrystallized) and Coated Ta-
30 Cb – 7.5 V at Various Temperatures

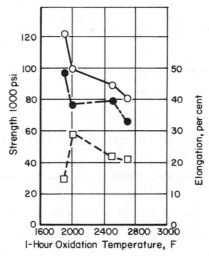

b. Room-Temperature Tensile Properties After Oxidation
for I Hr at Various Temperatures

FIGURE 45.   TENSILE BEHAVIOR OF (Sn-50Al-Si)-10TaAl₃-COATED
Ta-30Cb-7.5V SHEET[17,44]

substrate during the oxidation exposure. Obviously, these effects are not embrittling. Figure 45 shows tensile properties and thermal stability for the coated Ta-30Cb-7.5V alloy. Coating weakens the alloy to some extent and the diffusion-consumption-weakening effect of the oxidation exposure may be somewhat more severe than for the Ta-10W alloy (recrystallization was not a factor in the loss of strength of the Ta-30Cb-7.5V alloy; it was recrystallized prior to coating). Figure 46 shows that the Sn-Al coating does not significantly degrade the rupture strength of Ta-10W in times to 6 hours at 2800 F or 2 hours at 3000 F. Because of lack of baseline data, the situation is uncertain for the coated Ta-30Cb-7.5V alloy.

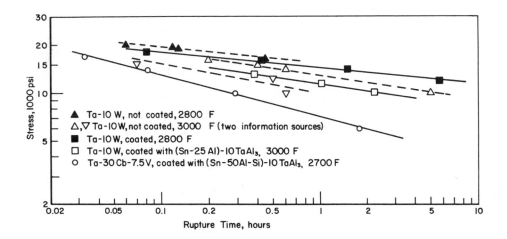

FIGURE 46. STRESS-RUPTURE CURVES FOR COATED AND UNCOATED Ta-10W AND Ta-30Cb-7.5V[17]

       Coated specimens tested in air. Uncoated specimens tested in vacuum.

       Results of cyclic and noncyclic plasma-arc oxidation tests conducted by the University of Dayton on 2 by 2-inch sheet specimens of Ta-10W protected by the Sn-50Al coating are given in Table 36. Specimens were heated in noncyclic tests for 5-minute intervals at progressively increasing temperatures. The cyclic tests consisted of heating specimens for 30 seconds and cooling in 10 seconds; specimens were cycled 15 times at each of several increasing temperatures. The maximum temperature at which the coating was protective was in excess of 3200 to 3300 F in the noncyclic tests, but was generally limited to about 2900 F in the cyclic tests. This difference may not be due to cycling alone, as prefailure chronotherms were different in the two tests.

	Noncyclic Tests at Progressively Increasing Temperatures		
	Maximum Surface Temperature, F	Time at Temperature, min	Remarks
Specimen 1	2070	5	
	2240	5	
	2530	5	
	2910	5	
	3230	5	Specimen warped, no failure
Specimen 3	2550	5	
	2910	5	
	3260	5	
	3340	5	No failure

Cyclic Tests[a]

	Maximum Surface Temperature, F	Number of Cycles	Remarks
Specimen 4	2730	15	
	2930	15	
	3150	4	Coating failed
Specimen 5	2740	15	
	2910	4	Coating failed
Specimen 6	2730	15	
	2910	11	Coating failed
Specimen 7	2730	15	
	2930	5	Coating failed
Specimen 8	2740	15	
	2910	8	Coating failed

(a) Specimens heated for 30 seconds and cooled for 10 seconds; 15 cycles at each test temperature.

Straight Silicide Coating on Ta-30Cb-7.5V Alloy[45]

An investigation of the performance of straight silicide coatings on tantalum alloys at Battelle has established that pack-siliconized Ta-30Cb-7.5V alloy exhibits good oxidation resistance and mechanical properties. The silicide coating is applied by pack cementation under argon in a pack consisting of 17 weight per cent silicon powder, 81 per cent particulate Al_2O_3, and 2 per cent NaF. Specimens are coated for 4 hours at 2200 F, repacked in fresh mix, and coated again for 12 hours at 2200 F. The resulting coatings are 4 mils thick. The principal coating layer is single phase in the as-coated condition and has the following composition based on electron-microprobe analysis:

	Atom Per Cent
Tantalum	12
Columbium	11
Vanadium	4
Silicon	73

This corresponds to a pseudo-compound having the composition $MSi_{2.8}$, where M represents the Ta-30Cb-7.5V substrate composition. Hence the tantalum, columbium, and vanadium occur in the coating in the same proportions as they do in the substrate. The coating system has been evaluated using 40-mil Ta-30Cb-7.5V alloy sheet stock.

The weight gain of the coating in cyclic oxidation tests is presented in Figure 47 and Tables 37 and 38. Whereas straight silicide coatings on unalloyed tantalum, Ta-10W, and Ta-8W-2Hf, suffered rapid oxidation (sometimes referred to as "pest") at 1800 F in a few hours, this vanadium-modified coating resisted the anomalous failure for 100 hours. The system does appear to be susceptible to early failure (50 hours) at 2000 F, however. The improved resistance of the coating to failure in the critical 1800 F temperature range is attributed to vanadium modification of the silicide coating. Oxidation weight gains were low at all temperatures except 1800 and 2000 F, but substrate protection was good for about 50 hours at either temperature. Coating life ranged from 2 to 12 hours at 2700 F, from 6 to greater than 17 hours at 2900 F, and 1 to 2 hours in oxyacetylene-torch tests at 3000 F. The coating was unable to self-heal at 20-mil holes that were drilled through the coating to expose the substrate.

Bend ductility of oxidized specimens was 0T at room temperature which is the same as that of the uncoated substrate (Table 37). Tensile properties of recrystallized 40-mil Ta-30Cb-7.5V sheet in the uncoated, coated, and coated plus exposed conditions are given in Table 39. Strength was based on the residual substrate cross-sectional area after coating. The tensile properties were not altered significantly by the coating at room temperature. The notched tensile data show that the coated substrate is not notch sensitive. At 2200 F, coated specimens were considerably stronger than uncoated specimens; this was interpreted as reflecting a strength contribution of the coating.

TRW Cr-Ti-Si Coating[46]

Thompson Ramo Wooldridge has applied its Cr-Ti-Si coating on tantalum using the process developed for columbium. The resulting coating protects the substrate from oxidation for 30 hours at 2700 to 2800 F.

R-506 Coating[17,47,48]

General Telephone & Electronics has applied its R-506 titanium-modified silicide coating to tantalum and columbium alloys. The coating process consists of titanizing by vacuum pack cementation at 2200 F followed by siliconizing with an atmospheric-pressure pack-cementation process. Table 40 shows that R-506 protects Ta-10W and Ta-30Cb-7.5V alloys from oxidation for several hours at 2800 F, and that it has long life at 1800 F where rapid oxidation normally occurs in unmodified silicide coatings on Ta-10W alloy.

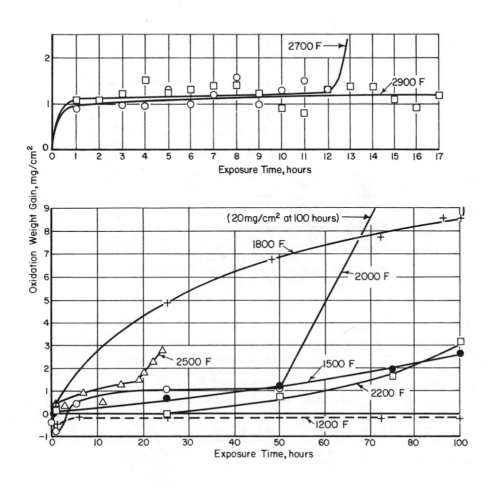

FIGURE 47. OXIDATION WEIGHT GAINS OF SILICIDE-COATED Ta-30Cb-7.5V ALLOY AT 1200 TO 2900 F DURING CYCLIC FURNACE TESTS[45]

TABLE 37. CYCLIC OXIDATION LIVES OF STRAIGHT SILICIDE-COATED
Ta-30Cb-7.5V ALLOY SPECIMENS IN FURNACE OXIDATION
TESTS[45](a)

Exposure Temperature, F	Oxidation Lives of Individual Specimens, hours		Room-Temperature Bend Properties of Substrate After Exposure
	Undefected	Defected[b]	
1200	>100, >100, >100	--	OT
1500	>100, >100, >100	--	OT
1800	>100, >100	<1, <1	OT[c]
2000	25-50, 50-75, 50-75	--	Embrittled
2200	>100, >100, >100	--	OT
2500	>24, >24, >24	--	OT
2700	2, 10, 12	<1, <1	--
2900	6, >17, >17	--	OT

(a) Specimens cycled to room temperature after 1, 25, 50, 75, and 100 hours at
temperatures up to 2200 F; after 1, 3, 7, 11, 15, 19, 20, 22, and 24 hours
at 2500 F; at 1-hour intervals at 2700 and 2900 F.
(b) 0.020-inch-diameter hole drilled through coating on one side of the sample.
(c) Defected specimens were embrittled.

TABLE 38. RESULTS OF CYCLIC OXYACETYLENE TORCH
OXIDATION TESTS OF SILICIDE COATING
ON Ta-30Cb-7.5V[a][45]

Test Temperature[b], F	Number of 1/2-Hour Cycles	Observation
3000	2	Failed at 3180 F
3000	4	Failed by cratering
2700	>10	Did not fail
2500	>10	Did not fail
1800	>10	Did not fail

(a) Samples were 0.040 by 0.5 by 2-inch flat sheet. Torch flame
was positioned normal to the sheet.
(b) Uncorrected, optically determined.

194

TABLE 39. TENSILE PROPERTIES OF SILICIDE-COATED Ta-30Cb-7.5V ALLOY 40 MILS THICK[45]

Specimen Geometry	Condition[a]	Test Temp, F	0.2% Offset Yield Strength, ksi[b]	Ultimate Tensile Strength, ksi[b]	Elongation in 1 Inch, per cent
Unnotched	Uncoated	RT	92.0	106.0	>20
Unnotched	Uncoated; 16 hours at 2200 F in vacuum (simulated coating treatment)	RT	83.6	100.3	26
Unnotched	Coated	RT	85.7	105.4	13
Unnotched	Coated and exposed 1 hour at 2700 F in air	RT	85.4	102.4	20
Unnotched	Coated and strained 1.5% in 1/4 hour at 2200 F in air	RT	87.6	104.6	27
Notched[c]	Uncoated; 16 hours at 2200 F in vacuum (simulated coating treatment)	RT	--	105.1	3-4
Notched[c]	Coated	RT	--	107.0	3-4
Notched[c]	Coated and exposed 1 hour at 2700 F in air	RT	--	102.6	3-4
Unnotched	Uncoated	2200	30.5	36.5	85
Unnotched	Uncoated; 16 hours at 2200 F in vacuum	2200	38.3	39.6	56
Unnotched	Coated[d]	2200	47.6	50.3	38

(a) All specimens recrystallized by annealing 1 hour at 2200 F in vacuum prior to the treatments listed.
(b) Strengths based on area of substrate core only; data were corrected for substrate consumed during coating formation.
(c) Center-hole notch with a calculated stress-concentration factor of 2.3.
(d) Single specimen, all other values are averages of two specimens.

TABLE 40. OXIDATION RESISTANCE OF R-506 COATING ON TANTALUM ALLOYS IN STATIC AIR[a] [17,47]

Substrate	Oxidation Temperature, F	Time to Coating Failure, hr
Ta-30Cb-7.5V	2800	1
Ditto	2800	5
"	2800	3
Ta-10W	2800	>8
Ta	2600	30
Ta-30Cb-7.5V	1800	213
Ta-10W	1800	221
Ta-30Cb-7.5V	1100	221
Ta-10W	1100	24

(a) Coatings were 1.2 to 3 mils thick.

COATINGS FOR TUNGSTEN

Thompson Ramo Wooldridge and General Telephone & Electronics are conducting the only Government-sponsored research programs on oxidation-resistant coatings for tungsten. These programs have established that the maximum protective temperature for silicide coatings is 3600 F; thus, higher temperature coatings will be required to fully realize tungsten's capabilities. Considerable effort has been expended to protect tungsten from oxidation at temperatures up to 5000 F with thick metal-reinforced layers, but this lies outside the scope of this report.

(Si-W) and Ti-Zr-(Si-W) Silicide Coatings[2]

Thompson Ramo Wooldridge is developing two silicide coatings for tungsten which are applied by vacuum pack cementation, as described below.

(Si-W) Coating

4 hours at 2000 F in pack consisting of 1 liter of silicon sponge, 10 grams tungsten powder, and 20 grams NaF.

Ti-Zr-(Si-W) Coating

(Cycle 1) Titanium deposited in 10 hours at 2000 F in pack containing titanium sponge and NaF.
(Cycle 2) Zirconium similarly deposited at 2000 F.
(Cycle 3) Same as the (Si-W) coating process described above.

The Ti-Zr coating layer is about 1 mil thick, and after siliconizing the coatings range in thickness from 3 to 5 mils. The coatings frequently receive an oxide conversion treatment in water-saturated hydrogen (72 F) for 2.5 hours at 2200 F to form a thin surface oxide, in which case the coating designations become (Si-W)-O or Ti-Zr-(Si-W)-O.

The coating procedure for the Ti-Zr-(Si-W) coating has not been optimized yet. The principal problem has been formation of an undersirable "crust layer" on the coating surface during the (Si-W) coating cycle which causes accelerated oxidation failure. The simple (Si-W) coating is relatively easy to apply, and conditions for applying it have been standardized.

The oxidation resistance of the two coatings in cyclic furnace tests is summarized in Table 41. Both systems exhibit accelerated coating oxidation at 1600 and 1800 F, forming a nonprotective, powdery, porous oxide. The oxidation mode appears to be similar to that described by Pranatis et al.[6] as occurring with straight WSi_2 coatings on tungsten at comparable temperatures. The popular term for this phenomenon is pest. Vitreous oxide forms at temperatures greater than 2500 F, and substantial protection is provided by the coatings at temperatures from 2500 to 3600 F. The coatings are not protective at 3650 F. Substrate delaminations are a common cause of premature coating failures at all temperatures. Chemical reaction with ceramic supports sometimes causes premature failures at temperatures above 3000 F. Generally, both coatings exhibit similar capabilities for oxidation protection.

TABLE 41. OXIDATION PERFORMANCE OF TRW SILICIDE COATINGS ON 60-MIL
TUNGSTEN SHEET IN CYCLIC FURNACE TESTS[a] [2]

Test Temperature, F	Coating	Time to Coating Failure, hr
1600	Si-W	1 hr max
	Ti-Zr-(Si-W)-O	3 hr max
1800	Si-W	10 - 50
	Ti-Zr-(Si-W)-O	1.5 - 25
2500	Si-W	30 - 50
	Ti-Zr-(Si-W)-O	3 - 40
3000	(Si-W)-O	10 - 47
	Ti-Zr-(Si-W)-O	20 - 72
3300	(Si-W)-O	8
3300	Ti-Zr-(Si-W)-O	4 - 25
3450	(Si-W)-O	1 - 8
	Ti-Zr-(Si-W)-O	1 - 17
3500	(Si-W)-O	3 - 7.5
	Ti-Zr-(Si-W)-O	2 - 5
3600	(Si-W)-O	1 hr max
	Ti-Zr-(Si-W)-O	1.5 hr max
3650	(Si-W)-O	A few minutes
	Ti-Zr-(Si-W)-O	A few minutes

(a) Oxidation tests were conducted in still air. Specimens generally cycled to room temperature once every 3 hours at and below 2500 F, and once each hour above 2500 F.

The performance of the coatings in thermal-shock and hot-gas-erosion tests is described in Table 42. Again the coatings appear to behave similarly.

Tensile properties of uncoated, coated, and coated-and-oxidized tungsten sheet specimens are presented in Figure 48. Uncoated material was tested in both wrought and recrystallized conditions. The thermal treatment associated with applying the Ti-Zr-(Si-W)-O coating recrystallized the substrate (except for a thin surface layer), but the (Si-W) coating treatment (no preoxidation treatment) did not result in recrystallization. In general, the yield and tensile strength values obtained reflected the residual cold work in the substrate; in general the coatings appeared to have only minor effects, except perhaps at room temperature where low fracture strengths suggest extreme embrittlement effects. Ductility was essentially nil at room temperature for uncoated and coated specimens, but it was about 10 per cent at 1000 F and it increased further at temperatures above 2000 F.

In conclusion, the tests conducted to date have not indicated which of the two coating systems is better.

197

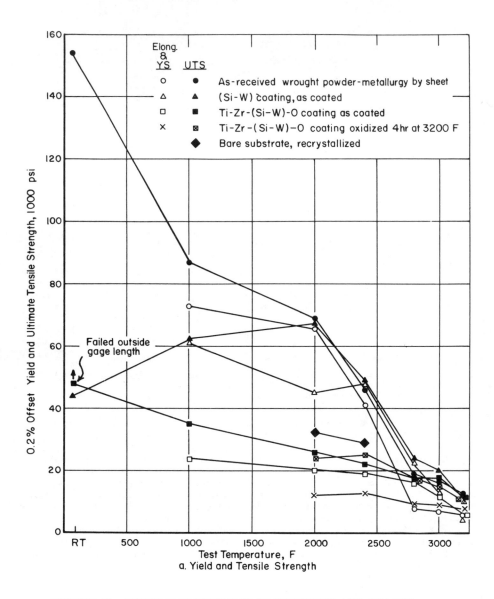

FIGURE 48. TENSILE PROPERTIES OF UNCOATED AND COATED
60-MIL TUNGSTEN SHEET TESTED IN INERT
ATMOSPHERE[2]

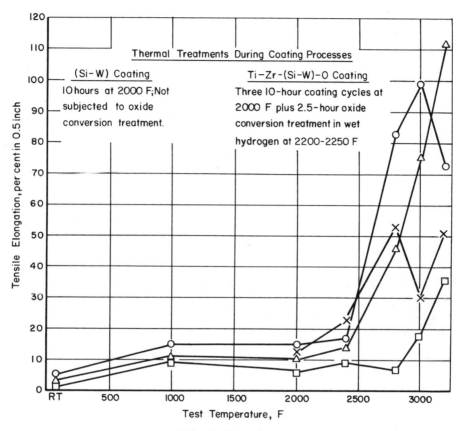

b. Tensile Elongation

FIGURE 48. (CONTINUED)

TABLE 42. PERFORMANCE OF (Si-W)-O AND Ti-Zr-(Si-W)-O COATINGS[a] ON 60-MIL TUNGSTEN SHEET IN THERMAL-SHOCK AND HOT-GAS-EROSION TESTS[2]

Thermal-Shock Tests[b]

Test Temperature, F	Prior Oxidation Exposure	Coating	Number of Cycles to Coating Failure
2000	--	(Si-W)-O	1000
2000	--	Ti-Zr-(Si-W)-O	1000
2500	--	(Si-W)-O	372
2500	--	Ti-Zr-(Si-W)-O	465
2800	--	(Si-W)-O	250
2800	--	Ti-Zr-(Si-W)-O	310
3000	--	(Si-W)-O	365
3000	--	Ti-Zr-(Si-W)-O	241
3000	0.5 hr at 3000 F	(Si-W)-O	>100
3000	0.5 hr at 3300 F	(Si-W)-O	>100
3000	1 hr at 3000 F	Ti-Zr-(Si-W)-O	>50
3200	--	(Si-W)-O	200
3200	--	Ti-Zr-(Si-W)-O	211

Hot-Gas Erosion Tests[c]

Test Temperature, F	Coating	Time to Failure, hr
3200	(Si-W)-O	2
3200	Ti-Zr-(Si-W)-O	2
3400	(Si-W)-O	1.7
3400	Ti-Zr-(Si-W)-O	2

(a) Test specimens were 1-inch-wide by 2-inch-long pieces of 60-mil tungsten sheet, curved to a 3/16-inch radius.

(b) Thermal-shock test procedure: Specimens heated on the front side to the test temperature with an oxyacetylene torch in 20 seconds and then cooled to 25° F with an air blast in 10 seconds.

(c) Procedure for hot-gas erosion test: Specimens exposed to effluent of a plasma-arc torch having an exit-gas velocity of 2000 ft/sec and a composition of 20 per cent oxygen and 80 per cent nitrogen.

R-507A Coating[48]

General Telephone & Electronics has a coating for tungsten, designated R-507A, which is applied by pack-cementation siliconizing followed by a proprietary coating process. The coating subsequently is heated in air at an elevated temperature to serve as a combined diffusion and preoxidation treatment. Coating lives of 18 to 40 hours have been obtained when the maximum temperature of resistance-heated rod specimens was 3450 F. Failures occurred by pest, however, in the zone that was between 2200 and 2500 F. The coating was protective for 4 to 8 hours at 3450 F in an oxyacetylene-torch test.

DISCUSSION

Evaluation of the performance data that are available for coating systems to define the relative merits of various coatings still is quite difficult, although the situation has improved within the past 2 or 3 years. Several problems complicate proper interpretation of the available data. Test procedures used by various investigators frequently are different; the appropriate direction should be toward standarized tests. To this end, the Materials Advisory Board has published a report describing standard tests that it advocates[49]. Most technologists want to be able to compare the mechanical properties of coated substrate with those of uncoated substrate. Ideally the bare substrate should be exposed to the "coating thermal treatment" and then tested under the same conditions as coated specimens, so the effect of the coating can be isolated. Frequently the thermal history of the substrate prior to coating (i.e., stress-relieved wrought structure or recrystallized) or the coating thermal treatment is not given in test data. If not specified, it generally has been assumed in this report that as-received material was in the stress-relieved condition. Thermal history of test specimens is important, because coating and subsequent oxidation treatments frequently transcend the recrystallization temperature. For instance, a comparison of the tensile strength of stress-relieved bare substrate with recrystallized coated substrate would be nebulous. Frequently it is not specified how the cross-sectional area of coated specimens is obtained for calculating strength. The most common method is to use the dimensions of a sheet tensile specimen prior to coating. It has been assumed, unless specified otherwise, that this method was used for calculating the strength data in this report. Another method is to measure the residual substrate thickness metallographically and use it to calculate strength. The first method usually results in "apparent" strength values for coated substrate which are below those for uncoated substrate. The "change in strength" values calcalated by the two methods diverge as sheet thickness decreases. Sheet thickness is decreased by up to 1 mil per side by diffusion formation of coatings, so the residual substrate thickness is as much as 2 mils less than the uncoated substrate. The 2-mil thickness reduction would amount to a 5 and 20 per cent reduction in cross-sectional area, respectively, for 40- and 10-mil sheet. Of course there could be some concurrent diffusion strengthening of the substrate by the coating elements.

Performance of a particular coating can be good or poor depending on test conditions, making it uncertain in some instances whether the coating is hypersensitive to test procedures or reproducibility of the coating is poor. Many coatings are standardized, but variations in thickness, intentional or unintentional, and other variables, frequently becloud analysis of data.

Occasionally some of the coatings described in this report have demonstrated different oxidation resistance on different alloys, even though the alloy base was the same (e.g., columbium-base alloys, tantalum-base alloys). The finding by Battelle that the substrate elements occur in silicide coatings on tantalum-base alloys in approximately the ratio of their occurrence in the substrate offers an explanation. Oxidation behavior is sensitive to the composition of a coating. Hence a given coating might provide different oxidation resistance on two different alloys because of the existence of the substrate alloying elements in the coating. Several examples are contained in this report that show the desirable influence of titanium in the columbium-base substrate on performance of the coating. The radically different performance of the Vought coating on D14 and FS85 columbium alloys also suggests an important effect of substrate.

Generally it is the ductility of a substrate rather than strength that is degraded most by coatings. This can be described as a manifestation of an increase in the ductile-to-brittle transition temperature by the coating and/or the coating thermal cycle. The question arises as to whether the tensile or bend test is the best method for ascertaining the ductility of coated material. In the work at Solar on testing coated foil, several coatings resulted in nil tensile ductility of the substrate but did not cause specimens to fracture in a 4T bend test (which requires a nominal <u>outer</u> fiber elongation of 10 per cent). Part of the difficulty with bend tests undoubtedly is in differentiating a coating crack from a substrate surface crack, the later signaling specimen failure according to MAB test procedures established for uncoated refractory metals[22]. In view of the apparent hypersensitivity of the tensile test for detecting substrate embrittlement by a coating, and the more quantitative nature of the test data obtained, it appears that the tensile test is superior for detecting embrittlement. In addition the yield and tensile strength data obtained conjunctively in the test are of paramount importance in any coating-evaluation program.

In conclusion, despite difficulties in the analysis of data, information generated within the past 2 years describes, to a considerable extent, the relative behavior of various coatings for columbium and molybdenum and their alloys. Some of the more recent evaluation programs have been able to utilize the growing wealth of data to minimize the selection of coating-substrate systems for more detailed evaluation. It is anticipated that current and future programs will continue to define the behavior of coated systems to further simplify the task of selecting the best coating for a given application.

REFERENCES

(1)   Gadd, J. D., and Jefferys, R. A., "Advancement of High-Temperature Protective Coatings for Columbium Alloys", ASD Technical Documentary Report 62-934, Thompson Ramo Wooldridge, Inc. (November, 1962).

(2)   Thompson Ramo Wooldridge, Inc., preliminary information under an Air Force Contract.

(3)   Thompson Ramo Wooldridge, Inc., preliminary information under a Navy contract.

(4)   University of Dayton Research Institute, preliminary information under an Air Force contract.

(5)   Kushner, M., "Coated Refractory Alloys for the X-20 Vehicle", The Boeing Company (June, 1963).

(6)   Klopp, W. D., "Summary of the Fifth Meeting of the Refractory Composites Working Group", DMIC Report 167 (March, 1962).

(7)   Private communication from M. Kushner, The Boeing Company, to W. A. Gibeaut (June 21, 1963).

(8)   Aves, W. L., Bourland, G. W., Featherston, A. B., Forcht, B. A., and O'Kelley, K. P., "Diffusion Coating Process for Columbium-Base Alloys", ASD Technical Documentary Report 62-333, Chance Vought Corporation (February, 1962).

(9)   Alvares, N. J., "Emittance Measurements of Disilicide-Type Coatings at the U. S. Naval Radiological Defense Laboratory", paper presented at the Seventh Meeting of the Refractory Composites Working Group (March, 1963).

(10)   Gibeaut, W. A., and Maykuth, D. J., "Summary of the Sixth Meeting of the Refractory Composites Working Group", DMIC Report 175 (September, 1962).

(11)   Grimm, T. C., "Evaluation of Pfaudler Coating for Oxidation Protection of Columbium Alloys", Report 8886, McDonnell Aircraft Corporation (August, 1961).

(12)   Culp, J. D., "Refractory Metal Coating Systems Utilized on a Typical Hypersonic Glide Re-Entry Vehicle", McDonnell Aircraft Corporation, paper presented at the Seventh Meeting of the Refractory Composites Working Group (March, 1963).

(13)   Krier, C. A., "Coatings for the Protection of Refractory Metals from Oxidation", DMIC Report 162 (November, 1961).

(14)   Private communication from J. D. Culp, McDonnell Aircraft Corporation to W. A. Gibeaut (July 17, 1963).

(15)   O'Connor, J. P., "Effects on the Mechanical Properties of LB-2-Coated Columbium-5% Zirconium Alloy", Report 9340, McDonnell Aircraft Corporation (January, 1963).

(16)   Weissman, N., "Investigation of Refractory Composite Materials at North American Aviation, Inc., NAA Report NA-62-606, paper presented at the Sixth Meeting of the Refractory Composites Working Group (June, 1962).

(17)   Sama, L., "High-Temperature Oxidation-Resistant Coatings for Tantalum-Base Alloys, ASD Technical Documentary Report 63-160, General Telephone and Electronics (February, 1963).

(18)   "Information on Properties of NAA-85 Coating System", North American Aviation, Inc., Report TFD-63-522 (June, 1963).

(19)   "Development of Extreme Elevated Temperature Test Methods", North American Aviation, Inc., Report TFD-61-1196 (December, 1961).

(20)   Jefferys, R. A., and Gadd, J. D., "Development and Evaluation of High-Temperature Protective Coatings for Columbium Alloys—Part II, Coating Evaluation", ASD Technical Report 61-66, Thompson Ramo Wooldridge, Inc. (September, 1961).

(21)   Gadd, J. D., and Jefferys, R. A., "Design Data Study for Coated Columbium Alloys", Final Summary Technical Report ER 5185 to Bureau of Naval Weapons, Thompson Ramo Wooldridge, Inc., (January, 1963).

(22)   "Evaluation Test Methods for Refractory Metal Sheet Material", Report MAB-192-M, National Academy of Sciences, National Research Council (April, 1963).

(23)   Solar, preliminary information under an Air Force contract.

(24)   Gibeaut, W. A., and Ogden, H. R., "Summary of the Seventh Meeting of the Refractory Composites Working Group", DMIC Report 184 (May, 1963).

(25)   Epner, M., "Activities of Chromalloy Division in the Development of Coatings for Refractory Metals", notes prepared for the Seventh Meeting of the Refractory Composites Working Group (March, 1963).

(26)   Private communication from J. D. Culp, McDonnell Aircraft Corporation to W. A. Gibeaut (July 10, 1963).

(27)   Wachtell, R. L., and Seelig, R. P., "Diffusion Coating of Nonferrous Metals", U. S. Patent 3,037,883, Assignors to Chromalloy Corporation (June 5, 1962).

(28)   "'Chromalloy W-2' The Investigation of a Protective Coating on Molybdenum", A. R. D. E. Memorandum (MX) 23/61, Armament Research and Development Establishment, Fort Halstead, Kent, England (May, 1961).

(29)   Christensen, R. H., and Denke, P. H., "Crack Strength and Crack Propagation Characteristics of High-Strength Metals", ASD Technical Report 61-207, Douglas Aircraft Company, Inc. (May, 1961).

(30)   Pfaudler Company, preliminary information under an Air Force contract.

(31) Ortner, M. H., "Development of Protective Coatings for Refractory Alloys", paper presented at the Seventh Meeting of the Refractory Composites Working Group (March, 1963).

(32) Rummler, D. R., Stein, B. A., and Pride, R. A., "Preliminary Results of a Comparative Study of Several Commercially Available Oxidation Resistant Coatings on Mo-0.5Ti Sheet", paper presented at the Sixth Meeting of the Refractory Composites Working Group (June, 1962).

(33 Stein, B. A., and Lisagor, W. B., "Preliminary Results of Diffusion Studies of Commercially Available Coatings on Mo-0.5Ti Molybdenum Alloy Sheet at 2500 F", paper presented at the Seventh Meeting of the Refractory Composites Working Group (March, 1963).

(34) Price, W. L., and Perkins, R. A., "High Temperature Oxidation Resistant Systems, Section 1, Behavior of Silicide Coatings in High Temperature Low Pressure Environment", paper presented at the Seventh Meeting of the Refractory Composites Working Group (March, 1963).

(35) Smith, H. E., and Wurst, J. C., "The Evaluation of High Temperature Materials Systems with an Arc-Plasma-Jet", ASD Technical Documentary Report 62-655, University of Dayton Research Institute (July, 1962).

(36) Peters, R. W., and Rasnick, T. A., "Investigation of Oxidation-Resistant Coatings on Graphite and Molybdenum in Two Arc-Powered Facilities", NASA Technical Note D-838 (July, 1961).

(37) King, E. J., and Anthony, F. M., "Experimental Evaluation of Coated Molybdenum Riveted Joints", paper presented at the Sixth Meeting of the Refractory Composites Working Group (June, 1962).

(38) Anthony, F. M., "Activities of Bell Aerosystems Company with Refractory Materials", paper presented at the Seventh Meeting of the Refractory Composites Working Group (March, 1963).

(39) Republic Aviation Corporation, preliminary information under an Air Force contract.

(40) Alvares, W. J., "Emittance Measurements at the U. S. Naval Radiological Defense Laboratory", paper presented at the Sixth Meeting of the Refractory Composites Working Group (June, 1962).

(41) Chao, P. J., Dormer, G. J., Payne, Jr., B. S., Priest, D. K., and Zupan, J., "Research in Protective Coatings for Refractory Metals", paper presented at the Sixth Meeting of the Refractory Composites Working Group (June, 1962).

(42) Browning, M. E., Schatz, E. A., and Leavenworth, H. W., "Recent Activities in High Temperature Coating and Material Programs at AMF", paper presented at the Sixth Meeting of the Refractory Composites Working Group (June, 1962).

(43)   Browning, M. E., Schatz, E. A., McCandless, L. C., and Pearson, E. G.,
         Supplemental Information on High Temperature Coating and Material Programs
         at AMF, paper supplementing the report to the Seventh Refractory Composites
         Working Group Meeting, AMF Report AR-63-502A (May, 1963).

(44)   Schmidt, F. F., Imgram, A. G., Klopp, W. D., Bartlett, E. S., and Ogden,
         H. R., "Investigation of Tantalum and Its Alloys", ASD Technical Documentary
         Report 62-594 Battelle Memorial Institute (July, 1962).

(45)   Hallowell, J. B., Maykuth, D. J., and Ogden, H. R., "Coatings for Tantalum-
         Base Alloys", ASD Technical Documentary Report 63-232, Battelle Memorial
         Institude (April, 1963).

(46)   Metalworking News (April 22, 1963).

(47)   "High Temperature Protective Coatings", Brochure distributed by General
         Telephone and Electronics.

(48)   Private communication from L. Sama, General Telephone and Electronics, to
         W. A. Gibeaut (June 4, 1963).

(49)   "Evaluation Procedures for Screening Coated Refractory Metal Sheet", Report
         MAB-189-M, National Academy of Sciences, National Research Council
         (February, 1963).

PART 3

Coatings on Refractory Metals

D. H. Leeds

I. THE PROBLEM AREA

The term "refractory metals" is used generally to include those metals which melt above the melting point of chromium - $3405^\circ F$ or $1875^\circ C$, the most refractory being tungsten (see Ref. 1 and Table 1). The rare and noble refractory metals are normally not used in structural applications because of limited availability leaving, unfortunately, the least oxidation resistant metals of the family for high temperature structural applications (see Fig. 1). As we become increasingly aware of the aerothermodynamic impositions on a vehicle attempting to leave or reenter the air atmosphere, we can vividly see why the designer is seeking new structural materials.

Reentry vehicles are divided into three major classifications based on velocity at the start of reentry: suborbital (18,000 to 24,000 ft/sec); orbital (24,000 to 26,000 ft/sec); and superorbital (above 26,000 ft/sec) (see Figs. 2 and 3). The ballistic missile nose cone is a familiar example of a suborbital vehicle. Peak heating rates ($\dot{q}$ = 1200 to 3000 BTU/ft^2-sec) are the highest for any class of vehicles, but the duration of the heat pulse is short. Ablative and heat sink materials are used in these structures and, consequently, do not necessitate the use of refractory metals. The copper nose cap of the Thor vehicles is an example here. Orbital vehicles, such as those currently designed for manned and unmanned reentry capsules such as the Mercury capsule and boost-glide vehicles, sustain the lowest flux ($\dot{q}$ = 200 to 500 BTU/ft^2-sec) but over a much longer duration. The total heat input is similar to that for ballistic reentry and is dependent upon the range. Radiation cooling can be used effectively for the thermal protection of leading edges and adjacent structures. These structures represent a major area of use for refractory metals and are a prime impetus for coating development. Superorbital vehicles which reenter the atmosphere on return from lunar or space missions present the most critical materials problem. Instantaneous heat fluxes on leading edges approach those for ballistic reentry ($\dot{q}$ = 200 to 1100 BTU/ft^2-sec) and must be sustained for long periods of time. The total heat input (Q = 50,000 to 300,000 BTU/ft^2) is the highest for any class of reentry vehicle. A combination of absorptive and radiative thermal protection systems is required.

Various possibilities exist for the design and construction of leading edges and adjacent structures. The lightest design is provided by an uninsulated radiation-cooled structure. Such structures are limited to relatively low heat fluxes ($\dot{q}$ = < 210 BTU/ft^2-sec) by the melting point of refractory metal components. It should be emphasized that higher heat fluxes can be sustained for short pulse heating cycles. At a sustained heat flux of approximately 200 BTU/ft^2-sec, maximum substrate temperatures approach 3000° to $5000^\circ F$ (see Fig. 4 and Table 2) which result in the need for the use of refractory metals in heat shields and structures (see Fig. 5 and Ref. 2).

Table 1. Properties of Refractory Metals.

Metals	Melting Point C	F	Boiling Point C	F	Crystal Structure[a]	Density, g/Cm^3	Thermal Conductivity, cal/(Cm^2) (Cm)(C)(sec)	Electrical Resistivity, microhm-cm At 20 C	Heat Capacity, cal/(g)(C) At 20 C	Coefficient of Linear Expansion, 10^{-6} per C near 20 C
Tungsten	3410	6170	6700	12000	Bcc	19.3	0.48	5.5	0.032	4.5
Rhenium	3180	5755	5630	10100	Hcp	21.0	0.17	19.3	0.033	6.7
Osmium	3000	5430	5500	9900	Hcp	22.5	--	9.5	0.031	6.6
Tantalum	2996	5425	6100	11000	Bcc	16.6	0.13	13.5	0.033	6.6
Molybdenum	2610	4730	4800	8600	Bcc	10.2	0.35	5.21	0.061	5.4
Iridium	2442	4428	5300	9500	Fcc	22.4	0.35	5.3	0.032	6.5
Columbium	2415	4380	3300	5900	Bcc	8.56	0.125	14.8	0.065	7.1
Ruthenium	2250	4080	4900	8800	Hcp	12.2	--	9.5	0.058	9.6
Hafnium	1975	3585	5400	9700	Hcp[b]	13.36	0.053	30.0	0.035	6.0
Rhodium	1960	3560	4500	8100	Fcc	12.4	0.36	4.7	0.059	8.5
Vanadium	1900	3450	3350	6060	Bcc	6.11	0.074	24.8	0.119	9.7
Chromium	1875	3405	2469	4476	Bcc	7.20	0.16	12.8	0.107	6.2

(a) Bcc designates body-centered cubic. Hcp designates hexagonal close packed. Fcc designates face-centered cubic.
(b) Hcp lattice transforms to bcc at 1310 C.

R. I. Jaffee, "A Brief Review of Refractory Metals," DMIC Memorandum 40 (3 December 1959).

The requirements of these refractory metals for oxidation protection in these temperature regions in flowing air are depicted in oxidation tests on unprotected refractory metals (Figs. 6 to 9). Figures 10 through 14 are examples of the complexity of the oxidation. Figures 10 and 11 illustrate the complexity of the oxidation kinetic mechanism in the variable of temperature. Figures 12, 13, and 14 emphasize aspects of this complexity by showing reactive non-uniformities in the oxidation of various alloys of the same metal (another variable) as the temperature environment variable changes. The latter set of figures demonstrates the need for parallel development of coatings in pace with alloy research because as the substrate metals are variantly alloyed, the coating requirements, quite aside from inter-reaction difficulties, can be changed drastically. Such a change in protective requirements can be seen in protective lifetime changes at constant temperature (Figs. 15a and 15b).

Just as the coating is influenced by the substrate, conversely, the properties of the substrate are influenced by the presence of the coating. Figure 16 illustrates residual stresses established in a **columbium** substrate by a flame-sprayed coating. Figure 17 illustrates the **stress rupture** properties of plasma-coated and uncoated columbium at 2000°F. Figures 18a and 18b illustrate the cold ductility variance of molybdenum which is (a) uncoated, (b) flame-spray coated, and (c) coated and **exposed** to oxidation. Figure 19 illustrates the results of a series of **room temperature** tensile tests on 0.5 Ti-molybdenum in both silicide-coated and uncoated condition.

Table 2. Approximate Environmental Conditions for Various Applications of High Temperature Coatings.

Variable*	Applications			
	Ballistic nose cone	Leading edge	Ramjet	Domes
Time (min.)	0.5–2	30–120	1–240	30–120
Surface temp. (°F.)	2500 to ablating	2500–5000	2500 to ablating	2500 to ablating
Max. particle velocity (ft./sec.)	2500	2200	1000	2500
Gas enthalpy (B.t.u./lb.)	6000–9000	7000–10,000	500–2000	6000–10,000
Heat flux (B.t.u./ft.²-sec.)	200–4000	10–300	3–100	10–500
Gas composition	Air (dissoc.)	Air (dissoc.)	Combustion Atmosphere	Air (dissoc.)
Mass flow (lb./ft.²-sec.)	1000	1000	10–150	1000
Temperature programming (sec.)†	0.1–0.5	600–6000	15–30	0.1–60
Pressure programming‡	10^{-3} to 29.9 in. Hg	10^{-3} to 29.9 in. Hg	1 to 3 atm. in 15 sec.	10^{-3} to 29.9 in. Hg
Cyclical operation	No	Yes	Yes	Yes
Specimen configuration	Cones Plates	Cylinders Cones Plates	Cones Plates	Cones Plates

* Numbers are only approximate and represent no actual present or future application exactly.
† Time to reach maximum temperature.
‡ Range of pressure which can possibly be achieved in a realistic experiment and not actually encountered.

J. D. Walton, Jr., "Present and Future Problem Areas for High Temperature Inorganic Coatings," Ceramic Bulletin, 40 (3), 136-141 (1961).

II. THE SEARCH FOR A SOLUTION

A. FABRICATION AND STRUCTURE

As the four main refractory metals (tungsten, tantalum, molybdenum, and columbium) became increasingly available in the late 1950's, their potential as structural materials was realized. Molybdenum, a metal used for high speed turbine buckets, has been given much study in the quest for extension of its oxidation lifetime. Around 1900 when the availability of molybdenum was limited, the electrical equipment manufacturers had become refractory metal protection pioneers in their efforts to find protection for tungsten and molybdenum. The current light bulb incorporates one solution to their problems, i.e., the use of vacuum and glass as barriers to oxygen. Later work of Bergeron, et al. (Ref. 3) at the University of Illinois, reported in January 1960, indicated that a directly applied glassy matrix phase coating containing zircon also was capable of protecting tungsten from oxidation. The protection afforded was 3-1/2 hours at 3600°F during which a coated wire was resistance-heated. The use of another type of refractory glass was successful for 1-1/4 hours at 3600°F; this type was formed by oxidation in service after application of a vapor deposited coating of silicon metal on tungsten. The main limitation was that when testing the silicide coatings all the failures occurred in those portions of the specimen which were at a temperature of 2500°F, rather than in the hot zone which reached temperatures in excess of 3600°F (see Fig. 20).

These low temperature failures, or "pest" failures (see Fig. 21) as they were called, were believed to be caused by the inability of the glass to mature at these temperatures, which resulted in its failure to block passage of the oxygen (see Fig. 22). Unfortunately, combinations of the siliconized coatings and vitreous-bonded coatings failed at the University of Illinois because of a reaction between the two which resulted in a decrease in oxidation protection. In subsequent years researchers found benefits by varying the coating fabrication to include other metals such as chromium, boron, titanium and aluminum in the siliconizing operation. The silicon was added by some researchers as a silicide such as molybdenum and tungsten silicides, and the coating was given a preoxidation treatment to develop the protective glass first. Although the technology has undoubtedly advanced in fabrication processes since 1959, no investigator since Bergeron has reported much greater protection for tungsten.

For high temperature protection the flame/plasma spray gun has shown mild promise in its application of a diffusion barrier coating required for refractory metal protection over 3000°F for extended periods (of more than an hour). This application method, however, has a serious limitation. Many parts, designed with undercuts, deep blind holes, keyways, and small internal diameters, are not suited to the plasma spraying technique. A variety of sprayed coatings, however, did offer satisfactory protection at $3000^{\circ}F$ when they were tested cyclically in moving air. Doane tested $2000^{\circ}F$ hydrogen or argon diffused sprayed metal coatings of 20 Al-80 Cr-Si alloy, Colomonoy No. 5 (Ni-Cr-B alloy), Coast Metals 50 Alloy (Ni-Si-B alloy), Al-Ni-Si and composites on 0.5 Ti-molybdenum specimens (see Ref. 4). Reproducible protection of greater than four hours was available for the 20 Al-80 Cr-Si Alloy coatings to between $2600-2800^{\circ}F$. Two samples, which had been subjected to $200^{\circ}F$ increments from $1800^{\circ}F$ withstood four hours at $3000^{\circ}F$ (see Fig. 23). The Ni-Cr-B (see Figs. 24 and 25) and Ni-Si-B samples withstood slightly greater than four hours at $2200^{\circ}F$ reliably. In 1960, Wlodek reported 100-hour cycled protection in moving air to $2700^{\circ}F$ for columbium when a coating of Linde LM-5 (Mo-Si-Cr-B-Al) was flame plated onto an intermediate layer of columbium alloy of Cb-Ti-Cr-Al-Ni (see Ref. 5). In 1962, G. D. Smith reported disagreement with Wlodek's 100-hour protection to $2700^{\circ}F$ for LM-5 (he found it less protective - see Ref. 6). He also demonstrated metallographi- cally the benefit of modifying $MoSi_2$ with additives for use as a plasma sprayed coating for unalloyed columbium (see Figs. 26 and 27). The benefit of the additive was revealed by improved densification in the subsequent diffusion heat treatment. In general, diffusion heat treating is a necessity after flame/plasma spraying. As sprayed, the coatings are usually porous - a factor which works in their favor for thermal insulation, but not for oxidation protection. The requirement for the diffusion heat treat- ment in an oxygen free environment (usually argon or hydrogen) after flame spraying was provocative in establishing the trend for a single operation coating technique which matured into the reaction vessel approach. Prominent in this category is the pack cementation process.

In pack cementation the substrate is placed inside a retort (refractory lidded container) together with a surrounding mixture of reactants or pack. The sagger is then sealed and brought to reaction temperature in a kiln.

The pack, or mixed powder materials, specifically can contain granular alumina, metals such as silicon and a halide such as ammonium chloride or solid iodine. The halide addition enables the reaction to occur at a much lower temperature. The reactions in such a pack are as follows:

$$2NH_4Cl \rightarrow N_2 + 4H_2 + Cl_2$$

$$Si + 2Cl_2 \rightarrow SiCl_4$$

$$\text{or} \quad Si + Cl_2 \rightarrow SiCl_2$$

$$Mo + 2SiCl_4 \rightarrow MoSi_2 + 4Cl_2$$

$$\text{or} \quad Mo + 2SiCl_2 \rightarrow MoSi_2 + 2Cl_2$$

The silicon is not deposited by direct contact metallic diffusion but rather it is carried by the halide. The retort must be kept at a specific, carefully controlled temperature (between 850° and 1450°C) for a definite period of time (between 10 and 24 hours) until the diffusion limited coating process has reached a desired thickness (between 0.5 - 5.0 mils) (see Figs. 28-30 and Table 3). The purity of the reactants is sensitive with respect to the vapor pressure of the pack. The water vapor content of the pack is critical as is the oxygen/moisture content of the substrate because the bleeding out or pressurized entrapment in these gases "poisons" the reactions and undermines the coating.

Difficulties arise during the process due to the embrittlement of the metals by hydrogen and nitrogen occlusion in the coating and absorption by the substrate. Hydrogen is always present in the retort atmosphere to maintain reduction conditions. Nitrogen and hydrogen appear in the retort from the ammonium chloride, but attempts to overcome the embrittlement such as operating at higher temperatures (since the occlusion in the substrate is exothermic) have met with recrystallization problems. Removal of hydrogen by post-heat-treatment under vacuum requires not only high temperatures (which cause recrystallization) but also is dependent on the permeability of the coatings to hydrogen.

One of the biggest problems in the pack cementation process is caused by the presence of alloying elements in the refractory metal. During the diffusion intermetallic compounds are formed which often are incompatible with the diffusion coating. The presence of zirconium and titanium in a substrate reduces the diffusion rate of certain elements, e.g., see Fig. 31. These intermetallics are always possible centers for premature coating failure from the standpoint of both chemical (reaction) and thermal (varied expansion rate) compatability and, thereby, they lower the reliability of the system. Again, it is emphasized that coating research should be paced with refractory metal substrate investigations. To design a system whereby a new columbium alloy uses a protective coating which has been successful with other columbium alloys is to invite trouble. In conclusion, pack cementation coatings generally have offered the highest-temperature, longest-time oxidation protection for all refractory metals to date (see Figs. 32 and 33).

Modification of the pack cementation retort in 1962 to develop two phase coatings and scale up the process to accommodate large hardware led to the fluidized bed reactor. Briefly defined, the fluidized bed retort is a pack cementation retort which has been adapted for external (to the kiln) introduction and/or deletion of gaseous material, i.e., the retort is no longer inviolate and reacting gases may be introduced or replaced at will. The retort contains a loose inert material which breaks up the air space and offers catalytic adsorptive surfaces that may or may not be in contact with the substrate to be coated. The reacting material may be packed into the bed (fluid or movable to aid in coating) or externally introduced as a gas at reaction temperature. It is hoped that external introduction at reaction temperature will decrease the embrittlement problems. It is also hoped that a more uniform coating through vapor

214

Table 3. The Thickness of Commercial Pack Cementation Coatings for 0.5 Ti Molybdenum.

Supplier	Designation	Avg. Coating[a] Thickness (in.)	Substrate Thickness (in.) [a]		Wt. Change (percent)
			Before Coating	After Coating	
American Machine and Foundry	AMF (Glassed)[b]	0.0017	0.0122	0.0092	2.20
American Machine and Foundry	AMF (Not Glassed)	0.0017	0.0122	0.0099	2.20
Boeing	Disil	0.0015	0.0108	0.0081	-3.81
Chance Vought	C-V	0.0014	0.0120	0.0106	3.43
Chromalloy	W-2	0.0012	0.0121	0.0109	4.40
Pfaudler	PFR-5	0.0023	0.0118	0.0091	13.67
Pfaudler	PFR-6	0.0019	0.0116	0.0097	7.92

NOTE: (a) Based on cross section of tumbled specimen

(b) Preglassed 1 hour at 2800°F by AMF

D.R. Rummler, et al., "Preliminary Results of a Comparative Study of Several Commercially Available Oxidation Resistant Coatings on Mo-0.5 Ti Alloy Sheet," NASA/Langley. Presented to the Sixth Refractory Composite Working Group Meeting, Dayton, Ohio (16-19 June 1962).

deposit-scrubbing will be accomplished by the process (which appears more suitable for coating larger parts). Figures 34 and 35 show, respectively, a schematic of a fluidized bed reactor, and a 0.5 Ti-molybdenum sample coated therein.

Limited success has been accomplished by coating refractory metals by hot dipping in molten aluminum, zinc, and tin (see Figs. 36 and 37), by electroplating with noble metals, nickel, chromium, iron, and silver, by electrodepositing hard metals from solution (see Fig. 38), by covering the substrate with tack-welded refractory metal strips and trowelling on a phosphate bonded refractory system, by organic lacquer suspension spraying of a mixture of powdered metals, by enameling electrophoretic depositions, by fused salt electroplating, by plasma/flame spraying refractory compatible oxides onto an intermediate sprayed expansion and barrier layer and by disproportionation of subvalent metal chlorides on an active surface immersed in a fused salt solution. In the past, tens of millions of dollars have been spent on this problem to gradually push oxidation resistance from $1800^\circ F$ to $2200^\circ F$, to $2400^\circ F$, to $2600^\circ F$, to $3000^\circ F$, to $3400^\circ F$, and finally to its present $3600^\circ F$ mark. At each increment the problems were new and different ones, hence the research continues toward $5000^\circ F$.

Before leaving the discussion of fabrication techniques for these coating systems, it may be well to mention a brand new deposition method on which the author has done some basic developmental graduate work at the University of Southern California. Actually, an attempt has been made to adapt a process to refractory metals i.e., salt glazing, which has been practiced since advanced development in Cologne, Germany around 1750. In salt glazing, wet sodium chloride grains are introduced to the firebox of a kiln at about $2300^\circ F$. The salt decomposes to chlorine and sodium oxide, the latter of which reacts with clay to give a sodium-silico-aluminate glazed surface. Sewer pipe is glazed by this method, as were the traditional Boston baked bean pots. The new deposition technique substitutes a zirconium halide, for example, for the powerful flux Na_2O and decomposes it over an 80 percent refractory diffusion barrier-20 percent clay mixture. Also to combat "pest", the zirconium alumina silicate glass, when formed with the 20 percent clay and fused, would yield the interstitial barrier glass which renders the coating impermeable to oxygen. If this process appears similar to the new fluidized bed process, it should be noted that salt glazing is totally uncritical in comparison to cementation diffusion in that an entire kiln may be utilized without enclosure because the substrate can be introduced within seconds after the neutral/reducing decomposition atmosphere has been induced. Secondly, the additions at temperature are in solid form and not gaseous. Thirdly, the process requires no inert bed.

B.   TESTING AND PROPERTIES

Although there are nearly a hundred organizations actively engaged in research for refractory metal protection, most of the available information has

Table 4. Some Companies Active in Protective Coatings for Refractory Metals.

Company	Metal(s) Protected	Company	Metal(s) Protected
American Machine and Foundry Company 1025 North Royal Street Alexandria, Virginia Attention Mr. J. C. Withers	Cb, Mo, Ta	General Telephone and Electronics Laboratories Bayside, New York Attention Mr. C. D. Dickinson	W
Battelle Memorial Institute 505 King Avenue Columbus 1, Ohio Attention Mr. W. D. Klopp	Ta	National Research Corporation Cambridge, Massachusetts	Ta
		*The Pfaudler Company Rochester 3, New York Attention Dr. D. K. Priest	Cb, Mo
Boeing Airplane Company P.O. Box 3707 Seattle 24, Washington Attention Mr. T. Bergstrom	Cb, Mo		
		*Sylvania-Corning Nuclear Corporation Bayside, New York Attention Mr. I. Sama	Ta
Chance-Vought Division Ling-Temco-Vought, Inc. P.O. Box 5907 Dallas, Texas Attention Mr. W. L. Aves	Cb, Mo	*Tapco Division Thompson-Ramo-Wooldridge, Inc. 23555 Euclid Avenue Cleveland 17, Ohio Attention Mr. R. A. Jeffries	Cb, Mo, W
*Chromalloy Corporation 169 Western Highway West Nyack, New York Attention Mr. R. Wachtell	Cb, Mo	*Thermomet Corporation 1851 East Randolph Street Los Angeles 1, California	Mo, W
*Chromizing Corporation 12536 Chadron Avenue Hawthorne, California Attention Mr. M. R. Commanday	Mo	U.S. Naval Research Laboratory Washington 25, D.C. Attention Dr. C. Sandoz	Cb
General Electric Company Flight Propulsion Laboratory Department Cincinnati 15, Ohio Attention Mr. M. A. Levenstein	Cb, Mo		

* Denotes companies who will perform service coating.

"Protective Coatings for Tungsten and Ta-10W Rocket Nozzles," Defense Metals Information Center, Battelle Memorial Institute, Columbus, Ohio (26 February 1962).

not been formally published, so in the past bibliographies of individual reports were the only source for further information on the subject. A recent literature survey by the author, however, disclosed 2,014 recent references directly applicable to the field, and a supplement which is soon to be published lists more than 3600 references (see Refs. 7 and 8). Table 4 lists addresses and contacts for the principal commercial coating vendors in USA.

Obviously, with all of these commercial coating suppliers and with an increasing amount of research being conducted, a problem was bound to arise concerning the testing of the various coatings. How should these coatings be tested? In the past five years because the plasma-arc has proven its usefulness in supplying some of the heat fluxes discussed previously (100, 300, 500, and 1000 BTU/ft^2-sec), this tool has been widely used for screening (not to be confused with simulation) tests of coating systems (Appendix I of this report lists most of the locations of these facilities). When a survey for WADD (Wright-Patterson Air Force Base) by Wurst (see Ref. 9) of the University of Dayton showed poor correlation between various plasma-arc facilities located around the country, a standardization facility for testing coated specimens was established at the University. Oxy-acetylene torches with calibrated heat fluxes have also been used successfully. A popular method for testing coated refractory metal wire has been the resistance heating method which used a wire as the resistor. In this method, the ends of the wire are held by water-cooled grips which impart a thermal gradient in the test wire - the center being the hottest. Because of this gradient, this test has shown to be more severe than, for example, an oxygen-acetylene torch test because of the occurrence of "pest" failures in the cooler zones. The plasma arc, on the other hand, seems to radiate more heat than the oxy-acetylene torch to flat plate "splash test" specimens, causing them to heat in an area larger than would normally be expected by the diameter of the jet. This radiant heating also causes thermal gradients which are most radically manifested at the edges of such a plate, where turbulence from behind meets hot laminar gases from the front side to cause premature edge failures. This special attention to edges, culminated in the research work of Rummler et al., (see Ref. 10) who found benefit in special processing of edges, the results of which showed up photomicrographically and in oxidation testing. (See Figs. 39 and 40, also Fig. 9).

Study of the thermal profiles of certain types of reentry vehicles (e.g., skip glide) gave rise to stipulation for thermal cycling in addition to requirements for moving air imposed on static oxidation conditions. The effect of thermal cycling on protective behavior is shown in Figs. 41 and 42. Figure 43, and Tables 5 and 6 show results of some excellent recent compilative research on protective systems utilizing cycled testing.

An essential prerequisite for protection is that a coating should be able to heal itself, i.e., it must be capable of filling voids which are formed in thermal stress to block paths for oxidation. The examination of coating systems for their capability to heal under test conditions has undoubtedly predicted many answers in screening potential coating materials as it had provided an answer for one outstanding mechanism of "pest". Figure 44 is an example of testing a coating system for "healing" characteristics.

A recent study of silicide systems by Perkins, et al., (see Ref. 2), has shown that the variable of pressure can lower proven oxidation protection by several hundred degrees (see Figs. 45 and 46) although some question exists on the method used. Such a parameter will undoubtedly be met in the vacuum of space. Other parameters, such as micrometeorite bombardment (see Fig. 47) and combinations of environmental factors must be made if a true picture of the protective system environment is to be made. These factors have only recently been taken into account in part by the work of Levinstein et al., at General Electric Co., Evandale, and to an extent by Marquardt Corp. and Chance-Vought Corp.

C.   FAILURE MECHANISMS

The question now arises "why are refractory metals needed in aerospace technology?" The answer is that we perhaps do not yet know how to design adequate structures with ceramics (since the environment certainly calls for a refractory material). Here now, the difference in chemical species between metals and nonmetals works in the favor of the former. Unfortunately for the designer, however, the oxidation properties work in

218

Table 5. Protective Life of Various Coating Systems for Tungsten in Air Under Cyclic Conditions Over the Temperature Range of 2500° to 3400°F.

System	Protective Life - Hours [1]						
	2500°F	2800°F	3000°F	3100°F	3200°F	3300°F	3400°F
W+Si	22	16	11	4	1	0.2	-
W+(Si-W)-O	28	27	25	18	11	5	-
W+Ti-Zr-(Si-W)-O	36	35	32	26	19	14	5
W+Ti-(Zr-B)-(Si-W)-O	-	34	29	23	18	16	-

[1] Tests involved one cycle at room temperature each hour (for inspection) for the total test period.

R. A. Jeffreys, "Current Activities at TRW in the Protective Coating of Refractory Metals," TAPCO, a division of Thompson Ramo Wooldridge Inc., Cleveland, Ohio. Presented at Sixth Refractory Composites Working Group Meeting, Dayton, Ohio (18-19 June 1962).

favor of the oxide members of the latter. The compromise is the ceramic (as the coating certainly becomes in end use - even if applied as an intermetallic) coating of the metal.

Differences within the metallic group, however, complicate the situation. For example, the surface of unprotected molybdenum after eight hours in 2000°F slow-moving air recedes four times faster than a tungsten surface which has receded twice as much as a columbium surface which, in turn, has receded only slightly more than tantalum surface. A possible explanation for these differences is that the molybdenum and tungsten systems yield volatile oxides which run molten or vaporize from their surfaces, whereas the columbium and tantalum systems release their oxides by spalling. As Fig. 11 shows, however, the oxidation of these metals follows complex mechanisms. Whatever the explanation may be, the differences exist and add to the complexity of coating problem. No single coating yet found will provide adequate maximum protection (to 3400°F at this writing) for the entire group. IN FACT, EACH REFRACTORY METAL MUST BE TREATED AS A DIFFERENT COATING PROBLEM REQUIRING A SEPARATE TYPE OF COATING. As has been previously stressed, this may also apply to variant alloys of the same metal, and could possibly apply to variant application environments of the same alloy.

Table 6. W-3 Coated Moly Alloys Oxidation Test Data.

MOLY 1/2 TI

Test Temp. 2500° F-- Coating Thickness- .0035"
Cycles- 2 hours
First Failure-732 hours- Last **Failure 913 hours**

Average 812 hours

MOLY 1/2 TI

Test Temp. 2700° F-- Coating Thickness- .0034"
Cycles- 2 hours
First Failure-26 hours- **Last Failure 395 hours**

Average 268 hours

TZM

Test Temp. 3000° F-- Coating Thickness- .0012"
Cycles- 15 minutes
First Failure- 75 min.   Last Failure 255 min.

Average 170 minutes

Coating Thickness .0032" Where No Reaction
with Boat No Failure After 250 and 302 min.

"Activities of Chromalloy Corporation in the Development of Coatings for
Refractory Metals," notes prepared for Sixth Refractory Composite Working
Group Meeting (18-19 June 1962).

220

The protection of these metals to date has been successful because these coatings

a)   do not react appreciably with their substrates over long time intervals at temperatures below 3400°F,

b)   readily form oxides or intermetallic compounds, or both, which offer substrate protection in their environment below 3500°F,

c)   are applied in a dense (99 + percent theoretical density) adherent form by dipping, pack cementation, fluidized bed exposure, or by another means of vapor deposition,

d)   do not boil away or are not blown off the surface (they form viscous melts due to their refractory properties or chemical affinity),

e)   fill voids in their own layers (heal) by the action and presence of their viscous melts, and

f)   prevent oxygen from reaching their substrates by a combination of the above mechanisms.

The coatings prevent oxidation because they

a)   do not present a series of interconnected pores to the substrate from the environment,

b)   do not carry oxygen to the surface of the substrate by replacement diffusion mechanisms,

c)   have an affinity for oxygen themselves and tie it up in a chemically stable manner before it can reach the substrate,

d)   have not been impregnated with an over-abundance of adsorbed or absorbed oxygen through formation technique nor are they in possession of oxygen yielders on reduction (such as water, hydrates, or reducible oxides).

Accordingly, we can account for the thermal limitations of these protective coatings by a categorical denial of these fundamentals; that is, above 3500°F, they

a)   begin to react with their substrates more violently,

b)   begin to react with themselves - their constituents undergo inversions and reactions (see Figs. 20, 22, 24, 25, 44, and 48-50),

c)   begin to increase in porosity as minute blowholes are caused by vapor pressure increases and the escape of volatile by-products of reactions (see Figs. 51 and 42),

d)   become less viscous, and in their more fluid forms are blown off surfaces or run off externally exposed surfaces,

e)   cannot heal new voids which appear because of diminution of their liquid phase, and

f)   no longer prevent oxygen from reaching their substrates.

The coatings do not prevent oxygen from reaching their substrates because they

a)   present a series of interconnected pores to the substrate from their environment,

b)   begin to carry oxygen to the substrate by replacement diffusion mechanisms, because (1) their own affinity for oxygen has been satisfied by the increased reaction rate at high temperatures, and (2) they become impregnated with oxygen (see Fig. 53) as sections of the coating are removed by the volatile substrate

221

oxide which forms to wash, blow, or spall off its
protection, leaving fresh substrate surfaces to face the
oxidizing environment and to carry oxygen internally
by diffusion.

Therefore, in light of the above experience, a philosophy of protection must
be evolved whereby mechanisms must be included in the system above
$3500^{\circ}F$ which will

a) provide refractory insulation to the system whereby
it can act as an inert porous retort which can be
graded into the denser subcoating near the substrate.
This feature must provide the thermal gradient in
the lower level of which the system of substrate
protection must function, so that the vital portion of
the system is not subject to extreme conditions of
substrate or coating vapor pressure and reactions.
This feature probably will entail the use of a refractory
oxide because such a material, which will be the hot
face of the coating, is most stable in this environment.

b) provide an intermediate protective phase that grades
the external porous oxide phase into the dense inert
phase which lies next to the substrate thereby not
subjecting the substrate to replacement diffusion
mechanisms,

c) provide healing liquid phases at low temperatures
(e. g., $2000^{\circ}F$) which will not boil at high temperatures
(e. g., $4000-5000^{\circ}F$) nor decompose. This feature
should probably be included into the lower (closer to
substrate) portions of the intermediate phase,

d) provide a refractory dense phase that lies next to the
substrate and will be the ultimate diffusion barrier
for the substrate. Such a phase would be best when graded
into the substrate.

This philosophy combined with suitable basic research on diffusion barriers,
high temperature reactions, etc., which is being carried on at Universities,
AVCO, General Telephone Laboratories, TAPCO and Aerospace Corporation, will perhaps continue to extend the lifetime of the refractory metals
in air at $5000^{\circ}F$ for extended periods of time.

222

REFERENCES

1. C. A. Krier, "Coatings for the Protection of Refractory Metals from Oxidation," DMIC Report 162 Defense Metals Information Center, Battelle Memorial Institute, Columbus, Ohio, (24 November 1961).

2. R. A. Perkins, et al., "Problems in the Oxidation Protection of Refractory Metals in Aerospace Applications," Lockheed MSC, Sunnyvale. Paper presented at Sixth Refractory Composite Working Group Meeting NASA/ASD, Dayton, Ohio (June 1962).

3. C. G. Bergeron, et al., "Protective Coatings for Refractory Metals," Department of Ceramic Engineering, University of Illinois, WADC TR 59-526 (January 1960).

4. D. V. Doane, "Oxidation Resistant Coatings of Molybdenum," WADC TR 54-492 Part III, Climax Molybdenum Co. of Michigan (April 1957).

5. S. T. Wlodek, "Coatings for Columbium," Metals Research Laboratories, Union Carbide Metals Company, Niagara Falls, Paper presented Third High Temperature Composites Working Group Meeting NASA/WADD, San Diego, Calif. (27-28 January 1960).

6. G. D. Smith, "Microstructures of Selected Sprayed Coatings on Unalloyed Columbium," Mechanical Research Laboratory, Engineering Department, E. I. du Pont de Nemours and Co., Wilmington, Delaware. Paper presented Sixth Refractory Composites Working Group Meeting, Dayton, Ohio, NASA/ASD (June 1962).

7. D. H. Leeds, "Reentry Protective Systems, A Bibliography of Refractory Metals Protective Systems Research," Aerospace Corporation, Materials Sciences Laboratory, DCAS-TDR-62-146 Report No. TDR-169 (3240-31) TR-1 (6 August 1962).

8. D. H. Leeds, "A Portfolio of Experience in Refractory Metal Protection" TDR-169(3240-31)TR-2 (March 1963) (AF Report SSD-TDR-63-51).

9. J. C. Wurst, et al., "Evaluation of Materials Systems for Use in Extreme Thermal Environments Utilizing an Arc-Plasma Jet," University of Dayton Research Institute, WADD TR60-926 (June 1961). See also, The Development of a Standardized Screening Test for High Temperature Materials," (16-19 June 1962).

10. D. R. Rummler, "Preliminary Results of a Comparative Study of Several Commercially Available Oxidation Resistance Coatings on Mo-0.5 Ti Alloy Sheet," NASA/Langley, presented Sixth Refractory Composites Working Group Meeting, Dayton, Ohio (16-19 June 1962), NASA/ASD.

Appendix I. PLASMA

Tillian. D. J.. "A Survey of Plasma Arc Heaters," Vought
Vought Corporation, A Subsidiary of Ling- Temco-

Firm Agency	Test Apparatus	Type Power Supply	Enthalpy Range	Pressure Range	Flow Rate
I. Private Owned /Operated					
1. Atlantic Research Corporation Alexandria, Va.	Plasma Torch	80 KW Rectifier	Up to 16,000 BTU/lb	1 ATM	to 600 ft^3 ft^3/hr
2. AVCO Corporation Wilmington, Mass.	(a) 500 KW Facility	DC Diesel Generators	800-10,000 BTU/lb	16 psia	—
	(b) 10 MW	2080, 12 Volt DC Batteries	450-10,000 BTU/lb	15-370 psia	0.035-5 lb/Sec
	(c) Overs II Arc (1 MW)	—	2000-25000 BTU/lb	0.005-5 ATM	—
	(d) AVCO Channel 3 (2.0 MW)	Battery banks	350-28000 BTU/lb	0.015-15 ATM	—
3. Boeing Company Aerospace Div. Seattle, Wash.	(a) Erosion Panel	—	1500-6200 BTU/lb	0.1-1 ATM	0.04-0.15 lb/Sec
	(b) Subsonic Splash	—	300-7000 BTU/lb	-1.2 ATM	0.03-0.15 lb/Sec

FACILITIES SURVEY

Astronautics Report 00.49 Astronautics Division, Chance Vought, Inc., Dallas, Texas (April 1962)

Mach. No.	Nozzle Exit Dia.	Heat Flux	Run Time	Vacuum Range and Type	Operational	Remarks
Subsonic	0.25-2.50 in.	15-1500 BTU/Ft^2 Sec	Cont.	Atmospheric	Operational	
—	0.5 to 0.75 in.	125-1500 BTU/Ft^2 Sec	5 min	—	Operational	Separate high and low enthalpy heads
Subsonic Mach 5.0	—	2-2500 BTU/Ft^2 Sec	60 Sec	—	Operational	
—	3-8 in.	88-2640 BTU/Ft^2 Sec	Cont.	—	Operational	
2-3	2 in.	5-800 BTU/Ft^2 Sec	15 min	100 Microns Hg absolute 10,000 ft^3 vacuum tank	Operational	Expect to reach enthalpy of 34,000 BTU/lb. Addition of 33,000 CFM continuous vacuum capacity in the future.
Subsonic Mach 2.0	—	1-75 BTU/Ft^2 Sec	1 hr	—	Operational	Support facilities for all units include: 4 parallel generators capable of 1000 KW continuous. 4 DC rectifiers of 160 KW total. 45 ft^3 compressed air storage. 4 stage steam ejector system.
Subsonic	2 in.	2-400 BTU/Ft^2 Sec	1 hr	Atmospheric	Operational	

Firm Agency	Test Apparatus	Type Power Supply	Enthalpy Range	Pressure Range	Flow Rate
	(c) Shroud Nozzle	—	400-3000 BTU/lb	1.2 ATM	-0.3 lb/Sec
	(d) 500 KW Supersonic Tunnel	—	300-9000 BTU/lb	0.1-8 ATM	0.0025-0.5 lb/Sec
	(e) 1-2 MW Hypersonic Tunnel	—	2000-6000 BTU/lb	1-8 ATM	0.03-0.4 lb/Sec
4. Ling-Temco-Vought, Inc. Dallas, Texas	(a) 40 KW Plasma Arc, Aeronautics Division	Selenium rectifier	-3500 BTU/lb	1 ATM	-0.003 lb/Sec
	(b) 180 KW Plasma Facility, Research Center	Selenium rectifiers	2000-15000 BTU/lb	-6 psia	—
5. Chicago Midway Laboratories Chicago, Ill.	(1) 1 MW Unit	Generators	-10,000 BTU/lb	-16 psia	—
	(2) 1 MW Unit	Shares same power supply	-8000 BTU/lb	-1.2 psia	0.04-0.2 lb/Sec
6. Chrysler	1 MW Facility	Rectifiers	4000-16000 BTU/lb	15-300 psia	—
7. Douglas A/C Santa Monica, Calif.	240 KW	6, 40 KW Selenium rectifiers	1000-3000 BTU/lb	15-45 psia	0.004-0.025 lb/Sec
			1000-10000 BTU/lb	7-320 psia	—
			(redesign) 1000-20000 BTU/lb (Figure 1 MW)	7-600 psia	—
8. General Dyn. Convair Ft. Worth, Texas	1.8 MW Hyperthermal Research Facility	Silicon rectifiers	-18000 BTU/lb (a) 60 psia	0.1-0.500 psia	—

Mach. No.	Nozzle Exit Dia.	Heat Flux	Run Time	Vacuum Range and Type	Operational	Remarks
Subsonic	—	10-100 BTU/Ft^2 Sec	30 min	Atmospheric	Operational	
2.4-3.0	1 in., 2 in., 2 × 2 in. square	3-2500 BTU/Ft^2 Sec	10 min	—	Operational	
4-11	8 in.	1-700 BTU/Ft^2 Sec	30 min	—	Operational	
Subsonic	$^5\!/_{16}$ in.	50-600 BTU/Ft^2 Sec	Cont.	Atmospheric	Operational	
2.5-3.0	0.84 in.	150-2000 BTU/Ft^2 Sec ($^3\!/_4$" dia. flat face model)	Cont.	300 CFM Stokes Vacuum Pump	Operational	
Subsonic	1.25 in.	-2000 BTU/Ft^2 Sec	2-3 min	Atmospheric	Operational	
2.2	2.75 in.	—	—	Vacuum Pumps	Operational	
—	—	-2000 BTU/Ft^2 Sec	Cont.	—	Under Construction	
1-5	1.0 in.	300-900 BTU/Ft^2 Sec	Cont.	1-6 mm Hg 2000 CFM NRC pumps	Development	Construction of new high pressure head under development, 1 MW capability in future.
—	0.5 in. etc.	300-1600 BTU/Ft^2 Sec	—			
—	0.5 in. etc.	300-2200 BTU/Ft^2 Sec				
Subsonic Mach 12	0.2 to 8 in.	20-4000 BTU/Ft^2 Sec	5 min (a) 1.5 MW 2 min (a) 1.8 MW	0.1 psia to 1 atm, Steam Jet Ejectors	Shakedown and calibration	

Firm Agency	Test Apparatus	Type Power Sypply	Enthalpy Range	Pressure Range	Flow Rate
9. General Electric Space Sciences Lab. King of Prussia Pa.	(a) Shroud Arc	200 KW Motor Generators	3400-6800 BTU/lb	15-75 psia	-.0085 lb/Sec
	(b) Supersonic Arc Tunnel	—	1300-7400 BTU/lb	4.3-14.7 psia	0.0005-0.0026 lb/Sec
	(c) Large Arc	—	-4800 BTU/lb	-160 psia	-0.31 lb/Sec
	(d) Hypersonic Arc Tunnel	—	-13.500 BTU/lb	-20 psia	-0.0015 lb/Sec
General Electric Flight Propulsion Lab. Evandale, Ohio	(e) 12 MW Hypersonic Wind Tunnel	AC Power	500-3500 BTU/lb	0-1500 psia	0-2 lb/Sec
10. Goodyear A/C Akron, Ohio	1.8 MW Arc Heated Wind Tunnel	Rectifiers	-14,000 BTU/lb	—	-3 lb/min
11. Grumman A/C Corporation Bethpage, N. Y.	Gas Stabilized Arc Jet	Selenium rectifiers (80-200 KW)	-12,000 BTU/lb	-20 ATM	5 CFM
12. The Johns Hopkins University Applied Physics Lab. Silver Spring, Md.	Blowdown Arc Tunnel	DC (Submarine batteries) up to 630 Volts, 25,000 Amp 5 MW	2500-8000 BTU/lb	-1200 psia	—
13. Martin Baltimore, Md.	200 KW Plasma Facility	Selenium rectifiers	2000-16000 BTU/lb	0.01-2 ATM	—
14. McDonnell A/C St.Louis,Mo.	-700 KW Vortex Stabilized Arc Jet	Ignitron	to 20,000 BTU/lb	-350 psi	-0.25 lb/Sec

228

Mach. No.	Nozzle. Exit Dia.	Heat Flux	Run Time	Vacuum Range and Type	Operational	Remarks
Subsonic	—	300-3000 BTU/Ft^2 Sec	30 Sec	Atmospheric	Operational	
4.8	—	3-100 BTU/Ft^2 Sec	1000 Sec	—	Operational	
Subsonic Mach 2.2	—	500-1600 BTU/Ft^2 Sec	10 Sec	—	Operational	
3-8	—	60-250 BTU/Ft^2 Sec	900 Sec	—	Operational	
4-12	27 in.	—	Cont.	To 0.01 atm Centrifugal staged compressor	Planned	
-5	6 in.	—	—	1.0 mm Hg, (a) 3 lb/min, 0.05 mm Hg,(a) 0.19 lb/min, Steam	Operational	
-4	1 in.	-2000 BTU/Ft^2 Sec	Cont.	Above 15mm Mechanical vacuum pumps	Operational for Subsonic tests	
Sonic- Mach 7	1.75 in.	0-50 BTU/In^2 Sec	40 Sec	1.5 in. Hg at 1 lb/Sec flow steam ejectors	Shakedown	Plans to increase pressure to 2500 psi and power to 15 MW
3	3.0 in.	20-500 BTU/Ft^2 Sec	Cont.	Mechanical blower and backing pumps	Under Construction	
Subsonic to Mach 6	4 in.	Several thousand BTU/Ft^2 Sec	Cont.	10^{-3}, 10^{-6} mm Hg	Operational	

Firm Agency	Test Apparatus	Type Power Supply	Enthalpy Range	Pressure Range	Flow Rate
15. North American Los Angeles, Calif.	1 MW Plasma Jet	Rectifiers	300-1000 BTU/lb	0.10 psia -350 psia	0.03-10 lb/Sec
16. Northrop A/C Hawthorne, Calif.	80 KW Plasma Facility	80 KW Selenium rectifiers	7000-30000 F	Atmosp.	—
17. Republic Aviation Farmingdale, N.Y.	1 MW Arc Heated Wind Tunnel	1 MW, Silicon diode rectifiers	1000-26000 BTU/lb	0-20 ATM	—
18. RCA, Applied Research Camden, N.J.	120 KW Plasma Facility	Rectifiers	-16,000 BTU/lb on N_2	Atmosp.	200 CFM
19. Sandia Corp. Albuquerque, N.M.	120 KW Plasma Facility	Rectifiers	700-3700 BTU/lb (on Argon)	0.3-5 psia	0.01-0.035 lb/Sec
20. Space Technology Labs., Inc. Redondo Beach, Calif.	120 KW Plasma Jet	3, 40 KW Rectifiers	1000-6000 BTU/lb	to 1 ATM	-3 ft^3/min
21. Stanford Research Inst. Menlo Park, Calif.	4, DC Arc Plasma Jets	Rectifiers 160 KW	—	Atmosp.	-10 CFM
22. University of Dayton Research Institute, Dayton, Ohio	(a) N-4 Plasmatron (b) Plasmadyne M-4 (c) Modified Plasmadyne SG-1	Rectifiers	(a) 9000 BTU/lb (b) 11,000 BTU/lb (c) 3000 BTU/lb (Argon) 6100 BTU/lb (N_2)	—	(a) 0.0082 lb/Sec (b) 0.0082 lb/Sec (c) 0.0032 lb/Sec (Argon) 0.0041 lb/Sec (N_2)

Mach. No.	Nozzle Exit Dia.	Heat Flux	Run Time	Vacuum Range and Type	Operational	Remarks
3 present 14 capable	3.4 in.	60-4000 BTU/Ft^2 Sec	1 hr	1 mm Hg. Mechanical vacuum pump	Shakedown and Calibration	
Subsonic	1.25 in.	—	Cont.	Atmospheric	Operational	Used for Plasma Spraying
Subsonic-Mach 10	1.25 in.	30-2100 BTU/Ft^2 Sec (a) 720 KW	Cont.	162 lb/hr 0.8 mm Hg. Steam ejectors	Atmospheric Exhaust at present	Run in blowdown tank 3-15-62, continuous vacuum system 1-1-63.
Subsonic	3/8 in.	—	10 min	Atmospheric	Operational	1 MW unit under construction (a) RCA, Morristown, N. J.
2-5	1.250 in.	-350 BTU/Ft^2 Sec	Cont.	4 mm Hg-Atmospheric Vacuum pumps	Operational	1 MW Facility under construction
0.7-2.5	0.75 in.	20-100 BTU/Ft^2 Sec	1 min	375 CFM Vacuum pumps	Development	Expect to get in operation late summer 1962
Subsonic	11/16 in.	-1000 BTU/Ft^2 Sec	Cont.	Atmospheric	Operational	Also have electrodeless, (inductively) coupled, atmospheric pressure, plasma generators.)
Subsonic	½ in.	(a) 500 BTU/Ft^2 Sec (b) 1200 BTU/Ft^2 Sec	Cont.	Atmospheric	Operational	

Firm Agency	Test Apparatus	Type Power Supply	Enthalpy Range	Pressure Range	Flow Rate
23. United Aircraft East Hartford Conn.	15 MW Arc Heated Tunnel	–	to 9000°R	to 3000 psia	–

II. Government Owned/Operated

Firm Agency	Test Apparatus	Type Power Supply	Enthalpy Range	Pressure Range	Flow Rate
24. NASA, Jet Propulsion Lab. Pasadena, Calif.	Spun Arc	600 KW Rectifiers	10,000 BTU/lb Max.	0-10 psia	0.001-0.1 lb/Sec
25. NASA Langley Research Center Hampton, Va.	(a) 700 KW AC Arc Jet	Three phase AC power	5400-9200 BTU/lb	75-150 psia	0.035-0.072 lb/Sec
	(b) 1500 KW AC Arc Jet	Three phase AC power	600-4500 BTU/lb	15 psia	-0.08 lb/Sec
	(c) 2500 KW AC Arc Jet	Three phase AC power	-3560 BTU/lb	14.7-15.2 psia	-0.35 lb/Sec
	(d) 1500 KW AC Arc Tunnel	Three phase AC power	3100-4000 BTU/lb	2.3-5.6 psia	0.083-0.226 lb/Sec
	(e) DC Arc Tunnel	DC Generators	-3582 BTU/lb	-1000 psia	–
	(f) 2" Supersonic Arc Tunnel	–	-2025 BTU/lb	-40 psia	–
	(g) 10 MW Arc Tunnel	–	-8000 BTU/lb	600-9400 psia	0.017-0.34 lb/Sec
26. NASA Ames Research Center Moffet Field, Calif.	(a) DC Arc Tunnel	80-160 KW Rectifiers	-9000 BTU/lb	–	–
	(b) Mass Transfer Facility (10 MW)	–	-10,000 BTU/lb	-6.7 ATM	–
	(c) Aero Facility (10 MW)	Shares same power supply	-2000 BTU/lb	-100 ATM	–

Mach. No.	Nozzle Exit Dia.	Heat Flux	Run Time	Vacuum Range and Type	Operational	Remarks
5-12	—	—	—	—	Planned	
0-3	$1/2$-2 in.	100-1500 BTU/Ft^2 Sec	Cont.	to 1 Micron Mechanical pump and blower	Under Arc Characterization	
1.9	0.52 in.	2140-3020 BTU/Ft^2 Sec (2" dia. hemisphere)	9-15 Sec	—	Operational	
0.01	6 in. or 2 x 12 in. rect.	125-200 BTU/Ft^2 Sec (2" dia. hemisphere)	300-600 Sec	—	Operational	
0.09-0.21	4-6 in.	150-220 BTU/Ft^2 Sec (2" dia. hemisphere)	Cont.	—	Operational	
-0.16	6 in.	133-156 BTU/Ft^2 Sec (2" dia. hemisphere)	80 Sec	—	Operational	
13.4	—	—	90 Sec	—	Under Construction	
2.68	2 in.	—	35 Sec	—	Operational	
8-9	24 in.	64-312 BTU/Ft^2 Sec (2" dia. hemisphere)	60 Sec	—	Under Construction	
5.6	4.1	—	Cont.	—	Operational	
—	30 in.	—	20 min	—	Under Construction	
—	—	—	20 min	—	Under Construction	

Firm Agency	Test Apparatus	Type Power Supply	Enthalpy Range	Pressure Range	Flow Rate
27. NASA Lewis Research Center Cleveland, Ohio	(a) Hypersonic heat transfer facility	DC Generator 500 KW	4000-10000 BTU/lb	0.5-3 ATM	-0.02 lb/Sec (N_2)

III. Plasma Jet and Associated Equipment Suppliers

Firm Agency	Test Apparatus	Type Power Supply	Enthalpy Range	Pressure Range	Flow Rate
33. Linde Speedway Labs. Indianapolis, Ind.	(a) Model N-60 Arc Heater	60 KW	1500-9700 BTU/lb	6-370 psia	0.003-0.025 lb/Sec
	(b) Model N-250 Arc Heater	250 KW	1200-4500 BTU/lb	6-560 psia	0.0125-0.10 lb/Sec
	(c) Model N-1000 Arc Heater	1000 KW	1250-9000 BTU/lb	15-1540 psia	0.01-0.40 lb/Sec
	(d) Model N-4000 Arc Heater	4000 KW	2500-4300 BTU/lb	32-1860 psia	0.2-1.0 lb/Sec
34. Plasmadyne Corp. Santa Ana, Calif.	(a) 300 KW Unit	8, 40 KW Selenium rectifiers	2000-16000 BTU/lb	0.01-2 ATM	0.0001-0.03 lb/Sec
	(b) 1000 KW Unit	24, 40 KW Selenium rectifiers	2000-16000 BTU/lb	0.05-1 ATM	0.002-0.04 lb/Sec
35. Thermal Dynamics Lebanon, N.H.	(a) 40 KW System	40 KW Rectifier	-11,300 BTU/lb	-15 psia	125 ft^3/hr
	(b) 80 KW System	80 KW Rectifier	3000-11300 BTU/lb	15-100 psia	250-760 ft^3/hr
	(c) 120 KW System	120 KW Rectifier	3000-11300 BTU/lb	15-300 psia	375-1130 ft^3/hr
	(d) 200 KW System	200 KW Rectifier	3000-8600 BTU/lb	15-300 psia	600-1880 ft^3/hr
	(e) 1000 KW System	1000 KW Rectifier	2900-8600 BTU/lb	15-300 psia	4100-9750 ft^3/hr
36. Vidya, Inc. Palo Alto, Calif.	1.5 MW Solenoid Arc Plasma Generator	1.5 KW Battery bank	1600-1800 BTU/lb (N_2)	20-650 psia	0.01-0.20 lb/Sec
37. Westinghouse Electric Pittsburgh, Pa.	10 MW Arc Air Heater	—	1000-5000 BTU/lb	35-1540 psia	0.07-0.97 lb/Sec

Mach. No.	Nozzle Exit Dia.	Heat Flux	Run Time	Vacuum Range and Type	Operational	Remarks
3.5	2.0 in.	—	Cont.	8 mm absolute minimum, delaval and roots exhaustors	Operational	
Subsonic	—	—	15 min+	Atmospheric	Head Performance Data	
Subsonic	—	—	15 min+	Atmospheric	Higher enthalpies reported in recent tests	
Subsonic	—	—	15 min+	Atmospheric		
Subsonic	—	—	15 min+	Atmospheric		
3	1.5-3.0 in.	20-160 BTU/Ft^2 Sec (2" dia. flat face model)	Cont.	0.1-25 mm Hg Vacuum pumps	Smaller 40, 80, 120 KW Units available	
3	3.0 in.	25-360 BTU/Ft^2 Sec (2" dia. flat face model)	Cont.	1-15 mm Hg Vacuum pump		
Subsonic	0.313 in. orifice	1600 BTU/Ft^2 Sec	Cont.	—	Head Performance Data	
Subsonic	0.124-0.500 in. orifice	-1260 BTU/Ft^2 Sec	Cont.	—		
Subsonic	0.132-0.625 in. orifice	-1200 BTU/Ft^2 Sec	Cont.	—		
Subsonic	0.170-0.62 in. orifice	-1600 BTU/Ft^2 Sec	Cont.	—		
Subsonic	0.42-2.0 in. orifice	-1000 BTU/Ft^2 Sec	Cont.	—		
Subsonic	0.250-0.706 in. throat	—	—	Atmospheric	Head Performance	
—	—	—	—	—	Prototype Arc Heater Performance	

235

Figure 1.

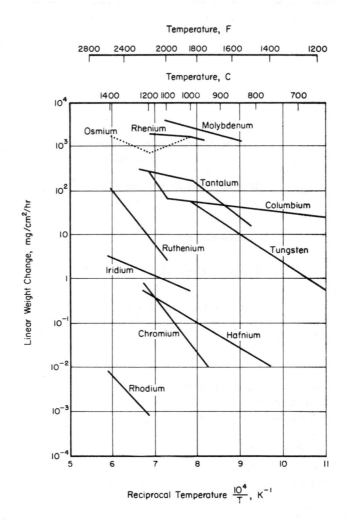

Changes in Oxidation Rate of Refractory Metals in Relation to
Temperature. (Data for molybdenum, rhenium, osmium,
ruthenium, iridium, and rhodium are weight-loss rates.)

R. I. Jaffee and D. J. Maykuth, "Refractory Materials," DMIC
Memorandum 44 (26 February 1960).

Figure 2.

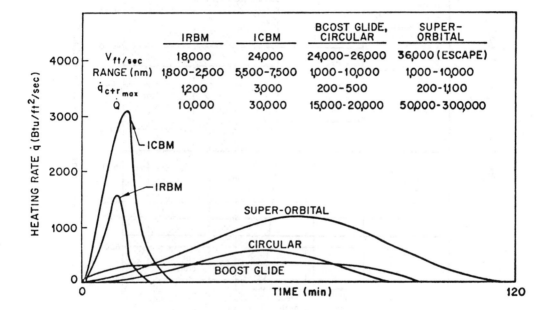

Comparison of Typical Reentry Parameters

R. A. Perkins, L. A. Riedinger, and S. Sokolsky, "Problems in
the Oxidation Protection of Refractory Metals in Aerospace
Applications," Lockheed Missiles and Space Co., Sunnyvale,
California, Paper presented Sixth Refractory Composites Working
Group Meeting, Dayton, Ohio (June 1962).

Figure 3.

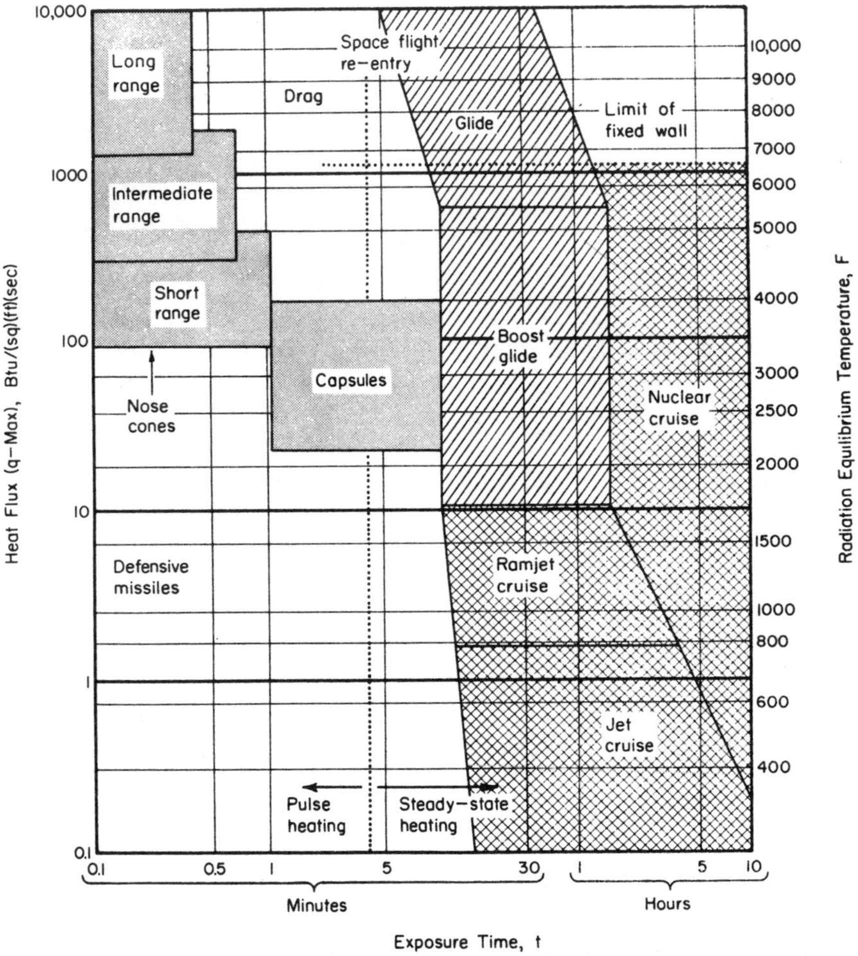

The Environmental Conditions of Various Classes of Vehicles Under Conditions of Steady-State Heating (Right) and Pulse Heating (Left). (The lines defining the vehicle zones are not rigid boundaries but indicate generally expected locations.)

W. S. Pellini and W. J. Harris, Jr., "Flight in the Thermosphere, Parts I-IV," Metal Progress (March-June 1960)

Figure 4.

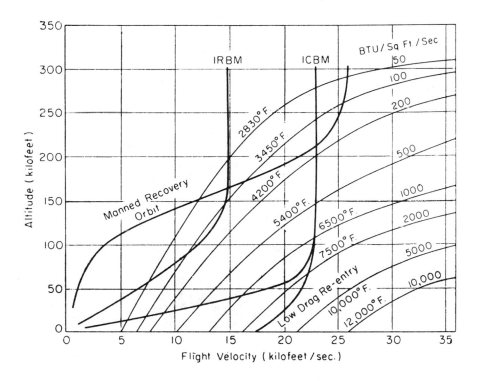

Heat Transfer to Various Re-entry Vehicles.

J. D. Walton, Jr., "Present and Future Problem Areas for High Temperature Inorganic Coatings," <u>Ceramic Bulletin</u>, <u>40</u> (3), 136-141 (1961)

Figure 5.

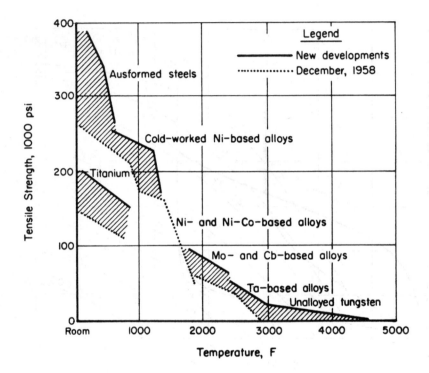

How Strength Levels of Typical High-Temperature Structural Alloys
Have Risen Since 1958. (Shaded areas indicate the extent of the increase as measured by tensile strength.)

E. S. Jones and L. P. Jahnke, "Updating High-Temperature Metallurgy,"
Metal Progress, 78 (4), 131-135 (October 1960).

Figure 6.

Tantalum Reacted with Air for 1 1/2 hr at 1000°C. (a) Before Removal
of Oxide Scale. (b) After Removal of Oxide Scale.

Tantalum Reacted with Air
at 1000°C for 2.6 Hours
Showing Oxide Penetration
into Base Metal Along (100)
Planes. X250.

(a)

(b)

W. M. Albrecht, et al., "Reaction of Pure Tantalum with Air,
Nitrogen, and Oxygen," Transactions of the Metallurgical
Society of AIME (February, 1961).

Figure 7.

Unalloyed Tungsten Before and After Exposure to Air at 2000°F (2 hours).

E. F. Atkins and R. I. Jaffee, "Oxidation of Clad Mo Containing Intentional Defects, " Battelle Memorial Institute, Columbus, Ohio. Paper presented Annual Meeting American Ceramic Society (1960).

Figure 8.

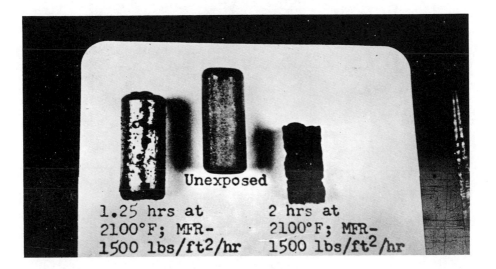

Tungsten/Cobalt Electroplated 0. 5 Ti Molybdenum.

E. F. Atkins and R. I. Jaffee, "Oxidation of Clad Mo Containing Intentional Defects, " Battelle Memorial Institute, Columbus, Ohio. Paper presented Annual Meeting American Ceramic Society (1960).

Figure 9a.

Metallographic Cross-Section of Niobium Specimen Oxidized for 300 min at 700°C and in Oxygen at 0.1 of Hg. Polarized Light. X500. Reduced Approximately 23% for Reproduction.

P. Kofstade and H. Kjöllesdal, "Oxidation of Niobium (Columbium) in the Temperature Range 500° to 1200°C, " Central Institute for Industrial Research, Blindern-Oslo, Norway. Transactions of the Metallurgical Society of AIME (April, 1961).

Appearance of CbO Samples after Gravimetric Runs. 160 Min at 1003°C,
100% oxidized, 45 min at 1202°C, 50% oxidized, X5.

W. T. Hicks, "Oxidation of Columbium Monoxide,"
Pigments Dept., Experimental Station, E. I. du Pont
de Nemours and Co., Inc., Wilmington, Del. Transactions of The Metallurgical Society of AIME (April,
1961).

Figure 10.

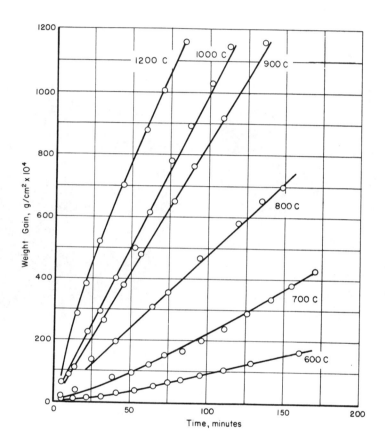

The Oxidation Rates of Columbium in Air at Various Temperatures.

H. Inouye, "Scaling of Columbium in Air," Proc. 1956 Reg. Conf. on Reactive Metals, AIME-IMD Special Report No. 5 (January 1957).

Figure 11.

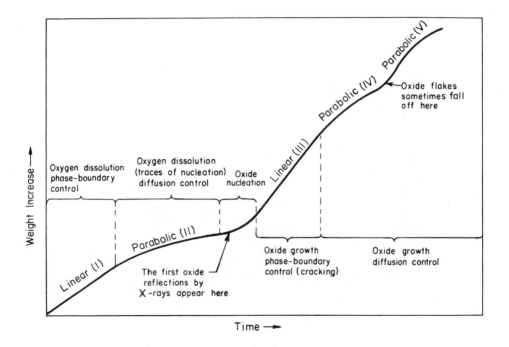

The Generalized Oxidation Behavior of Columbium.

T. Hurlen, et al., "Oxidation of Niobium," TN-1, Central Institute for Industrial Research, Norway, Contract AF 61(052)-90 (April 1959).

Figure 12.

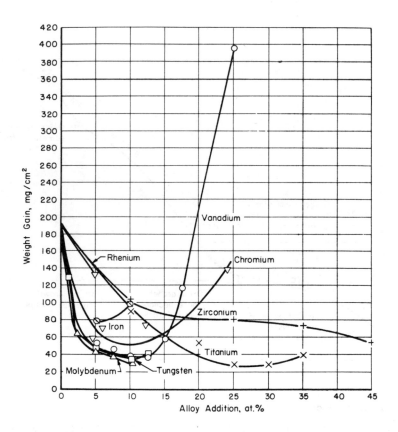

Weight Gains of Columbium Alloys Exposed 2 Hours in Dry Air at 1200 C (Continuous Weighing Tests).

W. D. Klopp, et al., "Oxidation and Contamination Reactions of Niobium and Niobium Alloys," BMI-1317 (3 February 1959).

Figure 13.

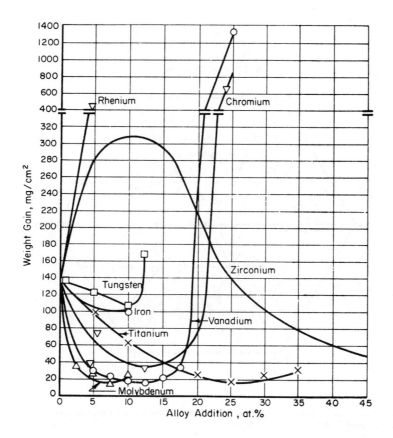

Weight Gains of Columbium Alloys Exposed 5 Hours in Dry Air at 1000 C (Continuous Weighing Tests).

W. D. Klopp, et al., "Oxidation and Contamination Reactions of Niobium and Niobium Alloys," BMI-1317 (3 February 1959).

Figure 14.

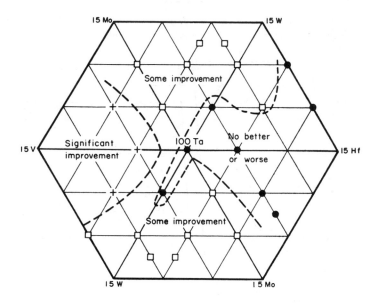

Effect of Substrate Composition on the 2700°F Cyclic Oxidation Life of Silicide-Coated Tantalum.

D. J. Maykuth, J. B. Hallowell, and H. R. Ogden, Battelle Memorial Institute, Columbus, Ohio, Paper presented at Sixth Refractory Composites Working Group Meeting, NASA/ASD Dayton, Ohio (June 1962).

Figure 15a.

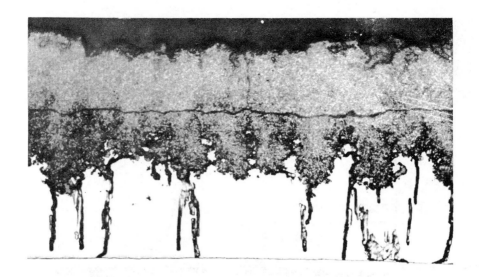

Microstructure of Silicide-Coated Tantalum Exposed in Air for 3.3 Hours at 2500 F (Initial coating thickness, 2.5 mils.)

W. D. Klopp et al., "Development of Protective Coatings for Tantalum-Base Alloys," Battelle Memorial Institute, Columbus, Ohio, paper presented at Fifth Meeting of the Refractory Composites Working Group, Dallas, Texas (8-10 August 1961).

Figure 15b.

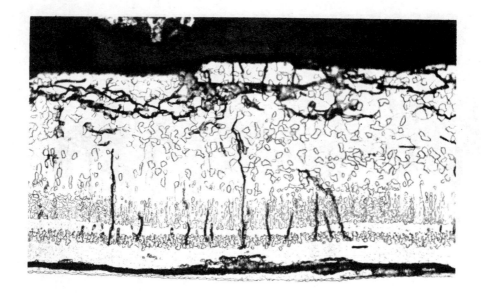

Microstructure of Silicide-Coated Ta-30Cb-10V Alloy After Exposure in Air for 7 Hours at 2700 F (No Failure). (Initial coating thickness, about 4 mils. Coating cracked from substrate during sectioning.)

W. D. Klopp et al., "Development of Protective Coatings for Tantalum-Base Alloys," Battelle Memorial Institute, Columbus, Ohio, paper presented at Fifth Meeting of the Refractory Composite Working Group, Dallas, Texas (8-10 August 1961).

Figure 16a.

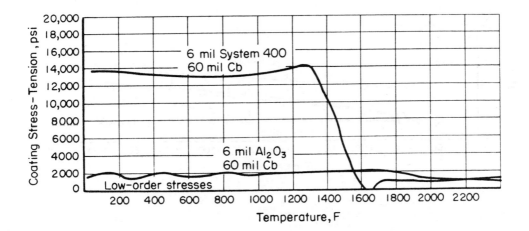

Apparent Residual Stress Development in Flame-Sprayed Alumina on
Columbium-System 400.

W. B. Hall and J. W. Graham, "System 400 Coating for the Protection
of Columbium," Report No. DM-60-97, Chemical Engineering Sub-
Operating Materials Information Memorandum, Aircraft Gas Turbine
Division, General Electric Co. (20 April 1960).

Figure 16b.

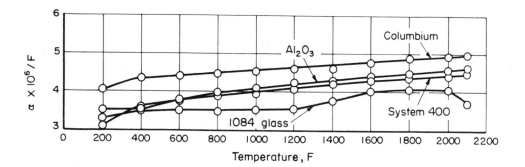

Thermal-Expansion Coefficients of Constituents in System 400.

W. B. Hall and J. W. Graham, "System 400 Coating for the Protection of Columbium,"
Report No. DM-60-97, Chemical Engineering Sub-Operating Materials Information
Memorandum Aircraft Gas Turbine Division, General Electric Co. (20 April 1960).

Figure 17.

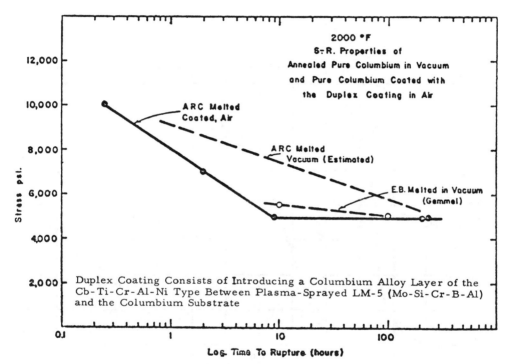

2000 °F
S-R. Properties of
Annealed Pure Columbium in Vacuum
and Pure Columbium Coated with
the Duplex Coating in Air

ARC Melted
Coated, Air

ARC Melted
Vacuum (Estimated)

E.B. Melted in Vacuum
(Gemmel)

Duplex Coating Consists of Introducing a Columbium Alloy Layer of the
Cb-Ti-Cr-Al-Ni Type Between Plasma-Sprayed LM-5 (Mo-Si-Cr-B-Al)
and the Columbium Substrate

Stress psi.

Log. Time To Rupture (hours)

S. T. Wlodek, "Coating for Columbium," Metals Research Laboratories,
Union Carbide Metals Co., Niagara Falls, Paper presented Third High
Temperature Composites Working Group Meeting NASA/WADD, San Diego
(27-28 January 1960).

Figure 18a.

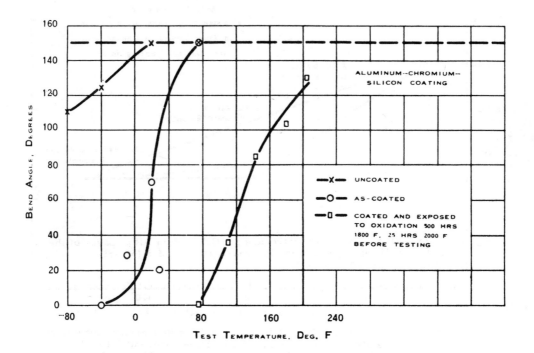

Results of Bend Tests.

D. V. Doane, "Oxidation Resistant Coatings for Molybdenum, " Climax
Molybdenum Co. of Michigan, WADC TR 54-492 Pt 3 (April 1957).

Figure 18b.

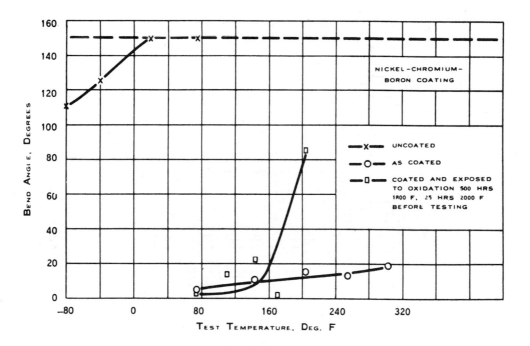

Results of Bend Tests

D. V. Doane, "Oxidation Resistant Coatings for Molybdenum, " Climax
Molybdenum Co. of Michigan, WADC TR 54-492 Pt 3 (April 1957).

Figure 19.

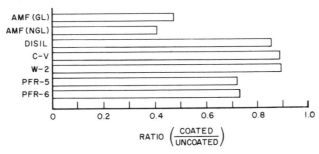

(A) TENSILE STRENGTH

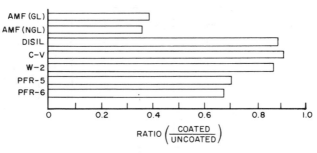

(B) YIELD STRENGTH

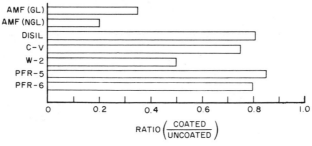

(C) ELONGATION IN 2 IN.

Results of Room Temperature Tensile Tests

Notes: 1 - Based on Area before Coating

2 - Specimens Tested as Coated

D. R. Rummler, et al., "Preliminary Results of a Comparative Study of Several Commercially Available Oxidation Resistant Coatings on Mo-0.5 Ti Alloy Sheet," NASA/Langley. Presented to the Sixth Refractory Composite Working Group Meeting, Dayton, Ohio (16-19 June 1962).

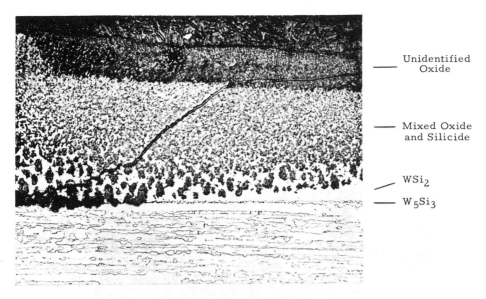

— Unidentified Oxide

— Mixed Oxide and Silicide

/ WSi_2

— W_5Si_3

(a) Structure of oxidation products formed in ~1300°C section. (250X)

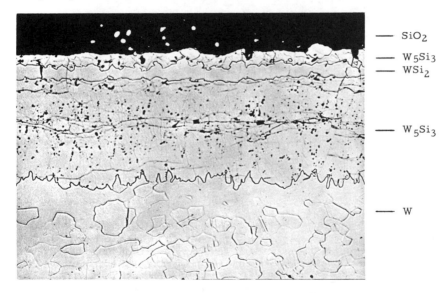

— SiO_2

— W_5Si_3
— WSi_2

— W_5Si_3

— W

(b) Structure of oxidation products formed at 1650°C. (250X)

The effect of temperature on layer growth during oxidation of a tungsten silicide coating on tungsten. Specimen tested 13 hours at 1650°C. Test stopped prior to failure.

Figure 20. Nicholas, M. G. and C. D. Dickinson, "The Development of Improved Coating Systems for the Protection of Tungsten from Oxidation and a Study of the Fundamental Factors Involved," Bayside Labs of General Telephone and Electronics Laboratories. Part II. Paper presented Sixth Refractory Composites Working Group Meeting, NASA/ASD, Dayton, Ohio (June 1962).

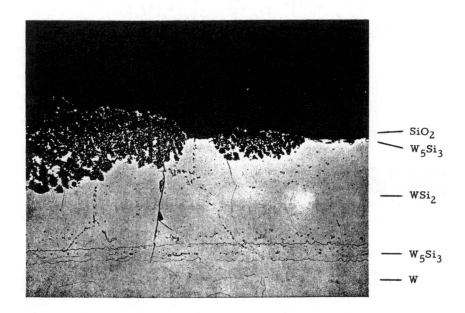

Figure 21.   Structure of tungsten silicide coating prior to failure
after 76 hours at 1400°C.   Structure shows abnormal
growth of oxide or pest.   Spec. No. 211-2Si:1.   Plate
No. 24973 (500X)

Nicholas, M. G. and C. D. Dickinson, "The Development of Improved
Coating Systems for the Protection of Tungsten from Oxidation and a
Study of the Fundamental Factors Involved," Bayside Labs of General
Telephone and Electronics Laboratories.   Part II.   Paper presented
Sixth Refractory Composites Working Group Meeting, NASA/ASD,
Dayton, Ohio (June 1962).

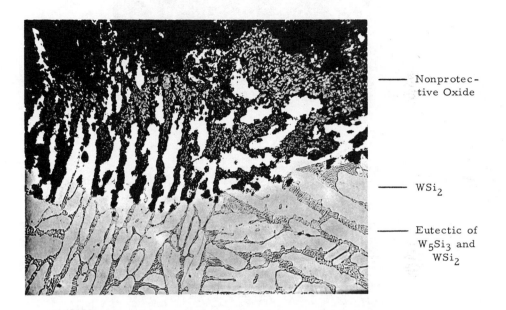

— Nonprotective Oxide

— WSi_2

— Eutectic of W_5Si_3 and WSi_2

Figure 22. Structure Showing Paths of Rapid Oxidation in WSi_2 + W_5Si_3 Eutectic in Arc-Melted Button of W-Si Tested 16 Hours at 1370°C. Plate No. 24166 (250X)

Nicholas, M. G. and C. D. Dickinson, "The Development of Improved Coating Systems for the Protection of Tungsten from Oxidation and a Study of the Fundamental Factors Involved," Bayside Labs of General Telephone and Electronics Laboratories. Part II. Paper presented Sixth Refractory Composites Working Group Meeting, NASA/ASD, Dayton, Ohio (June 1962).

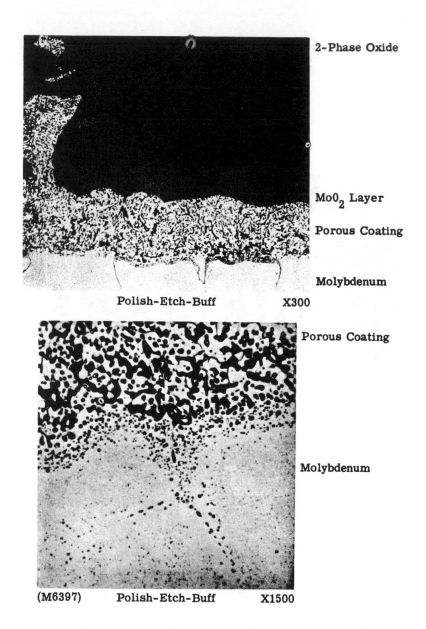

2-Phase Oxide

MoO_2 Layer

Porous Coating

Molybdenum

Polish-Etch-Buff   X300

Porous Coating

Molybdenum

(M6397)   Polish-Etch-Buff   X1500

Figure 23. Specimen E137. Al-Cr-Si Coating on 0.5% Ti-Mo Alloy. Diffusion
Treated at 2 hrs 2000°F in Dry Argon. Oxidation Tested 4 hrs 1800°F,
4 hrs 2000°F, 4 hrs 2400°F, 6 hrs 2600°F, 4 hrs 3000°F.

D. V. Doane, "Oxidation Resistant Coatings for Molybdenum, " Climax
Molybdenum Co. of Michigan, WADC TR-54-492 Pt 3 (April 1957).

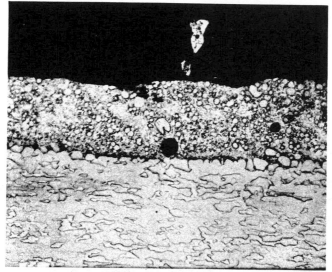

Polish-Etch-Buff   X100

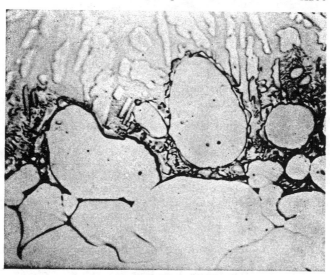

Polish-Etch-Buff   X1000

Figure 24. Specimen E227. Colmonoy No. 5 on 0.5% Ti-Mo alloy. Diffusion treated 2 hrs at 2000°F in dry argon. Oxidation tested 8 hrs 1800°F, 4 hrs 2000°F, 4 hrs 2200°F, 1/2 hr 2400°F (failed). Evidence of intergranular attack on molybdenum and "floating" of molybdenum to surface.

D. V. Doane, "Oxidation Resistant Coatings for Molybdenum, " Climax Molybdenum Co. of Michigan, WADC TR 54-492 Pt 3 (April 1957).

Figure 25.

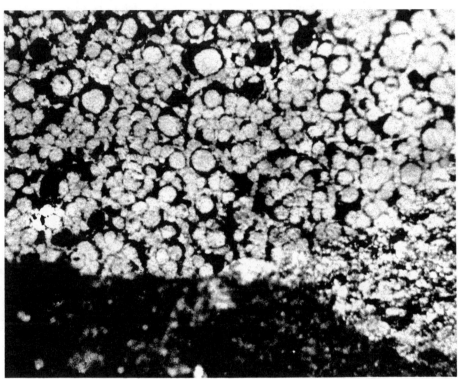

APPROX X45

Specimen E321. Macrostructure of Mo surface at coating
interface after chipping coating off. After 50 cycles
from 1800°F in thermal cycling apparatus. Note dark
molybdenum oxide in circular pattern.

D. V. Doane, "Oxidation Resistant Coatings for Molybdenum, " Climax
Molybdenum Co. of Michigan, WADC TR 54-492 Pt 3 (April 1957).

Plasmajet-Sprayed
MoSi$_2$ Coating

Diffusion Zone

Unalloyed Columbium

Figure 27a. Plasmajet-Sprayed MoSi$_2$
coating on an unalloyed columbium
substrate. Specimen subsequently
diffusion heat treated. 250X.

G. D. Smith, "Microstructures of Selected Sprayed Coatings
on Unalloyed Columbium," Mechanical Research Lab.,
Engineering Dept., E. I. du Pont de Nemours and Co., Inc.,
Wilmington, Delaware. Paper presented Sixth Refractory
Composites Working Group Meeting. ASD/NASA Dayton,
Ohio (16-19 June 1962).

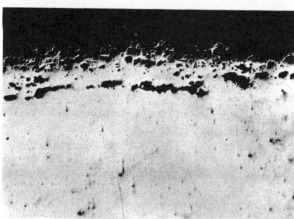

Plasmajet-Sprayed
Modified
MoSi$_2$ Coating

Unalloyed Columbium

Figure 27b. Plasmajet-sprayed modified-
MoSi$_2$ coating on an unalloyed columbium substrate. Specimen subsequently
diffusion heat treated. 250X.

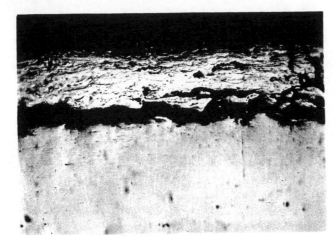

Figure 26a.

Linde LM-5 Coating

Unalloyed Columbium

Linde LM-5 Coating (Mo-Si-Cr-B-Al) on an Unalloyed Columbium
Substrate. Coating Applied by Linde's Detonation Gun Process.
250X; Bright Field Illumination.

G. D. Smith, "Microstructures of Selected Sprayed Coatings on
Unalloyed Columbium," Mechanical Research Lab., Engineering
Dept., E. I. du Pont de Nemours and Co., Inc., Wilmington,
Delaware. Paper presented Sixth Refractory Composites Working
Group Meeting. ASD/NASA Dayton, Ohio (16-19 June 1962).

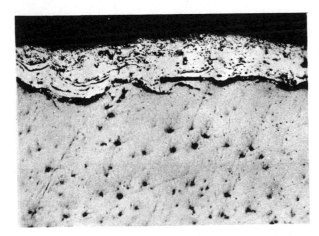

Figure 26b

Plasmajet-Sprayed

MoSi$_2$ Coating

Unalloyed Columbium

Plasmajet-Sprayed MoSi$_2$ Coating on an Unalloyed Columbium
Substrate. 250X.

266

Figure 28. Effects of WSi₂ Thickness on the Time to Failure in Oxidation Tests of Coated Tungsten Wire at 1400 and 1800°C.

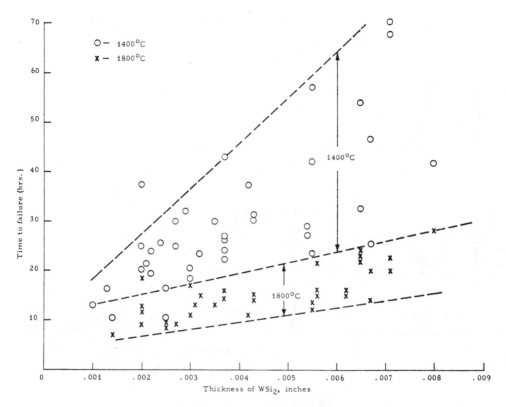

Nicholas, M. G. and C. D. Dickinson, "The Development of Improved Coating Systems for the Protection of Tungsten from Oxidation and a Study of the Fundamental Factors Involved, " Bayside Labs of General Telephone and Electronics Laboratories. Part II. Paper presented Sixth Refractory Composites Working Group Meeting, NASA/ASD, Dayton, Ohio (June 1962).

Figure 29.

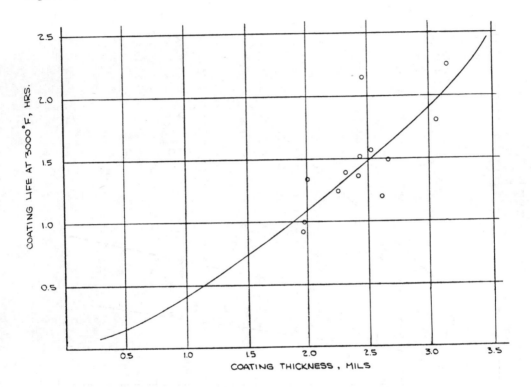

PFR-6 Coating on Molybdenum,
Coating Thickness Versus Coating Life.

P. J. Chao et al., "Recent Development of Oxidation Resistant
Coatings at Pfandler," Paper presented Fifth Refractory Composites
Working Group Meeting NASA/WADD, Dallas, Texas (August 1961).

Figure 30.

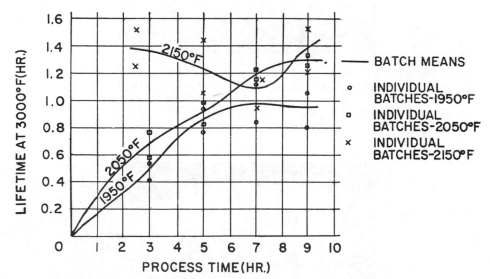

PROCESSING TIME AND TEMPERATURE VS. COATING LIFETIME-PFR-6

P. J. Chao, et al., "Research on Protective Coatings for Refractory Metals," The Pfandler Co., Paper presented Sixth Refractory Composites Working Group Meeting, NASA/ASD, Dayton, Ohio (16-19 June 1962).

Figure 31.

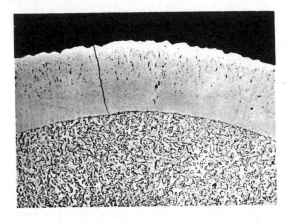

(a) Tungsten silicide coating, 0.0037-inch thick,
on tungsten coated at 1050°C for 16 hours
above H_2-Si-NaF mixture. Spec., No. 267Si:
B-1. (250X)

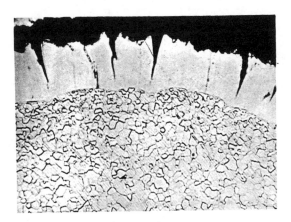

(b) Molybdenum silicide coating, 0.0023-inch thick,
on molybdenum coated at 1050°C for 16 hours
above H_2-Si-NaF mixture. Spec. No. 265Si:B-1.
(250X)

Tungsten and Molybdenum Silicide Coatings prior to Test.

Nicholas, M. G. and C. D. Dickinson, "The Development of Improved
Coating Systems for the Protection of Tungsten from Oxidation and a
Study of the Fundamental Factors Involved," Bayside Labs of General
Telephone and Electronics Laboratories. Part II. Paper presented
Sixth Refractory Composites Working Group Meeting, NASA/ASD, Dayton,
Ohio (June 1962).

Figure 32.

Run 89-Si-7 Penetration of Silicide Coating into Split End of 0.040"
Tungsten Rod by Pack Cementation with N and F Activation.

A Pranatis, et al., "Protection of Tungsten Against Oxidation at
Elevated Temperatures," Bayside Labs of General Telephone and
Electronics Laboratories, Part II. Paper presented Fifth Refractory
Composites Working Group Meeting, WADD/NASA, Dallas, Texas
(August, 1961).

Figure 33a.

Molybdenum Alloy Specimen as Coated with W-3.

"Activities of Chromalloy Corporation in the Development of
Coatings for Refractory Metals," notes prepared for Sixth
Refractory Composite Working Group Meeting (16-19 June 1962).

Figure 33b.

W-3 Coated Molybdenum Alloy Tabs After 3000° F Oxidation Testing.

"Activities of Chromalloy Corporation in the Development of Coatings for Refractory Metals," notes prepared for Sixth Refractory Composite Working Group Meeting (16-19 June 1962).

Figure 34.

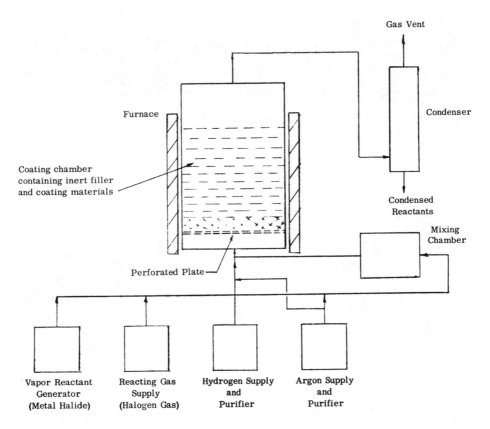

Gas Vent

Condenser

Furnace

Coating chamber
containing inert filler
and coating materials

Condensed
Reactants

Mixing
Chamber

Perforated Plate

Vapor Reactant
Generator
(Metal Halide)

Reacting Gas
Supply
(Halogen Gas)

Hydrogen Supply
and
Purifier

Argon Supply
and
Purifier

Flow Diagram of Laboratory-Scale Fluidized Bed Vapor Deposition
Apparatus.

P. J. Chao, et al., "Research on Protective Coatings for Refractory
Metals," The Pfandler Co., Paper presented Sixth Refractory
Composites Working Group Meeting, NASA/ASD, Dayton, Ohio
(16-19 June 1962).

Figure 35.

PFR-6 Coated Mo-0.5% Ti, 10% Chromic Acid and Gamma Alumina
Etch-Polish. Fluidized Bed Process. 100X. Note Smooth Coating
Around Corner.

P. J. Chao, et al., "Research on Protective Coatings for Refractory
Metals," The Pfandler Co., Paper presented Sixth Refractory
Composites Working Group Meeting, NASA/ASD, Dayton, Ohio
(16-19 June 1962).

Figure 36.

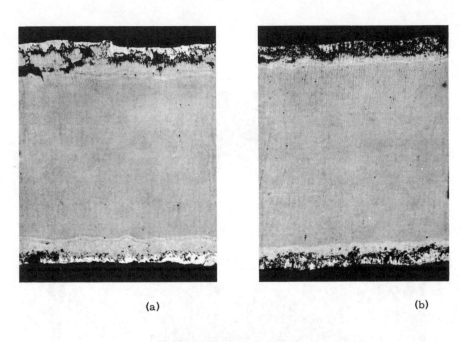

(a)   (b)

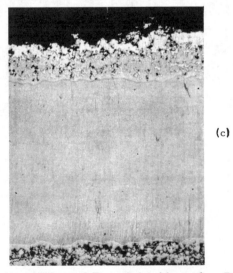

(c)

Samples of Tantalum Alloys and Pure Columbium after Double Coating
with Sn-25 Al.   (a) Ta-10W, (b) Ta-10Hf-5W, (c) Columbium.

L. Sama, "Protective Coatings for Columbium and Tantalum Alloys, "
Bayside Labs of General Telephone and Electronics Laboratories,
Part I. Paper presented Sixth Refractory Composites Working Group
Meeting, NASA/ASD Dayton, Ohio (16-19 June 1962).

276

Figure 37.

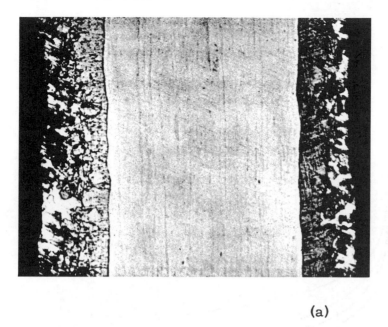

(a)

(b)

Samples of Tungsten and Molybdenum after Double Coating with
Sn-25 Al. (a) Tungsten, (b) Molybdenum. 200X.

L. Sama, "Protective Coatings for Columbium and Tantalum Alloys,"
Bayside Labs of General Telephone and Electronics Laboratories,
Part I. Paper presented Sixth Refractory Composites Working Group
Meeting, NASA/ASD Dayton, Ohio (16-19 June 1962).

Figure 38.

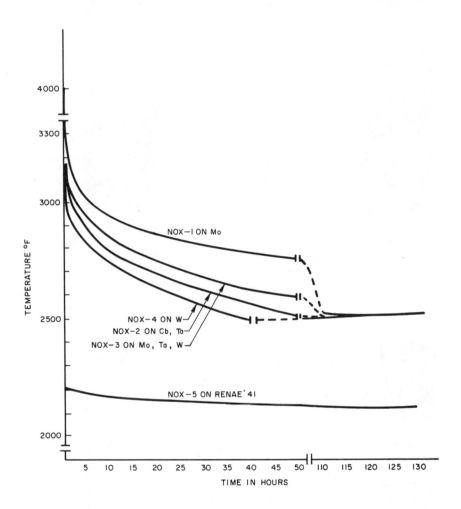

Protection of Refractory Metals by General Technologies Corporation's
Coatings.

J. Withers, "Refractory Coatings Research at the General Technologies
Corporation, paper presented at Sixth Refractory Composites Working
Group Meeting, Dayton, Ohio (June 1962).

Figure 39.

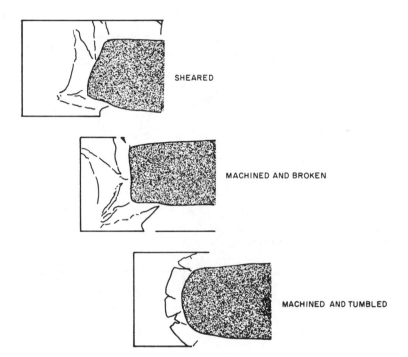

SHEARED

MACHINED AND BROKEN

MACHINED AND TUMBLED

Coating Appearance for Three Edge Conditions

D. R. Rummler, et al., "Preliminary Results of a Comparative Study of Several Commercially Available Oxidation Resistant Coatings on Mo-0.5 Ti Alloy Sheet," NASA/Langley. Presented to the Sixth Refractory Composite Working Group Meeting, Dayton, Ohio (16-19 June 1962).

Figure 40.

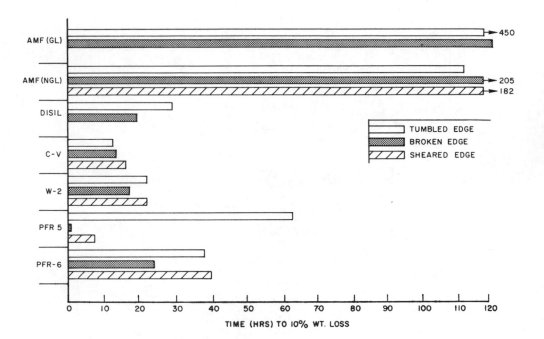

Continuous Exposure Coáting Life for Various Edge Conditions at 2500°F.

D. R. Rummler, et al., "Preliminary Results of a Comparative Study of Several Commercially Available Oxidation Resistant Coatings on Mo-0.5 Ti Alloy Sheet," NASA/Langley. Presented to the Sixth Refractory Composite Working Group Meeting, Dayton, Ohio (16-19 June 1962).

Figure 41.

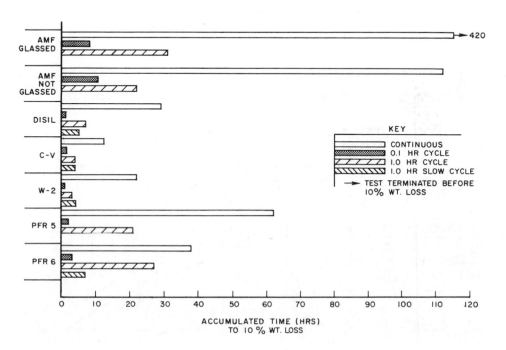

Comparative Results for Continuous and Cyclic Exposure Tests at 2500°F.

D. R. Rummler, et al., "Preliminary Results of a Comparative Study of Several Commercially Available Oxidation Resistant Coatings on Mo-0.5 Ti Alloy Sheet," NASA/Langley. Presented to the Sixth Refractory Composite Working Group Meeting, Dayton, Ohio (16-19 June 1962).

Figure 42a.

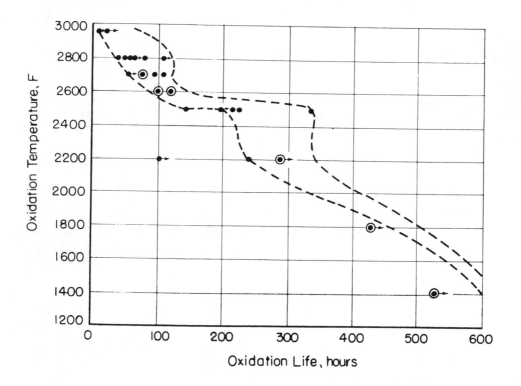

Oxidation Life of 34S(2 Cycle Coating of Powder Metal Lacquer Suspension-Spray, Diffusion-Spray, Diffusion)with a Composition 50 Al-50 Sn Coated Ta-10 W. Alloy Samples.

L. Sama and D. D. Lawthers, "Aluminide and Beryllide Protective Coatings for Tantalum," paper presented at Technical Conference on High Temperature Materials, Cleveland, Ohio (26-27 April 1961).

Figure 42b.

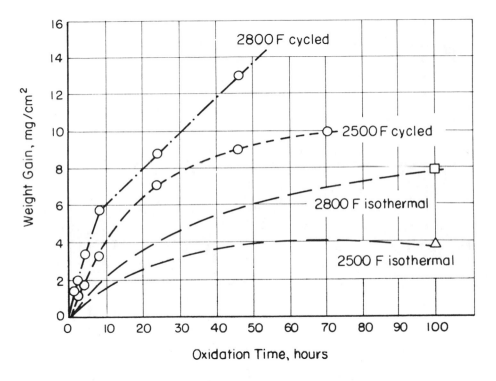

Weight Gains of 34S Coated Ta-10 W Samples Oxidized at 2500 and 2800 F.

L. Sama and D. D. Lawthers, "Aluminide and Beryllide Protective Coatings for Tantalum," paper presented at Technical Conference on High Temperature Materials, Cleveland, Ohio (26-27 April 1961).

Figure 43.

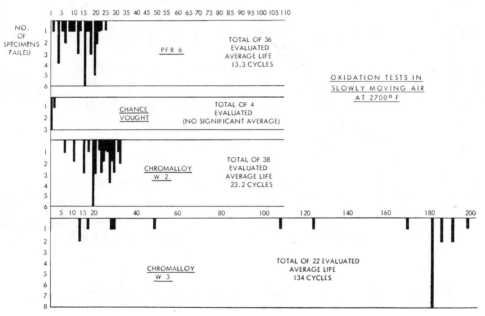

Oxidation Tests in Slowly Moving Air at 2700° F.

"Activities of Chromalloy Corporation in the Development of Coatings for Refractory Metals," notes prepared for Sixth Refractory Composite Working Group Meeting (16-19 June 1962).

Figure 44.

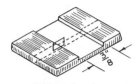

a. Slotted Specimen   A-39754

a.   Slotted Specimen

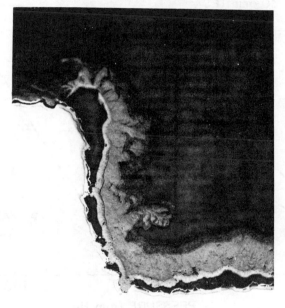

ZnO

Cb_2O_5

CbO_2

$CbZn_x$

b.   Microstructure of Defected Area After
20 Hours at 1800 F in Air

Sketch of Defected Zn-Coated Columbium and Microstructure of
Repaired Defect After Air Exposure.

B. F. Brown, et al., "Protection of Refractory Metals for High
Temperature Service," Progress Report 1, July 1, 1960, "The
Zinc-Base Coating for Niobium," NRL Report 5550 (Nov. 28, 1960).

285

Figure 45.

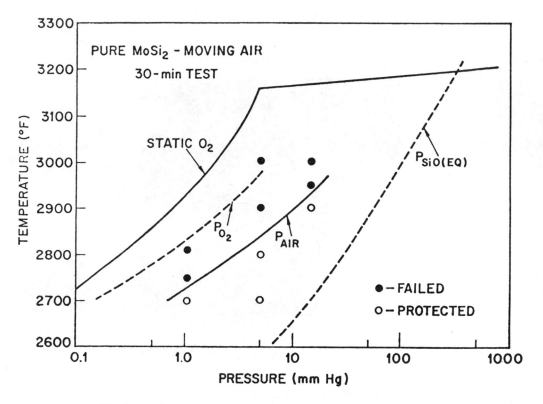

Maximum Temperature for 30-Min Life of $MoSi_2$ in Moving Air.

R. A. Perkins, L. A. Riedinger, and S. Sokolsky, "Problems in the Oxidation Protection of Refractory Metals in Aerospace Applications, Lockheed Missiles and Space Co., Sunnyvale, California.

Figure 46.

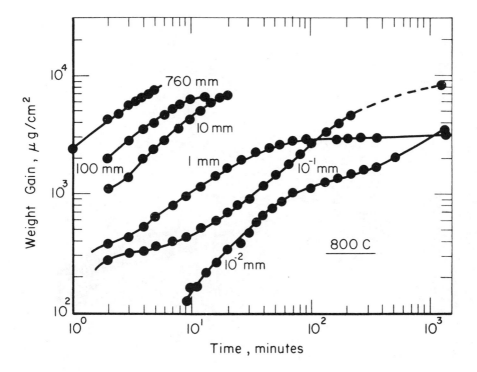

Reaction of Columbium at 800 C with Oxygen at Various Pressures.

T. Hurlen, et al., "Oxidation of Niobium," TN-1, Central Institute for Industrial Research, Norway, Contract AF 61(052)-90 (April 1959).

Figure 47.

Photograph of Ballistic Impact Test Furnace with Air Rifle in Position
for Impacting Coated Molybdenum Specimen.

J. R. Blanchard, "Oxidation-Resistant Coatings for Molybdenum,"
WADC TR 54-492, Part II, Climax Molybdenum Co. of Michigan
(June 1955).

Figure 48.

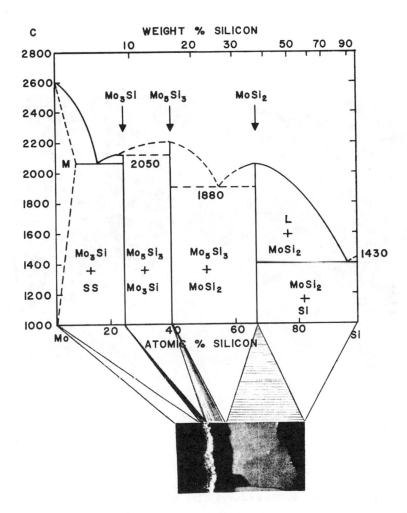

Correlating of Phases in the Mo-Si Phase Diagrams in a Siliconized Molybdenum Coating.

Gordon P. K. Chu, "Notes on Siliconizing of Molybdenum," Research Division, American-Standard Corporation, Union, New Jersey, Paper presented Sixth Refractory Composites Working Group Meeting, NASA/ASD, Dayton, Ohio (June 1962).

Figure 49.

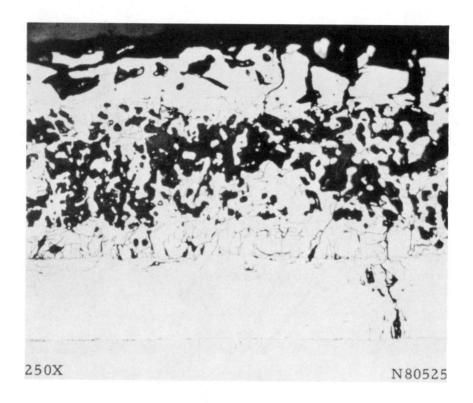

250X   N80525

Microstructure of Si-26 Atomic % Mn Coating on Tantalum after Exposure
in Air for 24 Hr at 2700°F (No Failure).   Initial Coating Thickness, 9 mils.

W. D. Klopp, et al., "Development of Protective Coatings for Tantalum-
Base Alloys," Battelle Memorial Institute, Columbus, Ohio. Paper
presented Fifth Refractory Composites Working Group Meeting, Dallas,
Texas (8-10 August 1961).

Figure 50a.

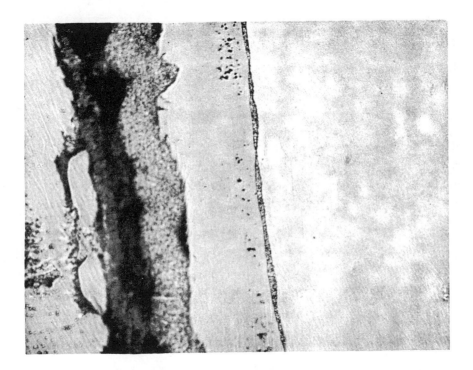

Microstructure of W-3 Coating As Applied

"Activities of Chromalloy Corporation in the Development of Coatings for Refractory Metals," notes prepared for Sixth Refractory Composite Working Group Meeting (16-19 June 1962).

Figure 50b.

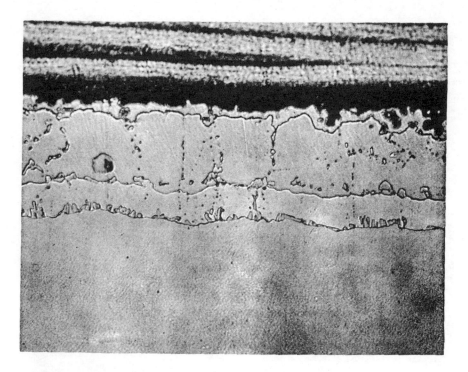

Microstructure of W-3 Coated Molybdenum After 4 Hour Exposure to 3000° F Oxidation.

"Activities of Chromalloy Corporation in the Development of Coatings for Refractory Metals," notes prepared for Sixth Refractory Composite Working Group Meeting (16-19 June 1962).

Figure 51.

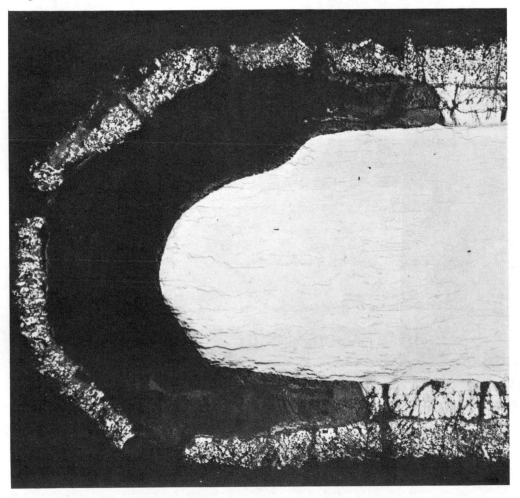

Specimen D289. Microstructure of Cross Section at Failed Edge of
Test Panel, Showing Progress of Oxidation.

D. V. Doane, "Oxidation Resistant Coatings for Molybdenum," Climax
Molybdenum Co. of Michigan, WADC TR 54-492 Pt 3 (April 1957).

Figure 52a.

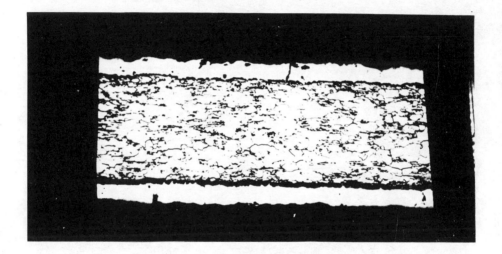

Photomicrograph - W-2 Coated 10 mil Molybdenum (As Received).

E. F. Atkins and R. I. Jaffee, "Oxidation of Clad Mo Containing Intentional Defects," Battelle Memorial Institute, Columbus, Ohio. Paper presented Annual Meeting American Ceramic Society (1960).

Figure 52b.

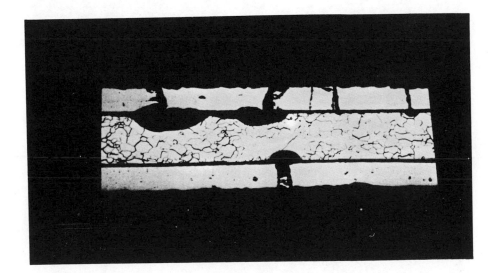

Photomicrograph - W-2 Coated 5 mil Molybdenum-After Thermal Cycling.

E. F. Atkins and R. I. Jaffee, "Oxidation of Clad Mo Containing Intentional Defects," Battelle Memorial Institute, Columbus, Ohio. Paper presented Annual Meeting American Ceramic Society (1960).

Figure 53.

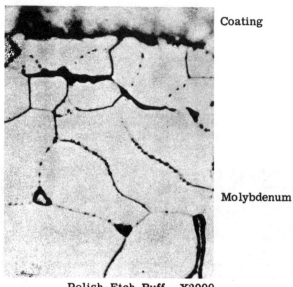

Coating

Molybdenum

Polish-Etch-Buff   X2000

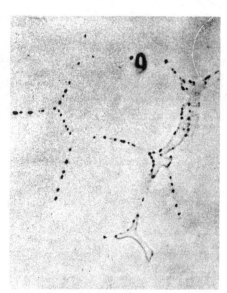

Polish-Etch-Buff   X2000

Specimen C422.   Showing Oxidation at Mo Grain Boundaries in
Recrystallized Layer Beneath the Coating.

D. V. Doane, "Oxidation Resistant Coatings for Molybdenum, " Climax
Molybdenum Co. of Michigan, WADC TR 54-492 Pt 3 (April 1957).